Theme Reader

The McGraw-Hill Companies

www.WrightGroup.com

Printed in the United States.

Send all inquiries to:
Wright Group/McGraw-Hill
P.O. Box 812960
Chicago, IL 60681

ISBN 978-0-07-656838-3
MHID 0-07-656838-5

3 4 5 6 7 8 9 QVR 16 15 14 13 12 11

Contents

UNIT 1

Life Stories

What is my heritage?

Focus Questions

Who are our ancestors?

How do people learn about their heritage or culture?

What kinds of things are passed on through the generations?

What can we learn from sharing our heritage or culture with each other?

Heritage—Who We Are

by Jeanette Bagnasco

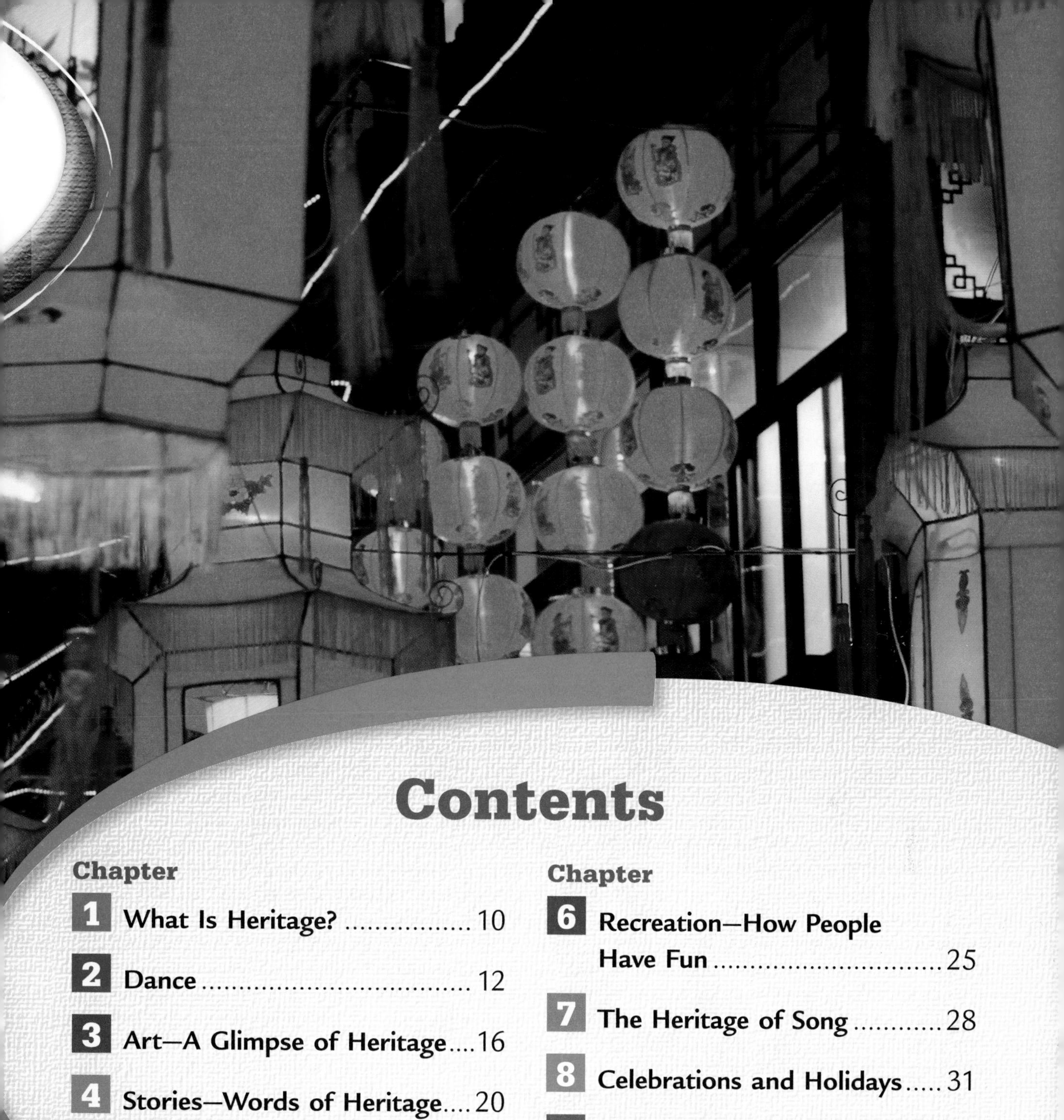

Contents

Chapter 1 What Is Heritage?

How much do you know about your classmates? You may know what they like to eat. You may know what makes them laugh. But do you know any songs their great-grandparents sang? Do you know about other languages they speak at home? If so, you know something about their **heritage**. Heritage is the beliefs, values, and customs that are handed down from the past.

Dancers celebrate their Mexican heritage at a cultural *fiesta*, or celebration.

Foods, games, holidays, and music are some parts of heritage. Our heritage frequently comes to us from our **ancestors**, the people who came before us. One day you may pass on your heritage to the next **generation**.

Learning about your heritage helps you understand yourself and your family. Knowing about the heritage of others helps you understand them. You can understand how others are different from you and how they are the same as you.

Meals called *bento* are often eaten in Japan.

Express Your Heritage

Have you ever seen someone wearing a T-shirt with a flag from another country? By wearing that T-shirt, that person may be giving you a clue about his or her heritage.

Heritage is passed along in many ways. Here are some examples.

Chapter 2 Dance

People share their heritage through dance. They sometimes express, or show, their heritage through dance forms that came from the countries of their ancestors.

Bhangra

Bhangra (BAHN grah) is a spirited folk dance with a pounding beat. It began hundreds of years ago in Punjab, an area in India and Pakistan, to celebrate the harvest.

Today college *bhangra* dance teams compete for prizes. Many team members grew up learning traditional *bhangra* moves. But now some teams mix hip-hop music with the old folk songs. Others add break dancing. By adding these changes, they are forming a new tradition to pass along.

An important part of the *bhangra* sound is the *tumbi* (TOOM bee). The *tumbi* is a stringed instrument. It makes a high-pitched sound, like an American banjo. Unlike the banjo, the *tumbi* has only one wire string! The *tumbi* sound is so lively and different that some American music artists have used it in their music.

The *tumbi* is played by continuously snapping the string with the forefinger.

The *bhangra* dance team at Cornell University, in New York, performed at the Boston Bhangra Competition.

Dancing Around the World

Dance can be an expression of heritage and identity. *Bhangra* is only one of many dances that have been passed on through generations. Many cultures have their own ways of moving to music. Let's look at some other dance forms.

From Greece comes the *kalamatianos* (kah lah mah tee ah NOS). It is a joyous circle dance. This dance is a celebration. It is often the first dance performed at weddings and baptisms.

Square dancing is an American tradition. A *caller* calls out moves, which groups of four couples then perform.

Square dancing is a lively partner dance. The movements in square dancing come from many different heritages. It has its roots in many Irish, Scottish, English, and French dances. Today square dancing is thought of as an American dance.

The *Ikariotikos* is another popular Greek circle dance. Dancers move quickly to the accompanying music.

Chapter 3

Art—A Glimpse of Heritage

Have you ever visited an art museum? Museums are good places to store and exhibit art for future generations. You can learn about your own heritage through art. You can learn about other cultures too. Art can show how people live. It can also show what is important to people.

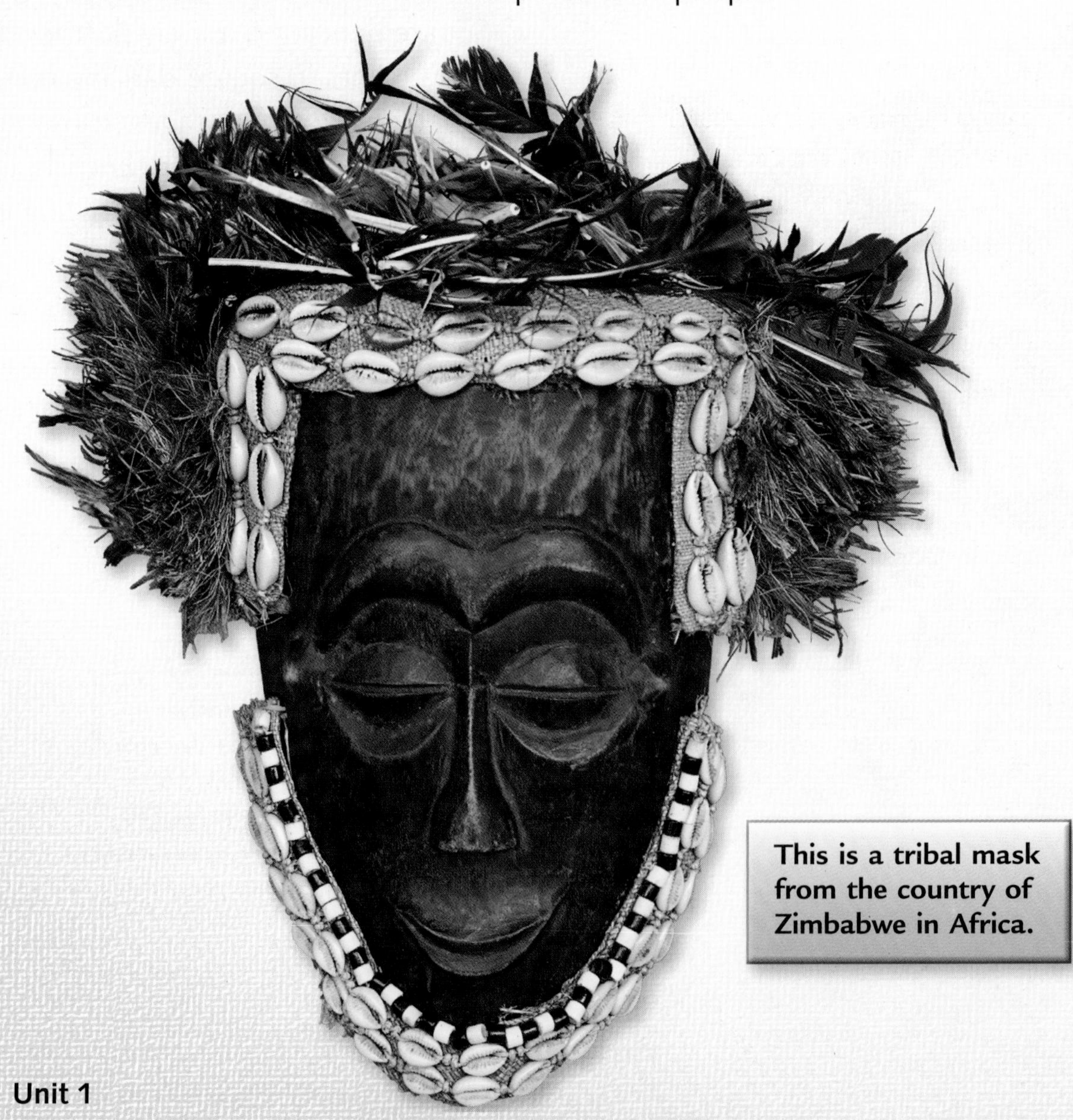

This is a tribal mask from the country of Zimbabwe in Africa.

Story Art and Sandpaintings

Faith Ringgold is an artist and author who expresses her African American heritage in her art. Some of her paintings show life in Harlem, her childhood neighborhood in New York City. Some of Ringgold's art is inspired by the cloth paintings that are part of the Tibetan heritage.

Another cultural art form is sandpainting. For hundreds of years, sandpaintings have been used in Navajo healing ceremonies, or services. Originally they were drawn on the ground in sand and erased after the ceremony. Today, Navajo artists make immobile, or fixed, sandpaintings to show Navajo signs and ways of life.

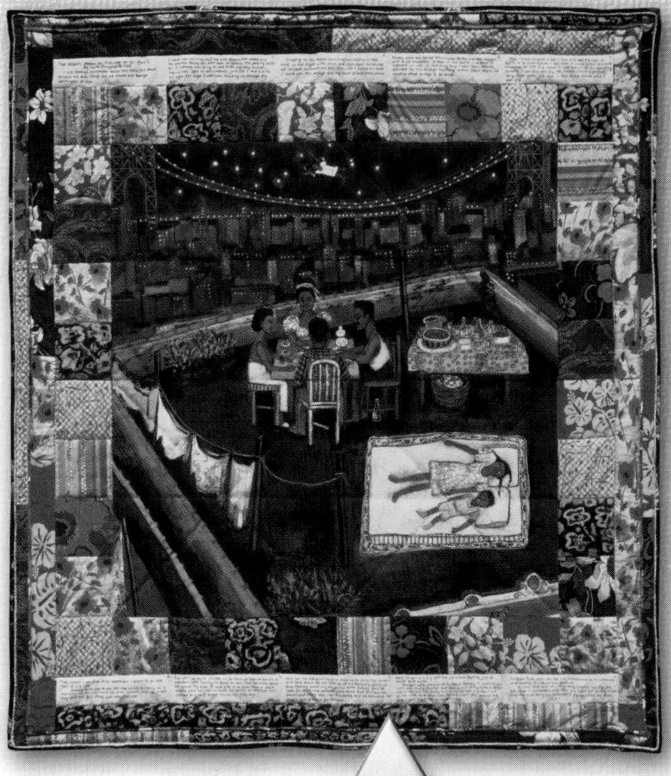

As a child, Ringgold and her family spent time on their rooftop in New York City. Ringgold's memories helped inspire *Tar Beach*, one of her famous story quilts.

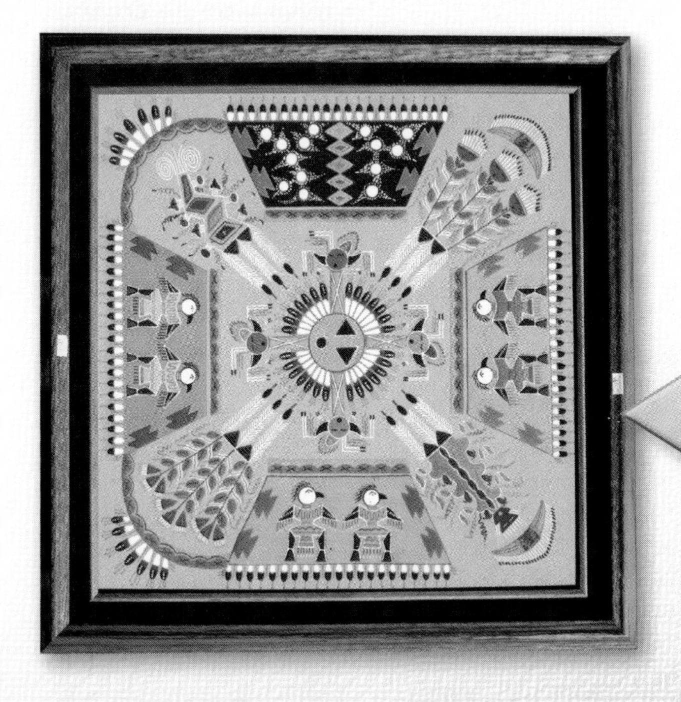

Sandpaintings are still used in Navajo healing ceremonies. Some are kept in museums for future generations.

Amish women create quilts like these at quilting bees. Quilting bees are also an opportunity for the women to socialize.

Quilts and Rugs

When people think of art, they often think of paintings. But there are many other forms of art. Sculpture and fabric design are art. Jewelry making and other crafts are also art.

Quilting has been done by the Amish people of Pennsylvania since the mid-1800s. This craft reflects the values of the Amish culture. Quilts are often made by groups of women. This shows a culture where community life is important.

Another craft that became an art form was rug making. In early America there was not much material available to cover cold floors. New England women used old clothing to make braided ropes for rugs. The strands were sewn together in oval shapes.

The craft of braiding rugs is still passed down, and braided rugs can be found throughout the United States. This form of art, along with all art forms, allows people to see their heritage and the heritage of others.

Handmade braided rugs may be made of many fabrics, but wool is usually used.

At a state fair in Raleigh, North Carolina, a woman shows how to make a braided rug.

Chapter 4 Stories—Words of Heritage

Did your family ever tell you bedtime stories? Using spoken words to pass along stories is called an oral tradition. Many cultures share the storytelling tradition. For hundreds of years Native Americans have told stories. Joseph Bruchac is a Native American writer. He relies on this oral tradition in his stories and poems. He uses them to tell about his Native American heritage.

Joseph Bruchac

BIRDFOOT'S GRAMPA

The old man
must have stopped our car
two dozen times to climb out
and gather into his hands
the small toads blinded
by our lights and leaping,
live drops of rain.

The rain was falling,
a mist about his white hair
and I kept saying
you can't save them all,
accept it, get back in
we've got places to go.

But, leathery hands full
of wet brown life,
knee deep in the summer
roadside grass,
he just smiled and said
they have places to go
too.

—Joseph Bruchac
Entering Onondaga

This poem tells about Grampa's love of nature. What can someone find out about you from the stories you tell?

Stories are another way that heritage can be shared. Julia Alvarez is an author who hands down her Latina heritage through her stories. In her book, *Once Upon a Quinceañera* (keen say ah NYAY rah), Alvarez writes about a special birthday celebration.

A *quinceañera* is a party Latinos give their daughters when they turn fifteen. At the party there are many traditions. A girl's "last doll" may be given away to a younger girl. Her flat shoes are replaced with heels, and a crown is placed on her head. She is now considered a woman.

It is tradition for the father of the *quinceañera* to lead her in her first dance as a grown-up.

Chapter 5

Food

Does your family have a favorite family **recipe**? A recipe is the list of things you need and directions for making a kind of food. Recipes can be part of your heritage. Perhaps there is a recipe that was passed down through generations of your family. Family recipes are often passed on this way. Over the years these recipes are used to prepare foods when families gather.

Mashed chickpeas are the main ingredients in *hummus* and *falafel*, two popular Arabic foods.

Chopsticks are the main eating utensil in Asia. Two thin sticks, held in one hand, are used to pick up food.

Foods from Many Cultures

We all can enjoy foods from many countries. Think about pizza, a baked pie. Many Italians came to the United States in the early 1900s. They brought recipes for pizza with them.

Wat is a spicy stew from the Ethiopian culture. It can be made with beans or meats, but it always has many strong spices.

People came to the United States from many locations. They brought with them knowledge of foods and recipes from their cultures. By passing down these recipes, people pass down their heritage.

Many Ethiopian meals are served on traditional *injera* (ihn JEER uh) bread.

Chapter 6

Recreation—How People Have Fun

People everywhere like to have fun. Cultures around the world have different sports and games. These sports and games can become part of people's cultural heritage.

Sports

There are many kinds of sports. But nearly every culture has a sport in which people kick a ball. Sports that are much like soccer have been played for more than 2,000 years!

The Japanese have been playing *Kemari* since ancient times. It uses many of the same movements as soccer.

Games

Games are also a part of many cultures. Some games use balls. Some games use sticks. Some games use marbles, stones, or other things. Other games use a board of some kind. Many parents teach their children games from their culture. Which games are part of your heritage?

Mancala **(man CA la) is a very old board game that traveled across the African continent. Players try to capture all of the seeds from the pits on the board.**

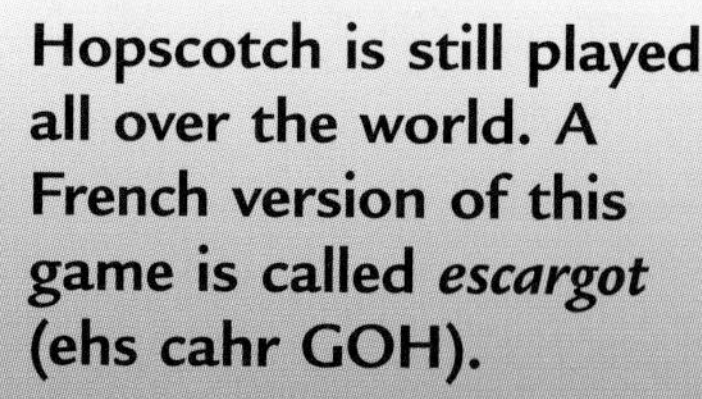

Hopscotch is still played all over the world. A French version of this game is called *escargot* (ehs cahr GOH).

Acrobatics

Acrobatics are full of action and fun to watch. Acrobats have been performing in China for more than 2,000 years. Through the years acrobatics have remained a part of the Chinese culture. Many acrobatic tricks, or stunts, come from ancient Chinese dances, sports, games, and **customs**. Customs are a culture's way of doing things. Today, Chinese acrobats share this part of their heritage with people all around the world.

The Peking Acrobats from China perform tumbling, balancing acts, and other gymnastics.

Chapter 7

The Heritage of Song

Songs are an interesting way to learn about your heritage and the traditions of others. The lyrics, or words to a song, can tell about a way of life.

One kind of music that tells a story is bluegrass. Bluegrass is a kind of country music played on stringed instruments. The banjo is an important instrument in bluegrass.

Passing Bluegrass Along

Today older bluegrass music players teach the next generation how to make this kind of music. They teach young bluegrass music players how to use the strings on their instruments to get the bluegrass sound.

These two men are playing bluegrass music at a South Florida Bluegrass Association music festival in Miami Beach, Florida.

The Sounds of Bluegrass

These instruments help to create the lively sound of bluegrass music.

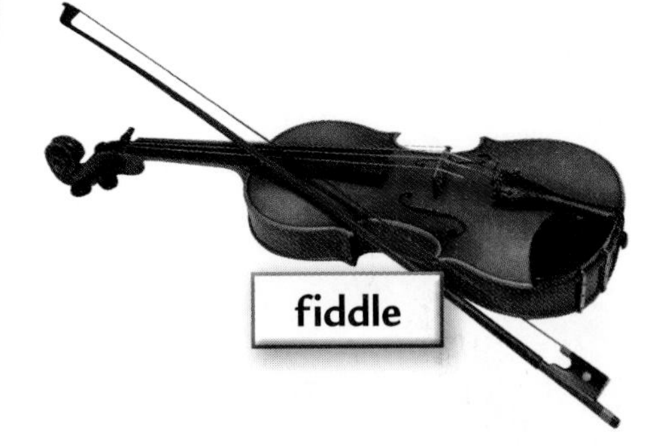

fiddle

mandolin

acoustic guitar

banjo

American Jazz

Jazz is an American form of music. It began when African Americans in the southern United States got together to make music. Many early jazz players could not read music. They played *by ear*. This means they played what sounded good to them without reading music. In 1987 the U.S. Congress called jazz a national treasure. This music form is part of our country's heritage.

Duke Ellington is considered to be one of the greatest jazz composers and bandleaders.

Chapter 8

Celebrations and Holidays

People all over the world enjoy their own special celebrations. All cultures participate in celebrations that have been handed down for generations. People can learn about the heritage of others by taking part in different holidays and celebrations.

Events in History

Some holidays help people remember what happened in the past. Cinco de Mayo (SEEN koh day MY oh) is a Mexican holiday that celebrates a battle that Mexican soldiers won against the French army. The holiday celebrates Mexico's spirit of independence.

At a Cinco de Mayo parade in Chicago, Illinois, dancers celebrate in traditional dresses.

Holidays Honor People

Some holidays honor people who did important things in the past. The United States remembers Presidents George Washington and Abraham Lincoln on Presidents' Day. Washington was the first president of our country. Lincoln governed our country during the Civil War.

Martin Luther King, Jr., worked to end racial discrimination in the United States. The third Monday of each January honors Dr. King.

The city of Denver, Colorado, celebrates Martin Luther King, Jr., Day with a torch-passing ceremony.

A torchlight procession begins the four-day Scottish New Year celebration, called *Hogmanay* (hawg meh NAY). The procession honors Scotland's Viking ancestors.

Other Kinds of Holidays

You have read about holidays that recognize people or historical events. Other holidays are **religious**, or about a certain faith. Religions all over the world have important celebrations.

Some holidays, such as a harvest festival, celebrate a special time of year. One of the oldest holidays in the world is New Year's Day. This holiday is enjoyed in many different ways by people all around the world. People who celebrate it say good-bye to the old year and express hope for the future.

Chapter 9

Our National Heritage

Do you eat foods from other people's cultures? Do you play games from other countries? Do you play a sport such as soccer? Do you know songs or dances from other lands? Do you take part in holidays and traditions from different places in the world?

Most Americans say yes to at least a few of these questions. The reason is that the United States has a culture that includes the traditions and customs of its people. And the people of the United States come from many parts of the world.

Many cities and towns across the United States celebrate St. Patrick's Day, an Irish holiday.

Americans salute the American flag, a symbol of freedom.

You may follow one or more traditions in your family. Even so, you are part of a national heritage—the American heritage.

Baseball and apple pie are part of the American heritage. But so are the ideas of freedom and democracy. Our country's heritage is passed on through free elections. It is passed on through our American holidays, such as Flag Day and Memorial Day.

Flamenco dancing is a beautiful part of Spanish culture.

Sum It Up

You may have a heritage that has been passed down through many generations of your family. It's part of who you are. But your American heritage is also part of who you are. Your American heritage comes from many cultures.

Learning about the traditions of others can help us understand that we all have differences that make us special. But we also share many things that are the same across cultures.

The Life of Celia Cruz
La vida de Celia Cruz

written by/escrito por Monica Brown
illustrated by/ilustrado por Rafael López

SUGAR! My voice is strong, smooth, and sweet.
I will make you feel like dancing.

Close your eyes and listen. My voice feels like feet skipping on cool wet sand, like running under a waterfall, like rolling down a hill. My voice climbs and rocks and dips and flips with the sounds of congas beating and trumpets blaring.

Boom boom boom! beat the congas.
Clap clap clap! go the hands.
Shake shake shake! go the hips.

I am the Queen of Salsa and I invite you to come dance with me.

¡AZÚCAR! *Mi voz es intensa, suave y dulce. Te dará ganas de bailar. Cierra los ojos y escucha.*

Mi voz se siente como unos pies que resbalan en la arena mojada, como correr bajo una cascada, como bajar por una loma. Mi voz trepa y se mece y sube y baja al ritmo de las tumbadoras y el sonido de las trompetas.

¡Bum bum bum! *resuenan las tumbadoras. Las manos aplauden y las caderas se menean.*

Yo soy la Reina de la Salsa y te invito a bailar conmigo.

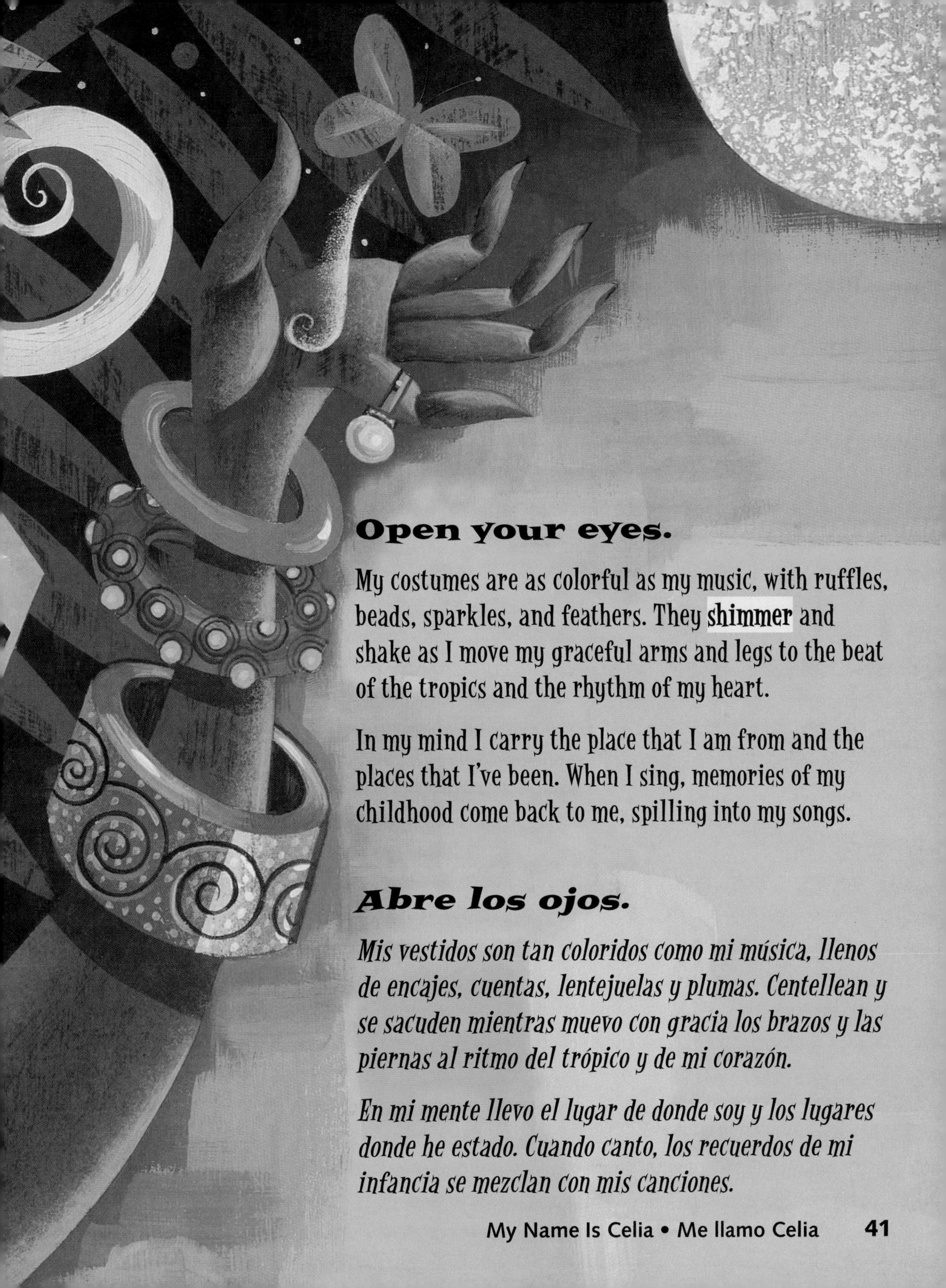

Open your eyes.

My costumes are as colorful as my music, with ruffles, beads, sparkles, and feathers. They **shimmer** and shake as I move my graceful arms and legs to the beat of the tropics and the rhythm of my heart.

In my mind I carry the place that I am from and the places that I've been. When I sing, memories of my childhood come back to me, spilling into my songs.

Abre los ojos.

Mis vestidos son tan coloridos como mi música, llenos de encajes, cuentas, lentejuelas y plumas. Centellean y se sacuden mientras muevo con gracia los brazos y las piernas al ritmo del trópico y de mi corazón.

En mi mente llevo el lugar de donde soy y los lugares donde he estado. Cuando canto, los recuerdos de mi infancia se mezclan con mis canciones.

I was born in Cuba, an island in the middle of the Caribbean Sea. My Cuba was the city of Havana.

Our family had a warm kitchen filled with the voices of women and men—grandparents, brothers, sisters, cousins, and friends. We ate rice, beans, and bananas and filled our bellies with love and warm coffee with milk and lots and lots of sugar.

In the evenings, I would help my mother put the younger children to sleep by singing them soothing, sweet lullabies.

Nací en Cuba, una isla del Caribe. Mi Cuba era La Habana.

En mi casa teníamos una cocina acogedora, llena de las voces de mujeres y hombres: abuelos, hermanos, primos y amigos. Comíamos arroz, frijoles y plátanos, y nos llenábamos la barriga con amor y café con leche bien caliente y mucha, pero mucha azúcar.

Por la noche, ayudaba a mi madre a acostar a mis hermanos chiquitos cantándoles canciones de cuna bien bajito.

My father worked long and hard on the railroad but loved coming home to us each day. He would sit in the backyard and sing with us. He gave us the gift of his music and filled our hearts with hope. Sometimes when I would sing with my father, the neighbors would hear the sound of my voice and walk over to listen to my melodies. We may have been poor, but music cost nothing and brought joy to us all.

Mi padre trabajaba muy duro en los trenes, pero se sentía feliz cuando volvía a la casa cada día para estar con nosotros. Se sentaba en el traspatio y cantábamos todos juntos. Nos dio el regalo de su música y llenó de esperanza nuestros corazones. A veces, cuando yo cantaba con mi padre, los vecinos oían mi voz y se acercaban a escuchar mis melodías. Éramos pobres, pero la música no costaba nada y nos alegraba.

My papa wanted me to become a schoolteacher, such an important job. At school I learned and grew. I studied history and art, mathematics and science, and even music.

I did well in school, and I loved to sing! When I sang, my body would fill with the rhythms of Africa and mix with the Spanish sounds of my Cuban mother tongue.

Finally, one of my favorite teachers took my two hands and said, “Go out into the world and sing, my child—you will be known across the land! Your voice is a gift from above and must ring sweet in the ears of our people!”

Mi papá quería que yo fuera maestra, que tuviera un buen trabajo. En la escuela aprendí mucho y maduré. Estudié historia y arte, matemáticas y ciencias, y hasta música.

Me fue bien en la escuela, ¡y me encantaba cantar! Cuando cantaba, mi cuerpo se llenaba de los ritmos africanos mezclados con el idioma español de mi patria.

Un día, una de mis maestras preferidas me agarró la mano y me dijo: “Sal al mundo a cantar, mi niña . . . ¡Te harás famosa! ¡Tu voz es un regalo del cielo y sonará muy dulce en los oídos de la gente!”

My cousin Nenita and I would travel far on the bus so I could have a chance to sing in competitions. Even though some people would not let me sing in their contests because of the color of my skin, I did not let this stop me from making my voice heard. I promised myself that I would keep singing and studying no matter what.

Mi prima Nenita y yo hacíamos viajes largos en ómnibus para que yo cantara en concursos. Aunque algunos no me dejaban cantar en sus concursos por el color de mi piel, no me di por vencida. Me prometí que seguiría cantando y estudiando pasara lo que pasara.

I was still a young woman when a revolution began in my country. Like many others, I left my Cuba forever. First, I traveled to Mexico. Then I traveled to the United States with my husband, the trumpeter Pedro Knight, and our musical group Sonora Matancera.

Todavía era joven cuando triunfó la Revolución. Como hizo mucha gente, me fui para siempre de mi Cuba. Primero fui a México. Después viajé a los Estados Unidos con mi esposo, el trompetista Pedro Knight, y nuestro grupo, la Sonora Matancera.

New York!

My new home with the lights and people—a blend of many cultures and traditions. From my window I saw the lights and heard the music, and I was the light and the music. Though I left my island and became a United States citizen, I carried my people in my heart. My songs were a gift to all those Cubans who left their island and all the children of the Americas.

Boom boom boom! The sounds of the congas and the trumpets returned to me.

¡Nueva York!

Mi nuevo hogar, con todas sus luces y su gente, con una mezcla de tantas culturas y tradiciones. Desde mi ventana veía las luces y escuchaba la música, y yo era la luz y la música. Aunque me fui de mi isla y me hice ciudadana de los Estados Unidos, yo llevaba a mi pueblo en el corazón. Mis canciones eran un regalo para todos los cubanos que dejaron su isla y para todos los niños de las Américas.

¡Bum bum bum! *Regresaban los sonidos de las tumbadoras y las trompetas.*

Miami! My home away from home.

One day in a restaurant, a young waiter asked me if I wanted sugar in my coffee. “SUGAR?!” I said. How could he even ask!? I am Cuban. “Yes, with SUGAR!” And when I sipped the milky sweetness I was back in my mother’s kitchen with my friends and family.

From that point on, when I walked out on stage I would simply say, “SUGAR!” And they would know exactly what I meant—home and love and lots of kisses.

The audience would bring their hands together and welcome me.

clap clap clap

¡Miami! *Mi segundo hogar.*

Un día, en un restaurante, un camarero joven me preguntó si quería azúcar con el café. ¿AZÚCAR?, exclamé. ¿Cómo se le ocurre preguntar eso? Yo soy cubana. Claro que sí, ¡con AZÚCAR! Y cuando tomé un poquito del café dulce recordé la cocina de mi madre con mi familia y mis amigos.

Desde ese momento, cuando entraba al escenario simplemente decía: ¡AZÚCAR! Y ellos sabían exactamente lo que yo quería decir: hogar, amor y muchos besos.

El público aplaudía y me daba la bienvenida.

I sang with my friends Tito and Johnny and Willie and people loved our music. Together we brought a new music to the Americas—salsa—a music that blended rock with rumba, mambo with jazz.

People loved to dance and swing to our music. **Shake shake shake!** went their hips as they laughed and danced!

Yo canté con mis amigos Tito, Johnny y Willie, y a la gente le encantaba nuestra música. Juntos trajimos una nueva música a América, la salsa, una música que mezclaba el rock con la rumba, el mambo con el jazz.

A la gente le encantaba bailar y girar con nuestra música. ¡Meneaban las caderas mientras se reían y bailaban!

Teachers and presidents honored me, and all because my songs sounded like the waves of the ocean hitting the roof of my mouth, like the streets of Havana, like my mother's kitchen, like a tummy full of beans and bananas and rice, like a cup of warm coffee with sugar. They named me the Queen of Salsa, and I wore that crown proudly.

Me rindieron honores maestros y presidentes, y todo porque mis canciones eran como las olas del mar golpeándome el cielo de la boca, como las calles de La Habana, como la cocina de mi madre, como una barriguita llena de frijoles, plátanos y arroz, como una taza de café caliente con azúcar. Me nombraron la Reina de la Salsa, y llevé esa corona con orgullo.

I crossed borders and broke **boundaries** because I was a survivor and no one ever stopped me from singing ever again! My records turned to gold and silver and streets and stars were given my name.

Boom boom boom! beat the congas.
Clap clap clap! go the hands.
Shake shake shake! go the hips.

When we sing together our words are like smiles flying across the sky. Come dance with me now, my friends, to the beat of the drums and the sound of the trumpets and the tropics.

Even when I am gone, my music will live on.

Crucé fronteras y rompí barreras porque fui fuerte y nunca más nadie consiguió que dejara de cantar. Mis discos llegaron a ser "discos de oro" y "discos de plata", y se les puso mi nombre a calles y estrellas.

¡Bum bum bum! *resuenan las tumbadoras. Las manos aplauden y las caderas se menean. Cuando cantamos juntos, nuestras palabras son como sonrisas volando por el cielo. Amigos, vengan ahora a bailar conmigo al ritmo de los tambores y al sonido de las trompetas y los trópicos.*

Aunque yo ya no esté, mi música seguirá viviendo.

¡Azúcar!
Sugar!

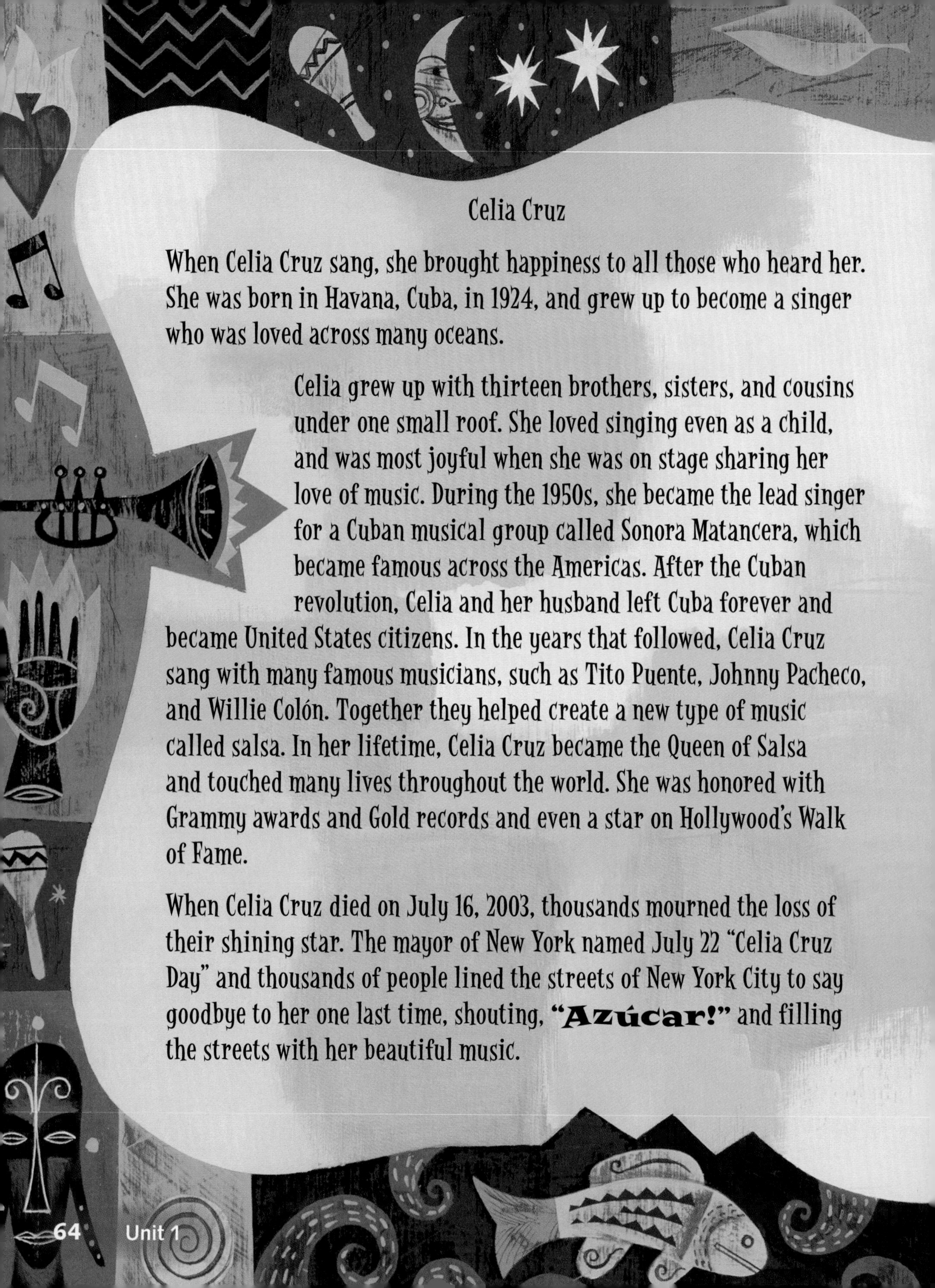

Celia Cruz

When Celia Cruz sang, she brought happiness to all those who heard her. She was born in Havana, Cuba, in 1924, and grew up to become a singer who was loved across many oceans.

Celia grew up with thirteen brothers, sisters, and cousins under one small roof. She loved singing even as a child, and was most joyful when she was on stage sharing her love of music. During the 1950s, she became the lead singer for a Cuban musical group called Sonora Matancera, which became famous across the Americas. After the Cuban revolution, Celia and her husband left Cuba forever and became United States citizens. In the years that followed, Celia Cruz sang with many famous musicians, such as Tito Puente, Johnny Pacheco, and Willie Colón. Together they helped create a new type of music called salsa. In her lifetime, Celia Cruz became the Queen of Salsa and touched many lives throughout the world. She was honored with Grammy awards and Gold records and even a star on Hollywood's Walk of Fame.

When Celia Cruz died on July 16, 2003, thousands mourned the loss of their shining star. The mayor of New York named July 22 "Celia Cruz Day" and thousands of people lined the streets of New York City to say goodbye to her one last time, shouting, **"Azúcar!"** and filling the streets with her beautiful music.

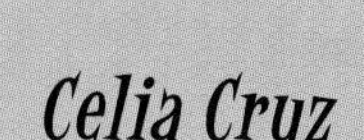

Celia Cruz

Cuando Celia Cruz cantaba, todos los que la escuchaban se sentían felices. Nació en La Habana, Cuba, en 1924 y llegó a ser una cantante muy querida en todo el mundo.

Celia se crió con trece hermanos y primos, en una casa pequeña. Le encantaba cantar ya de niña, y se sentía muy contenta cuando estaba en el escenario compartiendo su amor por la música. Llegó a ser la cantante principal de un grupo musical cubano llamado la Sonora Matancera, que fue famoso en toda América. Cuando triunfó la revolución cubana, Celia y su esposo se fueron para siempre de Cuba y se hicieron ciudadanos de los Estados Unidos. En los años que siguieron, Celia Cruz cantó con muchos músicos famosos, como Tito Puente, Johnny Pacheco y Willie Colón. Junto crearon un nuevo tipo de música llamada salsa. Durante su trayectoria, Celia llegó a ser la Reina de la Salsa y tocó muchos corazones en todo el mundo. Fue laureada con el premio Grammy y con varios Discos de Oro, e incluso con una estrella en el Paseo de la Fama de Hollywood.

Cuando Celia Cruz murió, miles de admiradores lloraron la pérdida de su estrella. El alcalde de Nueva York nombró el 22 de julio como el Día de Celia Cruz y millares de personas llenaron las calles neoyorquinas para darle el último adiós, gritando **¡Azúcar!** *y colmando las calles con la hermosa música de Celia.*

Celia Cruz

1924-2003

UNIT 2

A Green Future

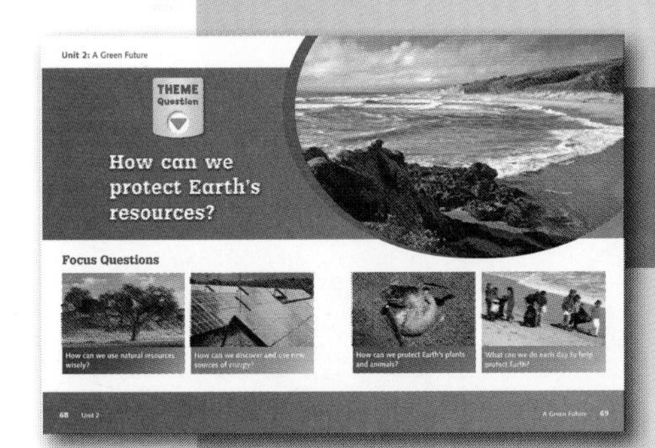
Unit 2: A Green Future

THEME Question

How can we protect Earth's resources?

Focus Questions

How can we use natural resources wisely?

How can we discover and use new sources of energy?

How can we protect Earth's plants and animals?

68 Unit 2

A Green Future 69

How can we protect Earth's resources?

p. 68

Living Green

by Ron Ottaviano

Contents

Living Green 71

Living Green *Nonfiction: Informational Text*

p. 70

A Symphony of Whales *Fiction: Realistic Fiction*

p. 99

How can we protect Earth's resources?

Focus Questions

How can we use natural resources wisely?

How can we discover and use new sources of energy?

How can we protect Earth's plants and animals?

What can we do each day to help protect Earth?

Living Green

by Ron Ottaviano

Contents

Introduction

Are You Green?

People who are "green" take care of nature. They are careful about how they use natural resources. Some natural resources are sunlight, air, soil, water, plants, and minerals.

We use natural resources to grow food. We use them to heat and cool our homes. We even use them to build shelters and to power our factories.

It is important to use natural resources wisely. Why? Because not all natural resources last forever. Without them, people and animals cannot live.

Renewable Resources

There are many kinds of natural resources. Some of them are **renewable**. Renewable resources are resources that can be used again. Some renewable resources return almost as fast as we use them. Take a deep breath—the air you breathe is a renewable resource. It's always there. Other renewable resources, such as trees, take longer to come back after being used. Trees grow back slowly.

Nonrenewable Resources

Some natural resources are **nonrenewable**. Nonrenewable resources can be used faster than they can be made. Coal, natural gas, and oil are nonrenewable resources. These resources are fuels formed from fossils. Fossils are what is left from plants and animals that died millions of years ago. Fossil fuels take years and years to form. This means when we use them up, they will be gone for a very long time!

Some oil rigs drill into the ocean floor for oil and natural gas, the most valuable fossil fuels.

Chapter 1

Reduce, Reuse, Recycle

How can you use natural resources wisely? How can you be green? You can

- reduce the amount of resources you use.
- reuse what you already have.
- recycle resources instead of throwing them away.

These are the three R's. There are lots of ways to practice the three R's. Let's learn about some of them!

Reducing, Reusing, and Recycling: A Lighter "Footprint"

What happens to the plastic containers and leftover food you throw away? What about sofas, broken toasters, and old toys?

A lot of trash ends up in landfills. There, trash is buried under the soil. This adds to our "human footprint," or the way our actions affect Earth.

In 2005 two people took green action. Sarah Pelmas and John Perry, along with eight friends, formed the Compact. Their mission was to reduce their consumption, or the buying and use of goods.

The Compactors vowed not to buy anything new during 2006. They borrowed or bought used things, except for goods such as food and medicine. "We thought . . . we could tread a little more lightly on the planet," Perry said.

Compact members created compost, decaying matter that fertilizes soil. They saved things from garbage bins and traded their used goods with other people.

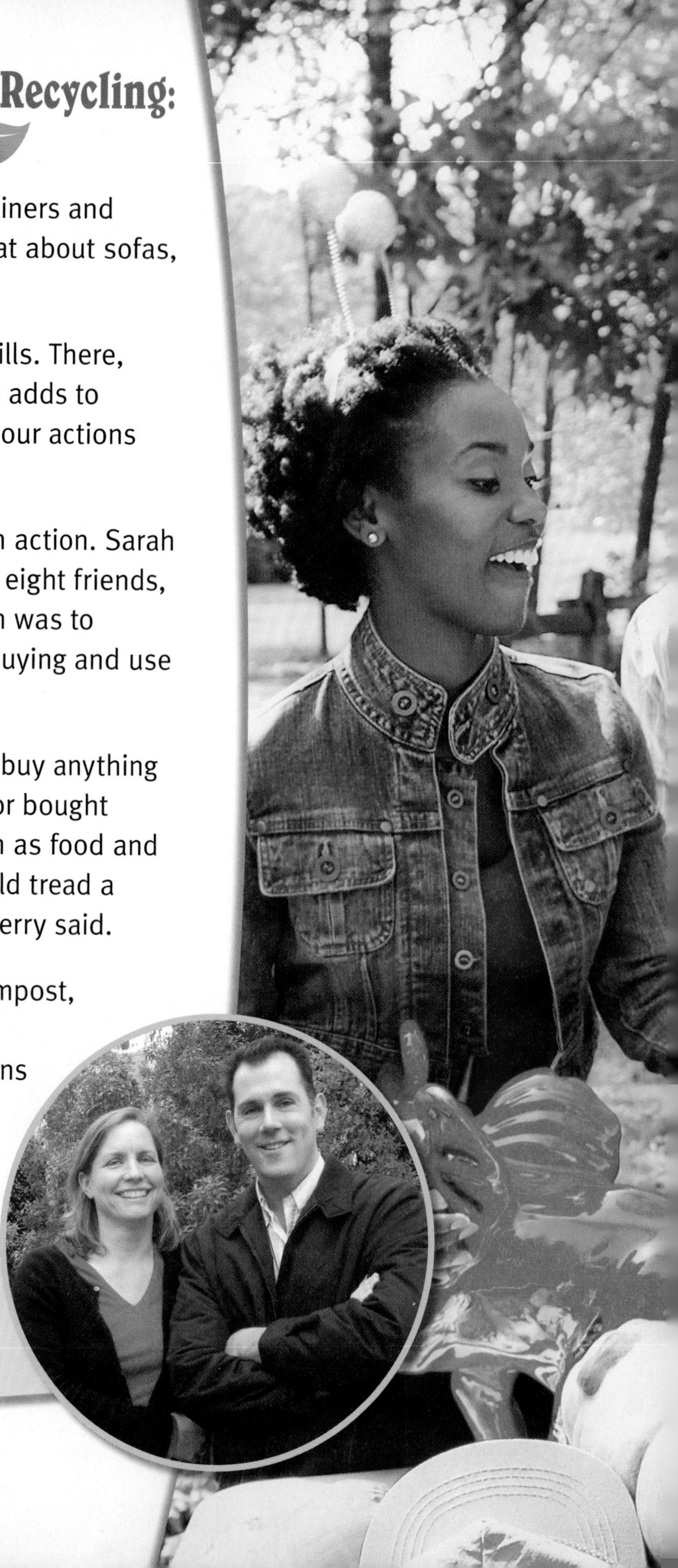

Sarah Pelmas and John Perry pledged to reduce their consumption in 2006. They still live this green lifestyle.

At garage sales, people sell their used belongings to recycle goods and to reduce trash.

Mountains of Waste

Landfills cover Earth with waste. The Environmental Protection Agency (EPA) reports that in 2006, Americans made 251 million tons of solid trash. That's 4.6 pounds per person, per day—about 1,700 pounds a year! Fifty-five percent of that waste gets buried in landfills.

Recycling: A Growing Solution

Recycling turns used products into valuable material. For example, recycled paper may be turned into a paper bag. By using paper that already exists, new trees won't need to be cut down to make the bag. This process reduces landfill waste, which releases methane, a gas that is harmful to the atmosphere.

Recycling reduces the burning of trash too. Waste incinerators burn trash and turn it into ash. The ash is harmful to the world's air, soil, and water.

Incinerators reduce the amount of trash that goes into landfills. However, burning waste is harmful to the environment.

Everyone can help by sorting and recycling paper, cans, and bottles instead of throwing them away. In 2006 the United States recycled 33 percent of its solid waste. That recycling helped lighten our country's footprint.

Machines like this one are used to recycle many different plastics. Recycled plastic may be turned into new plastic containers.

Chapter 2

Other Sources of Energy

Fossil fuels, which provide almost 90 percent of the world's energy, are nonrenewable. Once used, they take millions of years to come back. Some economists think that the world's oil could run out by 2040.

Burning fossil fuels also creates greenhouse gases. These gases trap heat in Earth's atmosphere and warm the planet.

Many countries are creating and improving **alternative** energy sources, such as nuclear, solar, and wind power. Most of these resources are renewable.

Electric cars don't use gasoline or create pollution. However, recharging them is difficult.

Wind Power 

Wind is an endlessly renewable resource we can harvest for energy. Right now, it is the fastest growing alternative energy source.

Wind power causes little air pollution. However, some people dislike the way wind farms look. Others are concerned about the danger to birds and bats. The main problem with wind energy is the high cost of constructing wind farms.

Wind Power in Action

1. **Wind spins the blades, which turn the shaft.**
2. **The shaft turns a generator that makes electrical energy.**
3. **A transformer changes the electrical energy to usable electricity.**
4. **The electricity is delivered to buildings that are part of the nation's power grid.**

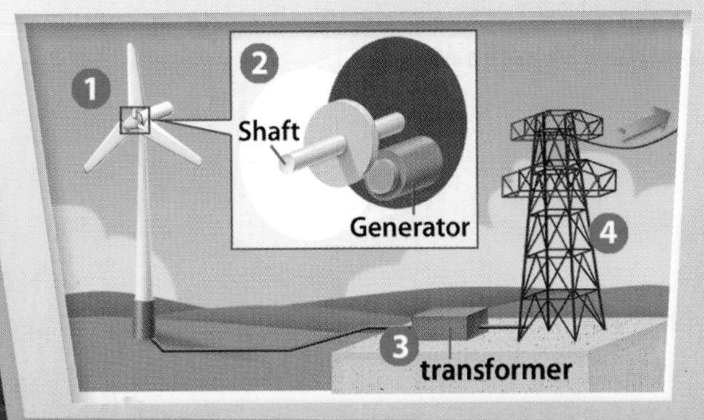

Using an alternative energy source, such as wind, can help conserve nonrenewable fossil fuels.

Solar Power

Sunlight is a renewable energy source that can be converted into solar power. To create solar energy, solar cells collect the sun's warmth. Solar energy can be used as heat or to produce electricity.

Using solar power has many benefits. It causes no pollution and can be created in most places. Sunlight is free and endlessly renewable.

However, the problems with solar power are the cost of the equipment and overcast days. A backup power source may be needed in places with many cloudy days.

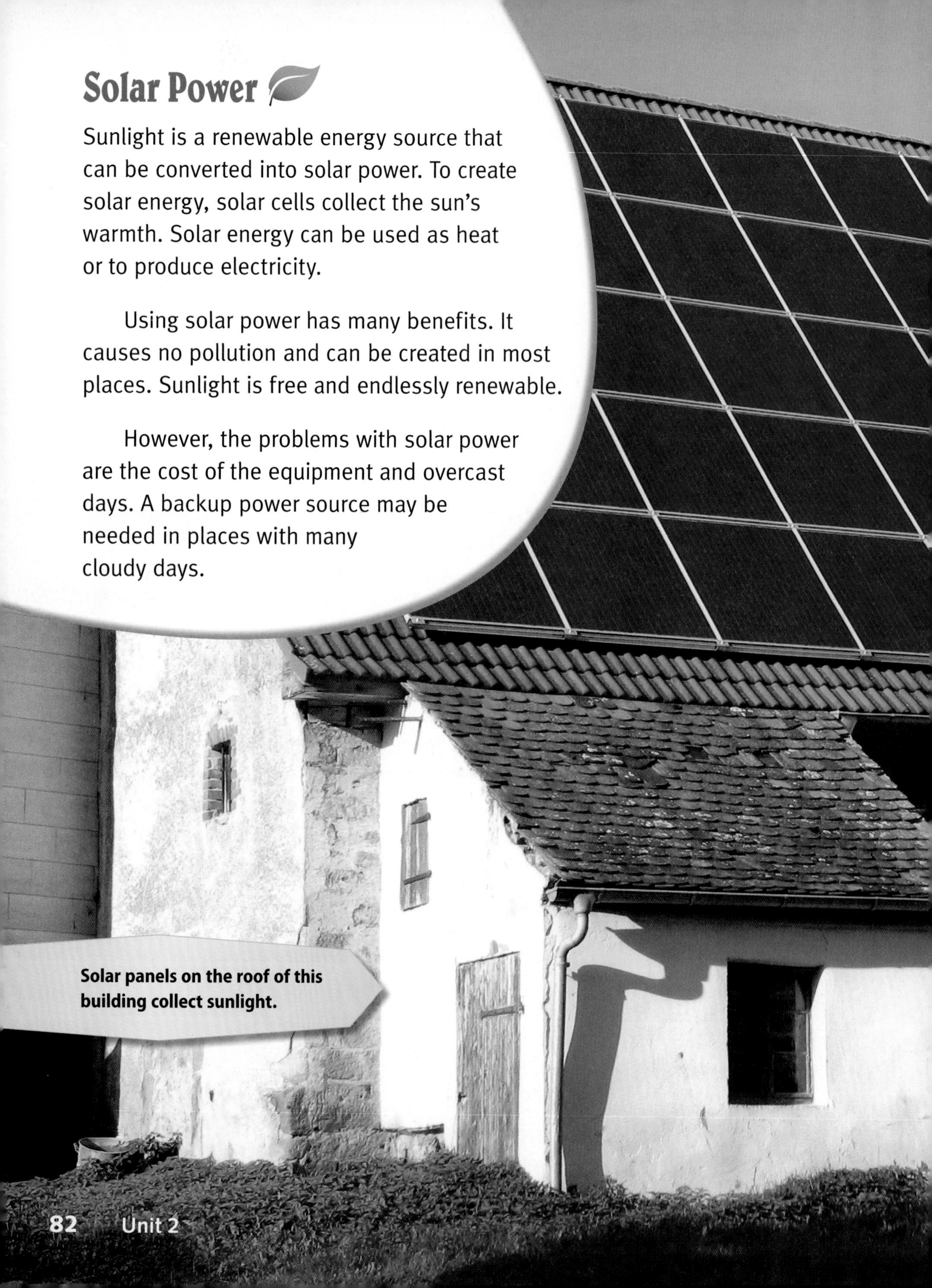

Solar panels on the roof of this building collect sunlight.

How Solar Energy Heats Water

In 2008 around 1.2 million buildings in the United States had solar energy systems. Homes used 80 percent of the generated power, often to heat water.

1. **Panels collect sunlight and store heat. A controller senses when the panels become hotter than the water in the tank.**
2. **The controller turns on a water pump. The pump brings cold water from the tank up to the collector on the roof.**
3. **Collected solar energy heats the water.**
4. **The system sends hot water back to the tank.**

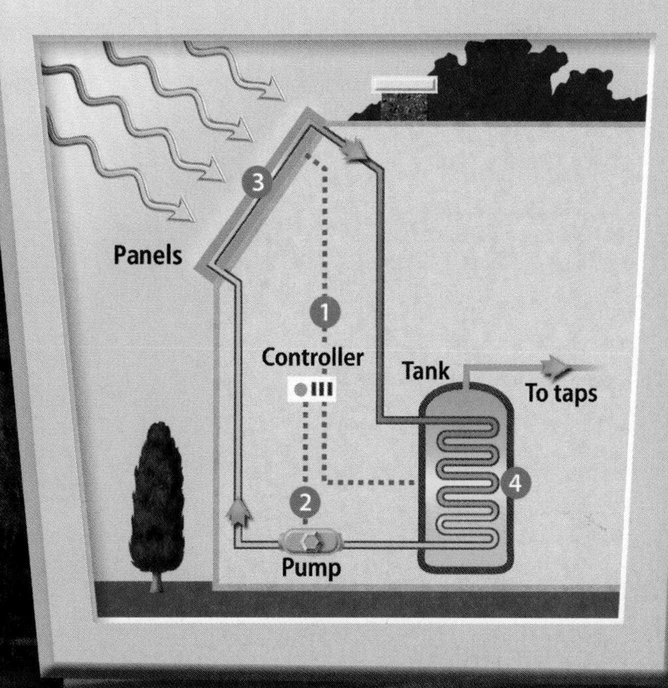

Biodiesel Power

Biodiesel is a renewable fuel made from vegetable oils or other agricultural resources. In the United States, soybean oil is used most commonly to make biodiesel. But other plants and recycled cooking oil are also used to make biodiesel.

Vehicles that use diesel fuel can use biodiesel and run almost the same way. High-grade biodiesels give off half the harmful greenhouse gas that diesel fuel gives off.

Crops such as soybeans can be converted into biodiesel fuel to run cars and trucks.

The Power of Pond Scum

Water plants called algae can also be used to make energy. Algae form slippery scum on ponds, lakes, and oceans. There is actually oil in the algae. Some plants are as much as 50 percent oil.

Algae is a promising source of fuel because it grows quickly. It also removes carbon dioxide, which contributes to global warming, from the air. But scientists are still working on a way to grow and harvest enough algae to make it a useful fuel source.

Algae grows all over the world in great amounts.

Research began in 1978 to study the use of algae as a renewable resource. Today researchers continue to search for the best algae to use for fuel.

Nuclear Power

Power from nuclear fission has provided alternative energy for many years. In nuclear fission, atoms are split apart, making smaller atoms. This releases energy. Atoms of uranium, a silvery metal found in the earth, are most often used.

A nuclear power plant converts the energy released from fission into electricity. Creating energy from nuclear fission is efficient and does not release greenhouse gases.

One problem with nuclear energy is nuclear waste. It can release cancer-causing radiation for hundreds of thousands of years. Another problem is nuclear accidents. Around fifty people died in Eastern Europe because of a nuclear accident that occurred in 1986.

Two uranium pellets make enough energy to power the average household for a month.

Nuclear power plants provide about 17 percent of the world's electricity.

Chapter 3

Gone Forever

Protecting Earth is important to *all* living things! But what happens if one plant or animal **species** becomes extinct, or goes away forever? Many other living things can suffer.

The extinction of one species can cause the extinction of another. In Singapore, a vine called *Tylophora* became extinct. The yellow glassy tiger butterfly fed from that vine's flowers. Now the butterfly is thought to be extinct.

The yellow glassy tiger butterfly lived in Singapore, a tiny island in Southeast Asia.

Today more than 1,200 species of animals are **endangered**. That means they could become extinct. Most animals become endangered because their **habitats**, or homes, are destroyed, and so fewer survive. A few, however, are hunted or fished too much. Some people believe these animals need to be protected by preserving their habitats and keeping them safe.

The right whale, the sea turtle, and the Florida panther are three animals that are in danger of becoming extinct. Let's take a look at them.

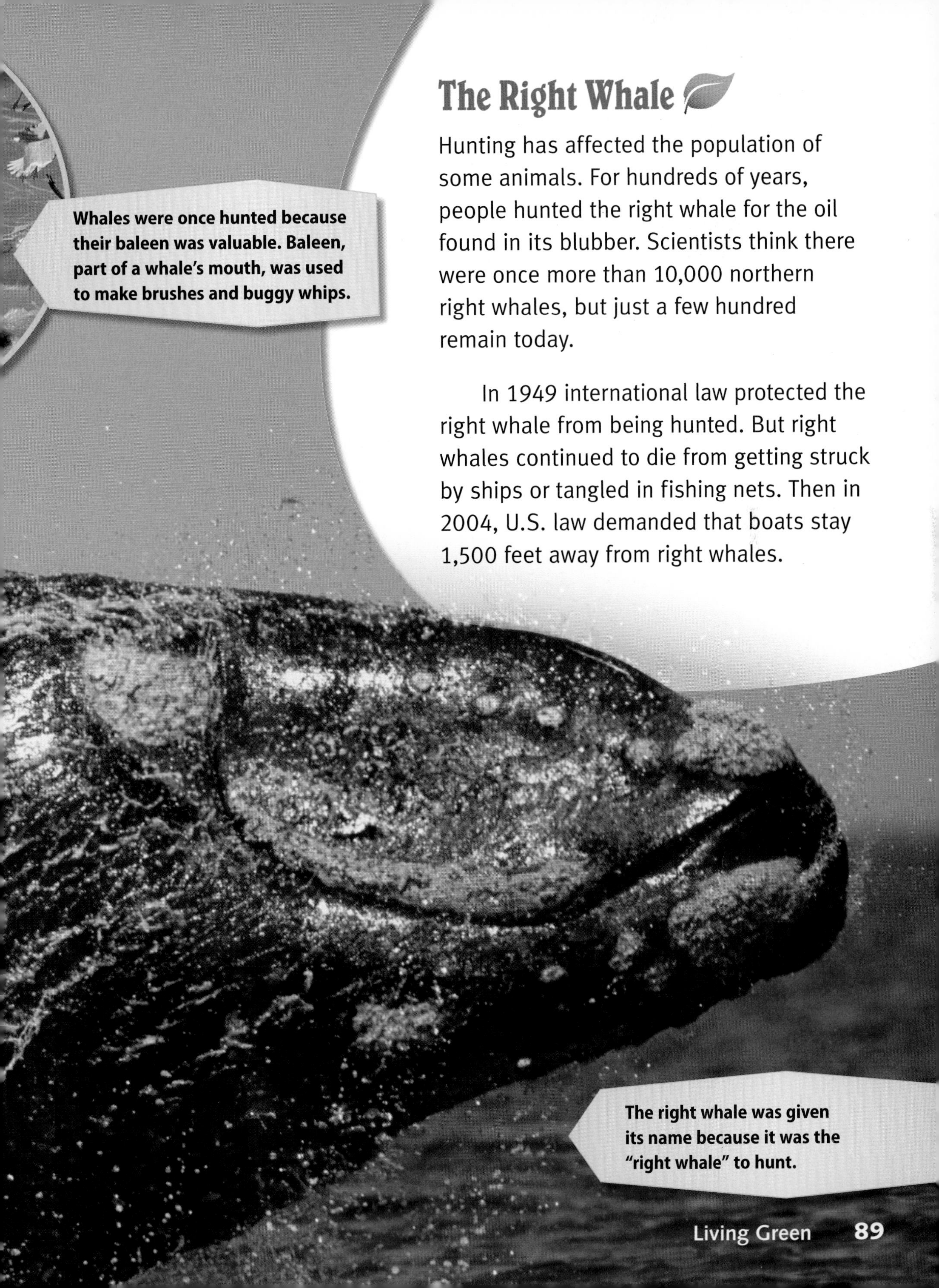

The Right Whale

Hunting has affected the population of some animals. For hundreds of years, people hunted the right whale for the oil found in its blubber. Scientists think there were once more than 10,000 northern right whales, but just a few hundred remain today.

In 1949 international law protected the right whale from being hunted. But right whales continued to die from getting struck by ships or tangled in fishing nets. Then in 2004, U.S. law demanded that boats stay 1,500 feet away from right whales.

Whales were once hunted because their baleen was valuable. Baleen, part of a whale's mouth, was used to make brushes and buggy whips.

The right whale was given its name because it was the "right whale" to hunt.

Sea Turtles

Other animals could disappear because their habitats have been harmed. The sea turtle is one example. Garbage left on beaches where sea turtles lay eggs affects baby sea turtles. Hatchlings walk to the sea at night, guided by moonlight. On the way, they can get stuck in fishing line or bags. Others mistake house lights for moonlight, and head inland and die.

The six sea turtle species in the United States are protected. Groups like Defenders of Wildlife volunteer to clean beaches and reduce lights in nesting areas.

baby green sea turtle

Florida Panthers 

Other animals are endangered because the areas where they live are shrinking. One of these animals is the Florida panther. Florida panthers need lots of space to hunt for food. Houses, farms, and highways have taken their hunting grounds away. Because of this, Florida panthers cannot find enough food to live.

Today about 100 Florida panthers are left in Florida. While it's against the law to kill them, many still die of hunger, disease, and other causes.

Large neighborhoods in Florida take land away from the Florida panther's habitat.

Florida panther

Chapter 4

Kids Are Planet Protectors

Are you too young to protect Earth's plants and animals? Here are some kids who would say, "No way!"

The kids of Enchanted Lake Elementary School in Kailua, Hawaii, are making a difference. They became Earth Protection Agents after agreeing to help preserve the environment. These kids are keeping the beaches clean where they live. They protect sea turtles by making sure the path to the ocean is clear.

Volunteers remove trash from beaches where endangered sea turtles nest.

Students at Country Meadows School in Buffalo Grove, Illinois, celebrate Earth Day by making paper and participating in other Earth-friendly activities.

The Earth Club kids are also making a difference. They attend Kildeer School in Buffalo Grove, Illinois. These kids asked their classmates to pack lunches that do not include anything they can throw away. Did their classmates meet the challenge?

Yes! They slipped sandwiches into reusable plastic tubs. They carried juice in jugs, not small plastic bottles. Instead of paper napkins, the kids used cloth. They ate with reusable nonplastic forks and spoons.

Green Goes to School

Many schools across the country are also going green. How? Some schools ban disposable plastic water bottles. Others trade regular light-bulbs for bulbs that use less energy. How can your school make a difference in protecting the planet?

How Green Can You Get?

You have read a lot about what other people are doing to save Earth's resources. But what can you do to protect the planet and use Earth's resources wisely? You can practice the three R's: reduce, reuse, recycle. Let's look at some ways you can practice the three R's every day.

Recycled plastic bottles can be made into many things, such as fiber for clothing, street signs, and structures like this greenhouse.

Waste Less and Make Less Waste

You can help Earth by buying less and wasting less. Recycle and reuse plastic bottles; it takes centuries for them to rot.

More than half of landfill waste is organic material that can be composted. You can compost your organic trash. Instead of putting that banana peel or grass clippings in the trash, put them in a compost pile. Compost can be used to help enrich the soil. You might even help start a community composting program.

Instead of throwing materials away, you can use them for creative projects.

By putting organic trash in a compost, you can reduce landfill waste and the pollution caused by waste removal systems.

A PET You Can Recycle

PET is an abbreviation for polyethylene terephthalate. That sounds strange, but it's just a kind of plastic. You've probably even used it! PET was created to make light, clear, and safe plastic bottles. Remember, don't throw them in the garbage. Place them in the recycling bin.

In 2005 around two million tons of electronic waste (e-waste) went to landfills. TVs, cell phones, and computer screens contain dangerous metals that pollute the air and poison drinking water.

If you need to get rid of an old computer or cell phone, take it to an e-waste center. There, e-waste can be safely handled and recycled.

Buying locally grown and organic produce lightens your affect on Earth by helping to reduce energy usage.

According to the Environmental Protection Agency, about 130 million cell phones were thrown away or recycled in 2008.

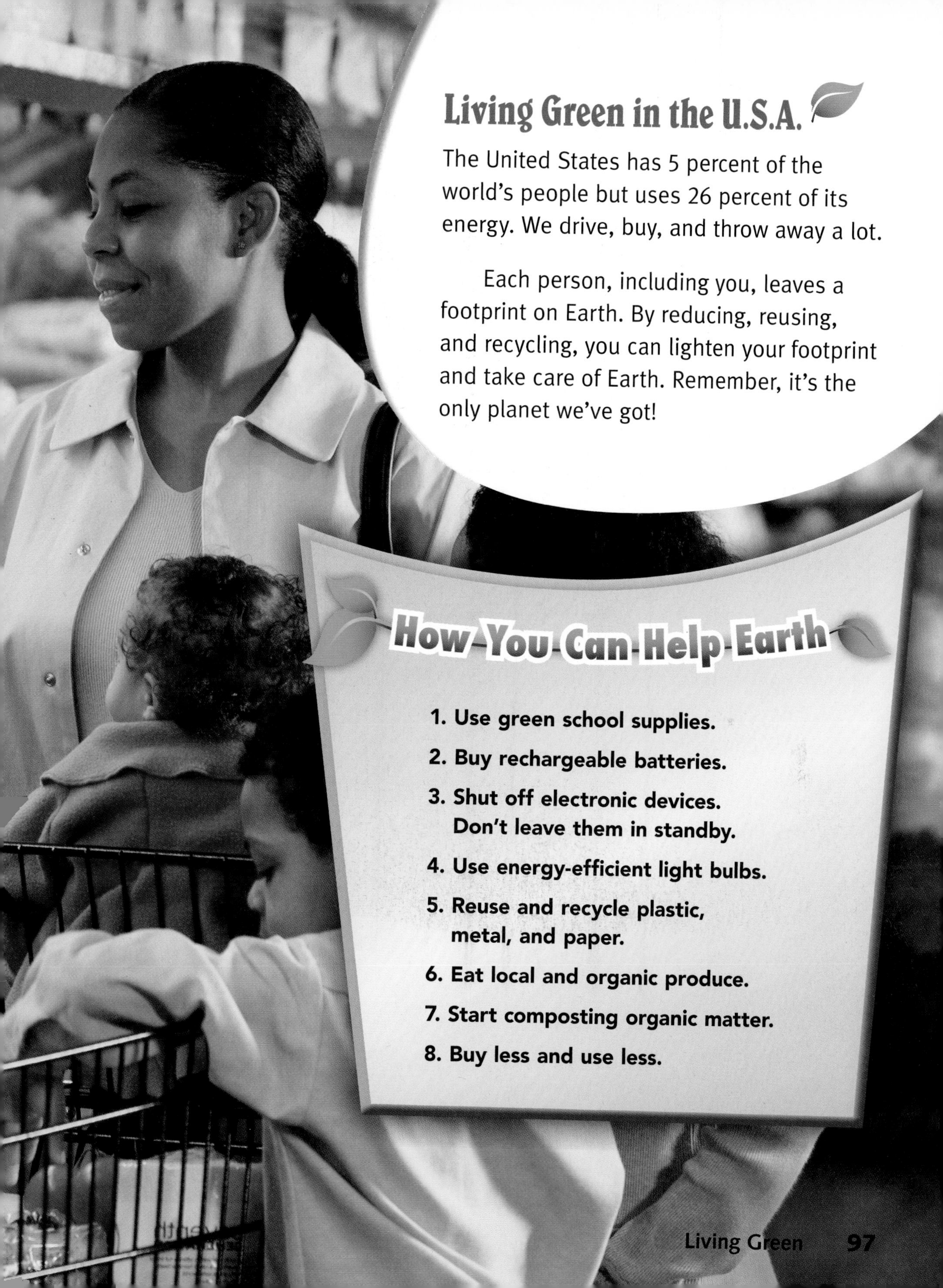

Living Green in the U.S.A.

The United States has 5 percent of the world's people but uses 26 percent of its energy. We drive, buy, and throw away a lot.

Each person, including you, leaves a footprint on Earth. By reducing, reusing, and recycling, you can lighten your footprint and take care of Earth. Remember, it's the only planet we've got!

How You Can Help Earth

1. **Use green school supplies.**
2. **Buy rechargeable batteries.**
3. **Shut off electronic devices. Don't leave them in standby.**
4. **Use energy-efficient light bulbs.**
5. **Reuse and recycle plastic, metal, and paper.**
6. **Eat local and organic produce.**
7. **Start composting organic matter.**
8. **Buy less and use less.**

The Big Ideas

Some resources are renewable, and some resources are nonrenewable. It is important to use all of Earth's resources wisely and protect Earth.

- We can protect Earth by practicing the three R's: reduce, reuse, recycle.
- Many of our current energy sources are disappearing. Some harm the environment. We must develop new, Earth-friendly sources of energy.
- We can protect other living creatures, such as plants and animals, by preserving their homes.
- There are many strategies we can use every day to conserve energy and protect our planet.

A Symphony of Whales

by Steve Schuch illustrated by Peter Sylvada

From the earliest time she could remember, Glashka had heard music inside her head. During the long dark winters, blizzards sometimes lasted for days. Then her family stayed indoors, close to the small fire. Glashka heard the songs calling to her out of the darkness, beyond even the voice of the wind.

The old ones of her village said, "That is the voice of Narna, the whale. Long has she been a friend to our people. She was a friend of our grandparents' grandparents; she was a friend before we saw the boats of strange men from other lands. But it is long now since one of us has heard her. It is a great gift you have." And Glashka would fall asleep, wrapped in her sealskin blanket, remembering their words.

The sea gave life to Glashka's village. The seals gave meat and warm furs to protect against the winter cold. In summer the people caught salmon and other fish, then salted them to keep for the hard times to come. And from Narna, the whale, the people received food for themselves and their sled dogs, waterproof skins for their parkas and boots, and oil for their lamps in the long winter darkness.

One year the snows came early. For three days a blizzard bore down on the village. When it finally stopped, Glashka's family needed supplies from the next village. Glashka asked if she might help drive the sled dogs. "It is not so easy to drive the sled," her parents said. "The dogs will know if you are uncertain of the way. But you will know the way home. Perhaps on the way back, you may try. Now go to sleep."

That night in her dreams, Glashka drove the dogsled. But the dogs did not follow her commands. Instead they led her to open water surrounded by ice. Glashka heard the singing of Narna, louder than she had ever heard it before. She awoke in the darkness of her sealskins, wondering what the dream had meant.

The morning was clear and cold as the family set out. The dogs made good time to the neighboring village. Before starting back, Glashka's parents packed the supplies into the sled. Glashka checked the dogs' feet for cuts. She rubbed their ears and necks. Glashka's parents gave her the reins. "We'll follow behind you. If your heart and words are clear, the dogs will listen and take you where you wish to go."

They set off. Across the ice, snow swirled as the wind began to pick up. Suddenly the sled dogs broke from the trail, yelping and twitching their ears. "What is it?" Glashka's parents shouted.

"I think they hear something," Glashka called back.

The sled dogs pulled harder. Their **keen** ears could pick up high-pitched notes that most humans couldn't hear. But Glashka, if she turned just right, could make out the eerie moans and whistles that grew louder until even her parents could hear them.

The dogs stopped short. They were right at the edge of a great bay of open water, surrounded on all sides by ice and snow.

Everywhere Glashka looked, the water seemed to be heaving and boiling, choked with white whales. Her father came up beside her. "Beluga whales," he said softly.

Glashka stared. "There must be more than a thousand of them."

The cries of the whales rose and fell on the wind as they swam slowly about. The dogs whined and pawed anxiously at the ice. "Let's hurry to the village," cried Glashka. "We'll get help!"

Glashka's father, though, knew there was no help. "They must have been trapped when they came here last fall looking for food," he said quietly. "There's nothing we can do to free them. When the last of the water freezes over, the whales will die."

But Glashka's mother remembered that an icebreaker, several winters ago, had **rescued** a Russian freighter trapped in the sea ice. "Could we call on the emergency radio? Maybe an icebreaker can clear a channel for the whales," she said.

Glashka and her parents raced back to their village. They gathered everyone together and told them what had happened. Glashka's father got on the emergency radio and put out a distress call. "Beluga whales, maybe thousands of them, trapped. We need an icebreaker. Can anyone hear me?"

Far out at sea, a great Russian icebreaker named the *Moskva* picked up the faint signal. "We read you," the captain radioed back. "We're on our way, but it may take us several weeks to reach you. Can you keep the whales alive until then?"

Some of the people from Glashka's village started setting up a base camp near the whales. Others set out by dogsled to alert the surrounding settlements.

Everyone came—young and old, parents, grandparents, and children. Day after day they chipped back the edges of the ice, trying to make more room for the whales to come up to breathe. "Look," said Glashka's grandmother. "See how the whales are taking turns, how they give the younger ones extra time for air."

As Glashka took her turn chipping back the ice, the song of Narna filled her ears again. She sang to the whales while she worked, trying to let them know help was on the way. Each day, Glashka looked anxiously for a ship. But each day, a little more water turned to ice. Each day, the whales got weaker from hunger.

Glashka knew how it felt to be hungry. The year before, her village had caught barely enough fish to make it through to spring. Sometimes the memory still gnawed at her. Even so, she gave the whales part of the fish from her lunch. The other villagers noticed and began to feed some of their own winter fish to the whales, too.

One morning Glashka awoke to the sounds of excited voices and barking dogs. The icebreaker had broken through the main channel during the night. "Hurry, Glashka," her parents called. Glashka pulled on her boots and parka and ran down the path to the water.

Everyone was gathered. Off to one side, the old ones stood, watching. They beckoned Glashka to join them. "Now," they said, "let us see what the whales will do."

The whales crowded together in fear, keeping as far from the icebreaker as possible. On board the ship, the captain gave orders. He hoped the whales would see the pathway cleared through the ice and follow the ship to safety. The icebreaker slowly turned around and faced back out to sea.

But the whales wouldn't follow the ship. "They may be afraid of the noise of our engines," the captain radioed to shore. "I've heard that trapped whales will sometimes follow the singing of other whales. We'll try playing a recording of whale songs."

Glashka felt a shiver down her back. "Narna's songs," she whispered to the sled dogs. "They're going to play Narna's songs."

Then the songs of the whales echoed over the water—deep moans and high whistling calls, ancient sounds from another world.

But the whales would not go near the ship. Again and again, the captain inched the giant icebreaker closer to the whales, then back toward the sea. But the whales stayed as far away as they could.

"It's no use," the captain radioed in despair. "And we can't stay beyond tomorrow. Already the channel is starting to refreeze!"

Glashka was near tears as she asked the old ones what could be done now. "Wait," they said. "Let us see what tomorrow brings."

That night the song of Narna came to Glashka again. Only this time it was different. She heard the music and voices of whales, but she heard other music, too . . . melodies she'd never heard before . . . . While it was still dark, Glashka woke her parents. "I've heard Narna again," she said. "And I've heard other music, too!"

"You have to tell the old ones," Glashka's parents said.

The old ones of the village listened carefully as Glashka told them what she had heard. "So, it is other music Narna is asking for," they said thoughtfully. "Long is the time, but once, it is said, humans and whales made music together. Perhaps the time has come again. Let us speak with the captain!"

Quickly Glashka and the old ones radioed the ship. "Have you any other music, people music, to play for the whales?" they asked. The captain said he would see what his crew could find.

First they tried playing rock and roll. The electric guitars and drums boomed, but the whales would not follow the ship.

Next the crew tried Russian folk music. It was softer, with many voices singing together. The whales swam a little closer, but still they would not follow the ship.

On shore, Glashka ran back to the radio transmitter. She had to talk with the captain. "I *know* there's other music that will work. Please keep trying!" she told him.

The crew found some classical music. First the sweet sounds of violins and violas, next the deeper notes of the cellos and, deepest of all, the string basses . . . and way up high, a solo violin . . . .

Everyone fell silent as the melody carried over the water. The whales grew quiet, too, listening.

A few whales started to sing back to the ship, and to each other. Gradually more whales joined in.

Then . . . they began to swim toward the ship!

Cautiously the captain started the huge engines and headed slowly out to sea. One whale followed, then another, then a few more. Soon all the whales were following the ship through the narrow channel, past the broken chunks of ice, back to the safety of the open ocean.

On shore, people laughed and cried and hugged each other. The sled dogs jumped up and barked, trying to lick the noses and faces of anyone they could reach. Glashka buried her wet face in the fur of the dogs' necks. "Such good, good dogs," she told them over and over. "Such good dogs. Now the whales are going home!"

On board the ship, the captain and his crew raised every flag. The music played as the captain radioed to say the whales were safe. He and his crew were finally going home, too.

Glashka and her family looked out to sea. They waved to the icebreaker and the disappearing whales. "And do you hear Narna singing now?" her grandmother asked.

"Yes," Glashka said, "but it isn't just Narna I hear now. It's something bigger than that . . . something like a whole symphony of whales!"

HISTORICAL NOTES

This tale was inspired by a true story. In the winter of 1984–1985, nearly three thousand beluga whales were found trapped in the Senyavina Strait of Siberia, a narrow body of water across the Bering Strait from Alaska. With the bitter cold, the water was freezing rapidly. In places the sea ice was twelve feet thick. For seven weeks, the people of the Chukchi Peninsula and the crew of the icebreaker *Moskva* risked their lives to save those whales. Against all odds, they succeeded.

There are several other recorded instances of rescuers leading trapped whales to safety by playing whale songs. But to my knowledge, the Chukchi rescue was the first time whales ever followed an icebreaker playing classical music. Was it Beethoven? Or Mozart? Or Tchaikovsky? The Soviet newspaper accounts don't say. That part of the story is still untold.

—Steve Schuch

UNIT 3

A Nation's Beginnings

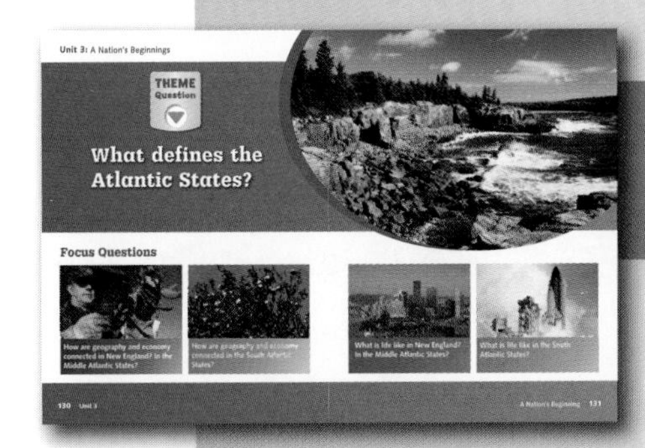

What defines the Atlantic States?

Focus Questions

How are geography and economy connected in New England? In the Middle Atlantic States?

How are geography and economy connected in the South Atlantic States?

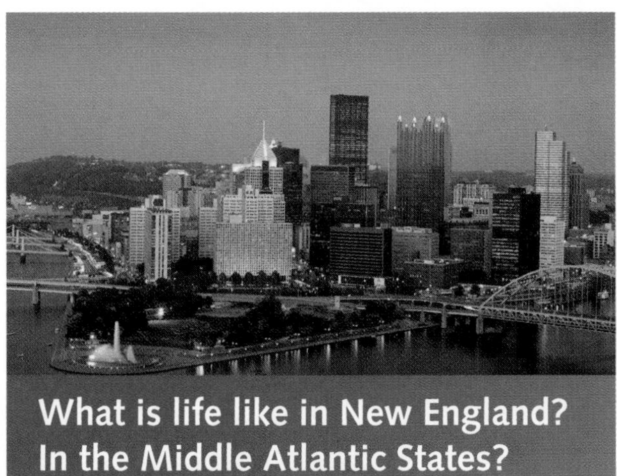

What is life like in New England? In the Middle Atlantic States?

What is life like in the South Atlantic States?

A TOUR of the Atlantic States

by Liane Onish

Contents

Introduction: The Atlantic States

Let's visit the Atlantic States, which extend from Maine in the north to the southern tip of Florida. These states are often called the East Coast of the United States. A coast is land that touches water, and much of the area known as the East Coast lies along the Atlantic Ocean. The East Coast includes three **regions**, or areas, of the United States: New England, the Middle Atlantic, and the South Atlantic. Seventeen states, along with Washington, D.C., our capital, make up the East Coast.

The East Coast is a big place. We'll learn about it by looking at its

- geography—the area's land and water,
- **economy**—how people in the area make a living,
- history—how the area's past shaped the present, and
- culture—the area's traditions, beliefs, and ways of life.

Got a warm coat? Good! We'll begin our visit to the East Coast by heading north to New England.

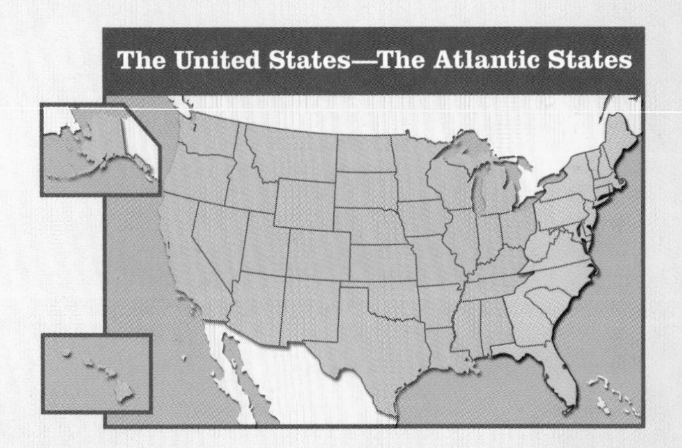

The United States—The Atlantic States

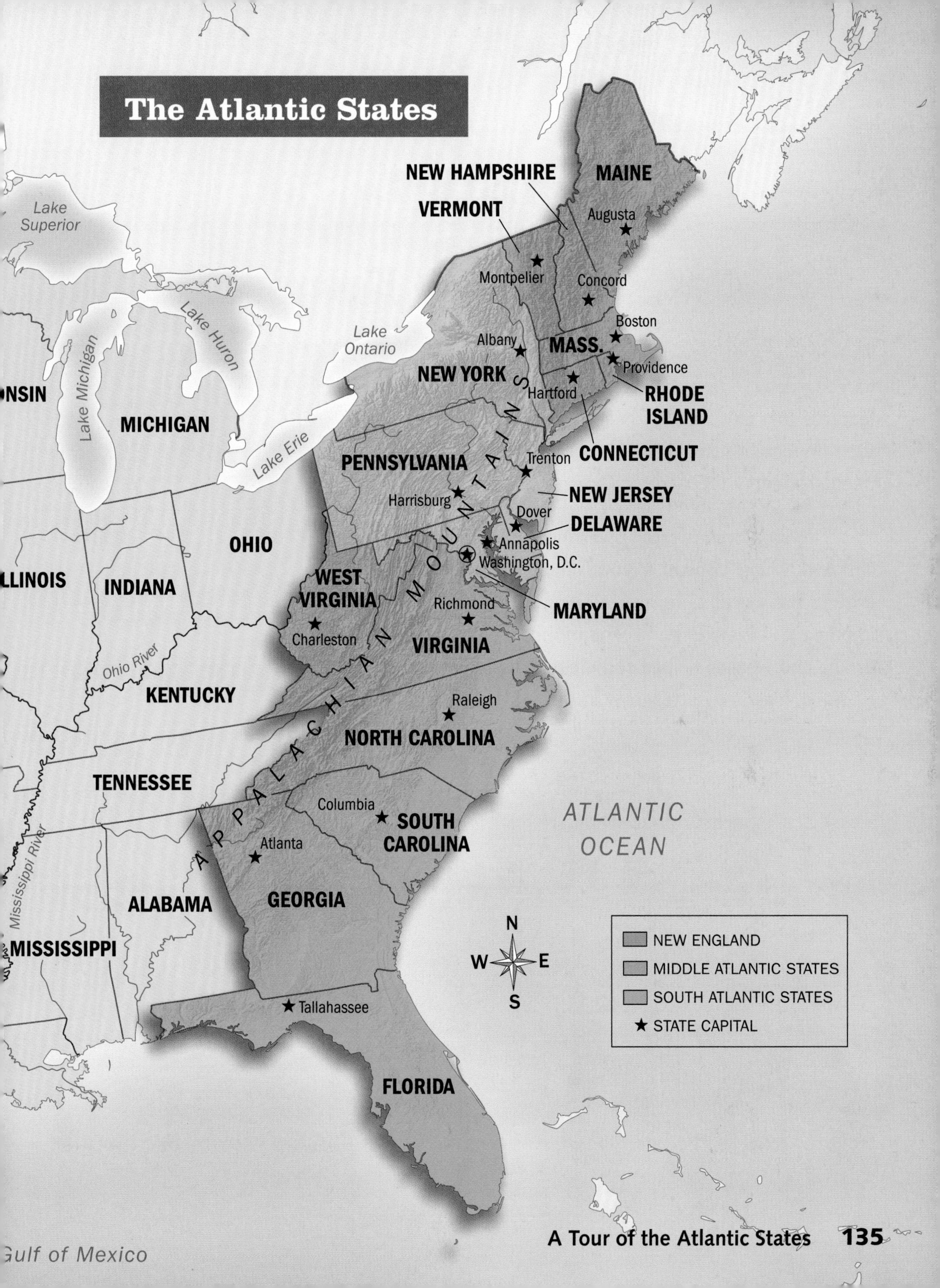
The Atlantic States
NEW HAMPSHIRE
MAINE
VERMONT
Augusta
Montpelier
Concord
Lake Superior
Lake Huron
Lake Michigan
Lake Ontario
Lake Erie
Boston
Albany
MASS.
Providence
NEW YORK
Hartford
RHODE ISLAND
NSIN
MICHIGAN
CONNECTICUT
Trenton
PENNSYLVANIA
NEW JERSEY
Harrisburg
Dover
DELAWARE
Annapolis
OHIO
Washington, D.C.
LLINOIS
INDIANA
WEST VIRGINIA
Richmond
MARYLAND
Charleston
VIRGINIA
APPALACHIAN MOUNTAINS
Ohio River
KENTUCKY
Raleigh
NORTH CAROLINA
TENNESSEE
Columbia
SOUTH CAROLINA
ATLANTIC OCEAN
Atlanta
Mississippi River
ALABAMA
GEORGIA
N
W
E
S
MISSISSIPPI
NEW ENGLAND
MIDDLE ATLANTIC STATES
SOUTH ATLANTIC STATES
STATE CAPITAL
Tallahassee
FLORIDA
Gulf of Mexico

New England

Geography *and* Economy

The economy of New England is connected to its geography. There are many land and water features that influence, or help build, the economy. One important feature is the coast, which has been shaped by the Atlantic Ocean.

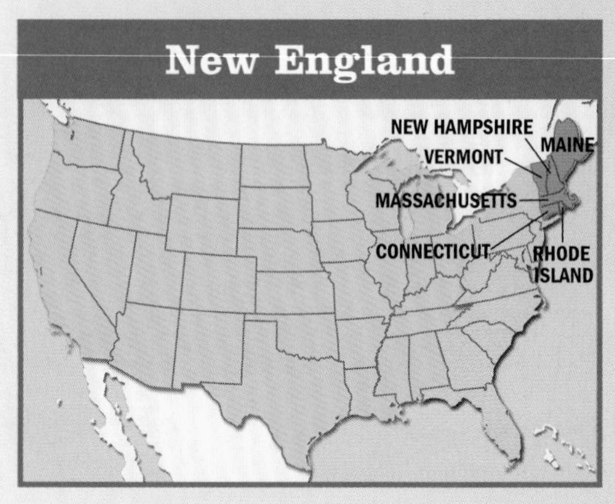

The cold ocean water is terrific for lobster and cod fishing. Lobster from Maine is shipped around the world. Long ago, whaling was important in New England. The money from fishing and whaling helped some cities, such as New Bedford, Massachusetts, grow into important ports.

Vermont is famous for its maple syrup. The syrup is made from the sap of sugar maple trees.

Lobster fishing provides thousands of jobs for Maine residents.

But New England is not just about water. You can also see great forests in Vermont, New Hampshire, and Maine. In the fall, deep reds and yellows fill the forests. Long ago the trees were cut down to build ships. Today the trees are used for more than just construction. Maple syrup also comes from trees growing in Vermont.

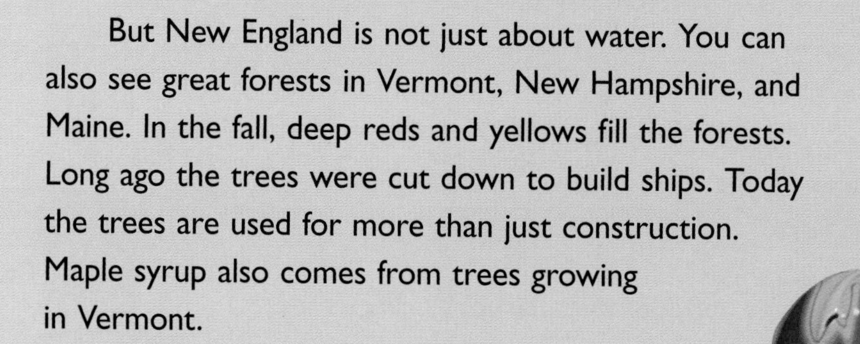

The mountains are another important land feature of New England. The Green Mountains of Vermont and the White Mountains of New Hampshire are home to many ski resorts. Tourism in these areas provides jobs for people.

New Hampshire is called the White Mountain State because it contains the White Mountain range.

The soil in New England is thin and rocky. Yet many wonderful foods grow well in New England. Cape Cod in Massachusetts has many bogs, or places where the soil is very soft and wet. Cranberries grow well here.

Because of the industries and jobs that harbors bring, many cities have grown along the New England coast. The New London Harbor in Connecticut is home to an important U.S. Navy submarine base.

In 1872 the New London Navy Yard was built. Today the base houses 17 submarines.

New England
History and Culture

The history and culture of New England are connected in many ways to its geography. The first people to live in the region were Native Americans. They used the many natural resources from the land and water to live. In the forests they hunted deer and other animals. They also grew corn, squash, and beans in small gardens.

Maize, or corn, was very important to Native Americans. Many Native American stories, traditions, and ceremonies celebrate maize.

One group of Native Americans who lived in New England was the Wampanoag. They used trees from the forests to make their canoes and homes. In the rivers and lakes, they fished with spears and nets. Along the Atlantic coast they gathered shellfish.

The Wampanoag made dugout canoes, like this replica, by hollowing out large trees.

The Pilgrims

In 1620 Pilgrims sailed from England across the Atlantic Ocean toward the colony of Virginia. But the ship was blown off course and the Pilgrims landed far north of Virginia. They called the region New England, in honor of their home country. Their first permanent settlement was in Plymouth, Massachusetts.

Afterward, more colonists came from England and they settled throughout New England. They held town meetings, which were open to almost everyone. They talked about the important matters, or **issues**, of the day. Every family could feel that it had a voice in the new colony.

Town meetings were beneficial around the time of the American Revolution.

The *Mayflower II* is a replica of the *Mayflower*, which landed at Plymouth on December 21, 1620.

A New Nation Is Born 

The colonists worked hard and the region grew. Cities, such as Boston, Massachusetts, and Newport, Rhode Island, became important centers of commerce and trade. Over time, the people of New England wanted a stronger voice in government. They disagreed with the laws and taxes that Britain made for the colonies.

In April 1775, colonists began fighting the British for their freedom. The people of New England played an important role in the Revolutionary War and the founding of the United States of America.

The Battle of Concord in 1775 marked the beginning of the American Revolution. American colonists protected Concord, Massachusetts, from British troops.

At the Rhode Island School of Design, students can learn to create many things, including furniture.

A Land of Learning

New England has long been a center of learning and culture. It is the home of North America's first college, Harvard University, which was built just 16 years after the Pilgrims landed. Today, Harvard is one of the top universities in the United States.

New England is home to many other important colleges and universities. The Rhode Island School of Design in Providence, Rhode Island, is noted as a center for education in the arts.

Route 128

Route 128 was built to ease traffic in Boston, but it did far more. It became "America's Technology Highway." The first modern industrial parks were built along the route. These were perfect for the needs of the growing technology companies in Massachusetts. Students from nearby colleges also benefit from the highway when they travel.

CHAPTER 3

Middle Atlantic States

Geography *and* Economy

Now let's head south to the region that includes the Middle Atlantic States. Just as in New England, the water and land features of the region have influenced the economy here. The Middle Atlantic States have rivers and deep harbors that are great for fishing and shipping. You will also find warmer weather and richer soil that is good for farming.

Middle Atlantic States

The Hudson River played an important role in the settlement of New York City. The Hudson also allowed settlers to move inland and ship their goods to market.

The Hudson River flows into a deep harbor. Harbors make it easy to ship goods. Therefore, industries and cities grow up around them. The mouth of the Hudson River meets the Atlantic Ocean in New York City.

As trade along the Hudson River grew, so did New York City. Today it is America's center of finance. The important financial industry **supports**, or gives jobs to, many people.

Other centers of commerce and industry include Philadelphia, Pennsylvania, and Baltimore, Maryland. Both of these cities have safe harbors for transporting goods to and from their regions.

Baltimore, Maryland, is located on the Patapsco River, which empties into the Atlantic Ocean. Baltimore's harbor is important to the state's economy.

Steel mills grew in Pittsburgh, Pennsylvania, where three great rivers meet: the Allegheny, Monongahela, and Ohio rivers.

Coal mining and steel production once played a major role in the economy of Pittsburgh and other areas of western Pennsylvania. Today the area has many jobs in finance, health care, and business services.

The rich farmlands of New Jersey and Pennsylvania produce fruits, vegetables, and dairy products. Known as the Garden State, New Jersey provides the region with many fresh foods. Pennsylvania's dairy industry is an important part of the state's economy.

Pennsylvania grows more than 73 million pounds of pumpkins each year.

CHAPTER 4

Middle Atlantic States

History *and* Culture

The first people to settle what are now the Middle Atlantic States were Native Americans. Many Iroquois tribes lived in the region. They used its rich natural resources to live. Tree bark covered their large homes, called longhouses. Iroquois women grew corn, beans, and squash. Iroquois men fished in the region's waters and hunted in its forests.

Most Iroquois built longhouses similar to this replica. Some longhouses were as long as 400 feet, or about the length of a football field.

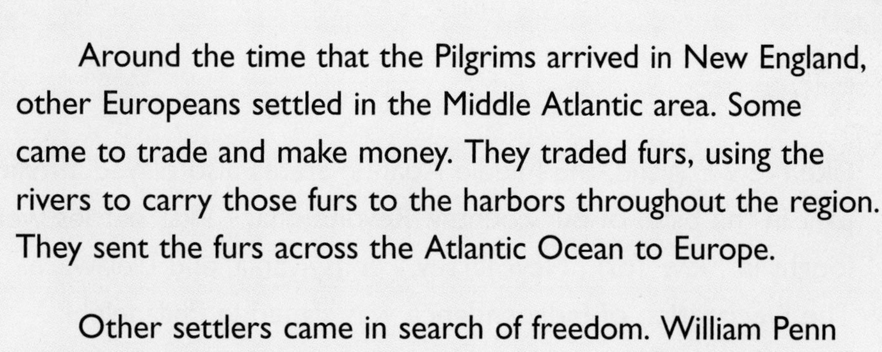

Around the time that the Pilgrims arrived in New England, other Europeans settled in the Middle Atlantic area. Some came to trade and make money. They traded furs, using the rivers to carry those furs to the harbors throughout the region. They sent the furs across the Atlantic Ocean to Europe.

Other settlers came in search of freedom. William Penn founded the state of Pennsylvania to give a religious group a place to practice their beliefs. They were called the Quakers.

People from all over the world still come to the Middle Atlantic States. For example, more than one-third of the workers in New York City today were born in other countries.

In 1681 William Penn founded the state of Pennsylvania. Today a statue of Penn sits on top of Philadelphia's City Hall.

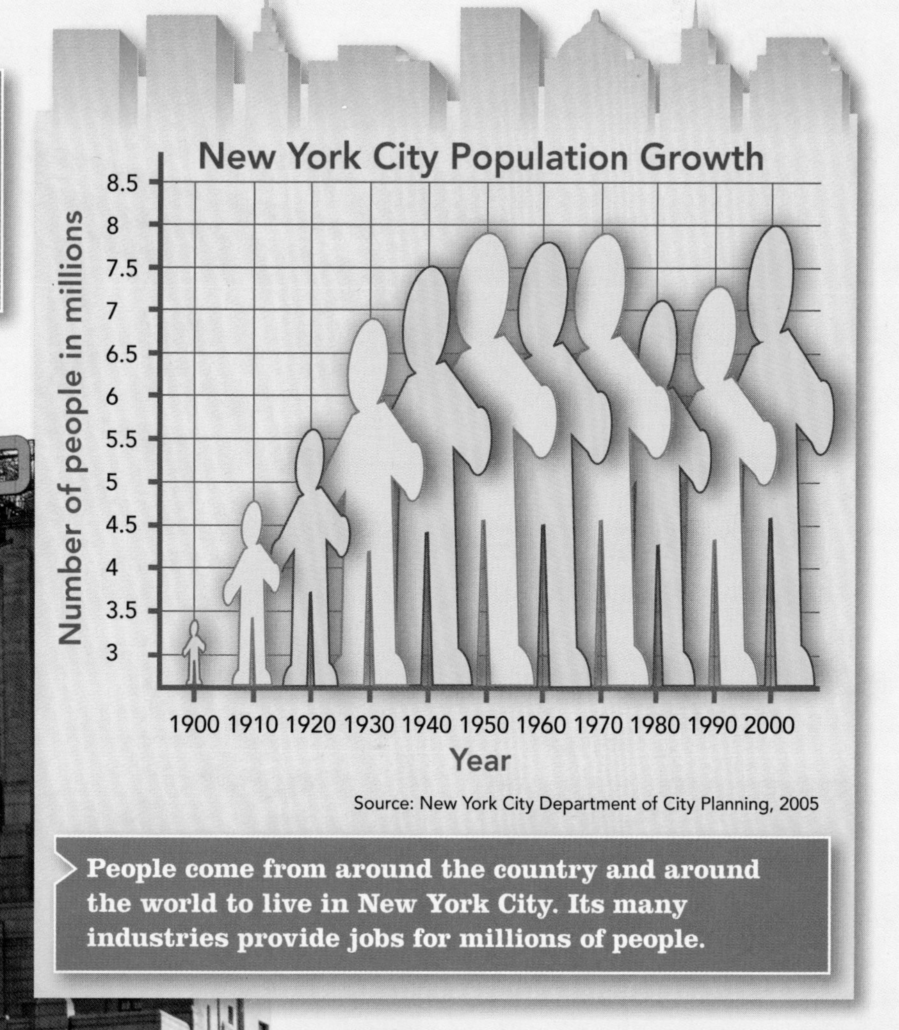

People come from around the country and around the world to live in New York City. Its many industries provide jobs for millions of people.

The Revolutionary War

Like New England, the Middle Atlantic States also played a major part in the birth of our country. Revolutionary War battles were fought in New York, New Jersey, Pennsylvania, and Delaware. The Declaration of Independence was signed in Philadelphia, Pennsylvania. Did you know that the first capital of the United States was New York City?

You can see that the Middle Atlantic States were important in our country's history!

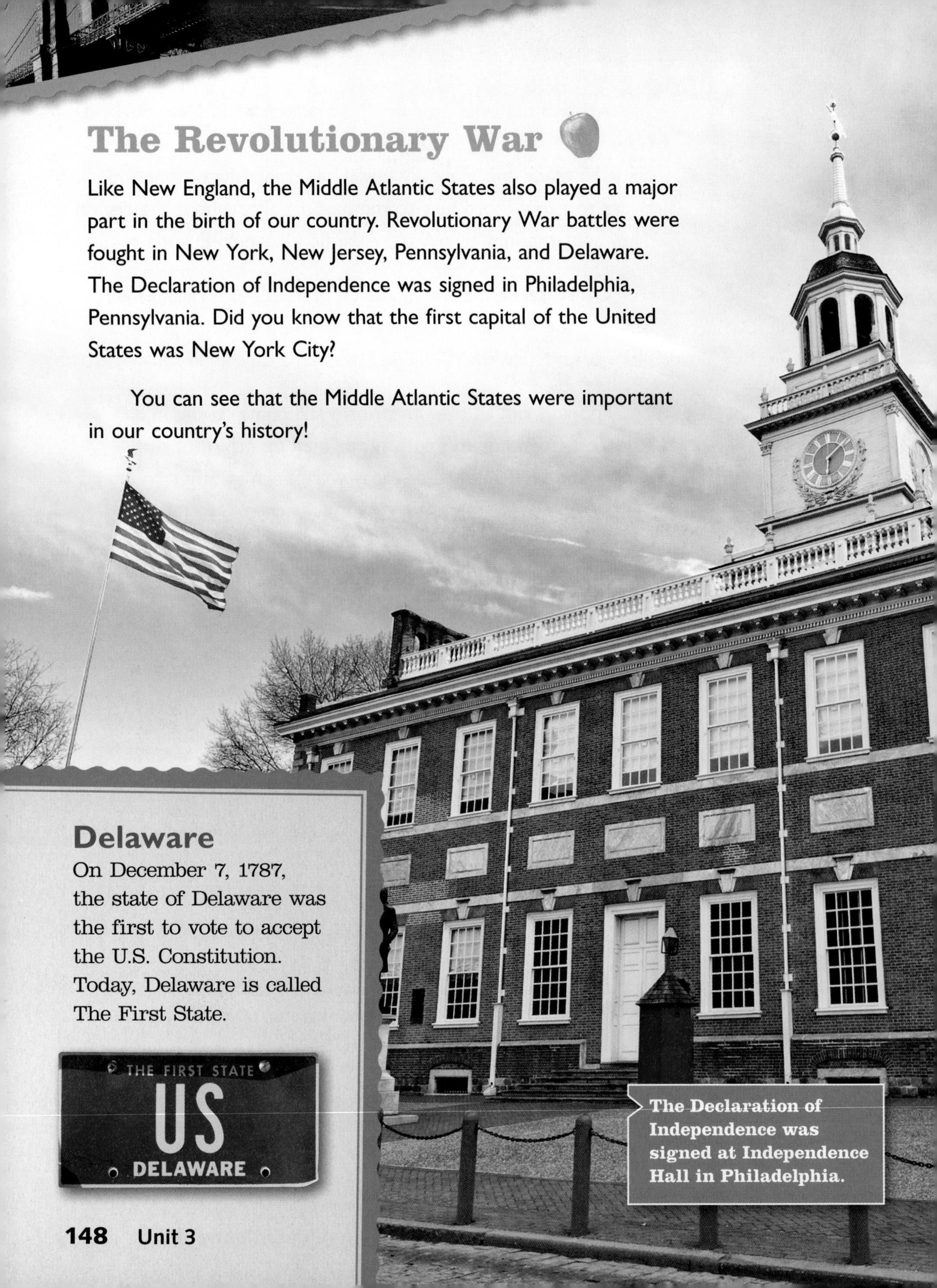

The Declaration of Independence was signed at Independence Hall in Philadelphia.

Delaware

On December 7, 1787, the state of Delaware was the first to vote to accept the U.S. Constitution. Today, Delaware is called The First State.

The Middle Atlantic States Today

The East Coast has many people living in cities that are close together. Three cities within the Middle Atlantic States played important roles in shaping the country's past and present.

New York City is a financial and cultural center of the United States. The earliest European settlers established it as a trading center. Today it plays an important role in economies around the world. New York is also noted for its vibrant cultural life.

The Wall Street Bull, in the Financial District of New York City, represents the power of the United States economy.

Philadelphia is an important historic city. Here independence was declared and the first government of the new nation was formed. Today, Philadelphia is an industrial center for the region.

The Liberty Bell, outside of Independence Hall in Philadelphia, is a symbol of freedom.

Washington, D.C., is the center of the federal government. The Supreme Court meets here and the President works in the White House.

The country's laws are created and passed in the U.S. Capitol, located in Washington, D.C.

CHAPTER 5

South Atlantic States
Geography and Economy

You won't need your warm coat where we're headed next! We're moving down the East Coast to the South Atlantic States. This region's geography and economy are different from those of New England and the Middle Atlantic States. But like these regions, the economy is affected by its geography.

Many of the states here touch the Atlantic Ocean, which allows for major fishing and shipping industries. Just off the west coast of Florida, there's another large body of water—the Gulf of Mexico. Here, in the warmer waters of the South Atlantic States, people catch shrimp and tuna.

The Gulf Coast

All that water is a rich resource for the region. Along the coasts of Virginia, the Carolinas, and Florida, you will find sandy beaches and resorts. Tourism is an important part of the economy here.

If you visit Florida, you won't want to miss the Everglades. This huge wetlands area is actually a slow-moving river that is miles wide but just inches deep. This important ecosystem is home to hundreds of different kinds of animals.

For many years animals in the Everglades were hunted in large numbers. Today, laws protect many of these animals, such as the alligator.

The Florida Everglades is home to many different plants. There are about 100 kinds of marsh plants, which live in water for all or most of the year.

Rich Farmland

The South Atlantic's soil along the Atlantic Ocean and the Gulf of Mexico is rich and **fertile**. Also, the weather here is much warmer than up north, which means a longer growing season. As a **consequence**, or result, many different crops can grow in this region.

Because peanuts need long summers and steady rain, the South Atlantic is an ideal place to grow them.

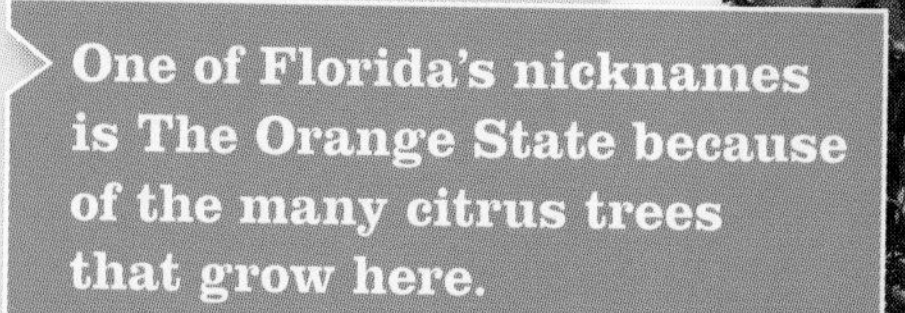
One of Florida's nicknames is The Orange State because of the many citrus trees that grow here.

Cotton is one of the many crops grown in the South Atlantic States. You can find fields of white puffs of cotton throughout Georgia. In Virginia and North Carolina, many farmers grow tobacco. Another significant crop grown in this region is peanuts. Georgia is the number-one state for growing them. That's not all! Did you have orange juice for breakfast? It most likely came from Florida, which grows most of the country's oranges.

West Virginia is a national leader in coal production.

Mining and Logging

The Appalachian Mountains are a major feature of the South Atlantic States. In the mountains of West Virginia, miners find coal, which is important to the state's economy.

There are also many forests in the South Atlantic States. Trees from these forests play a major part in the economy of North Carolina. These trees are used to build furniture and as Christmas trees. There's even a chance that the paper you write on is made from a North Carolina tree!

In 1926 the world's largest chest of drawers was built in High Point, North Carolina. It is a symbol of the region's furniture industry.

CHAPTER 6

South Atlantic States

History *and* Culture

Many Native American groups first settled the South Atlantic States. The Creek were Native Americans who lived in present-day Georgia and Florida. Like most Native Americans on the East Coast, they fished in the Atlantic Ocean for food. They also hunted in the Everglades, the large, wet marsh that covers more than 4,300 square miles in Florida.

The Catawba people settled in what is now the Carolinas. They used the fertile soil to grow crops. Did you guess that these crops included beans, squash, and corn?

In the hot, swampy Florida Everglades, the Creek people built chickees similar to this one. Stilts kept their homes dry, and open sides let in cooling breezes.

Colonial South Atlantic

In 1607, colonists settled in Jamestown, Virginia, the first English colony in America. At first, life in Jamestown was hard because the settlers didn't know how to farm the land. They often needed to trade their tools for food with the Native Americans. Later, colonists learned to grow tobacco, a valuable plant.

Colonists from Virginia played important roles in early America. George Washington led the Revolutionary Army and later was chosen to be the first President of the United States. Our country's capital, Washington, D.C., is named after him. Thomas Jefferson, also from Virginia, wrote most of the Declaration of Independence. He became the country's third President.

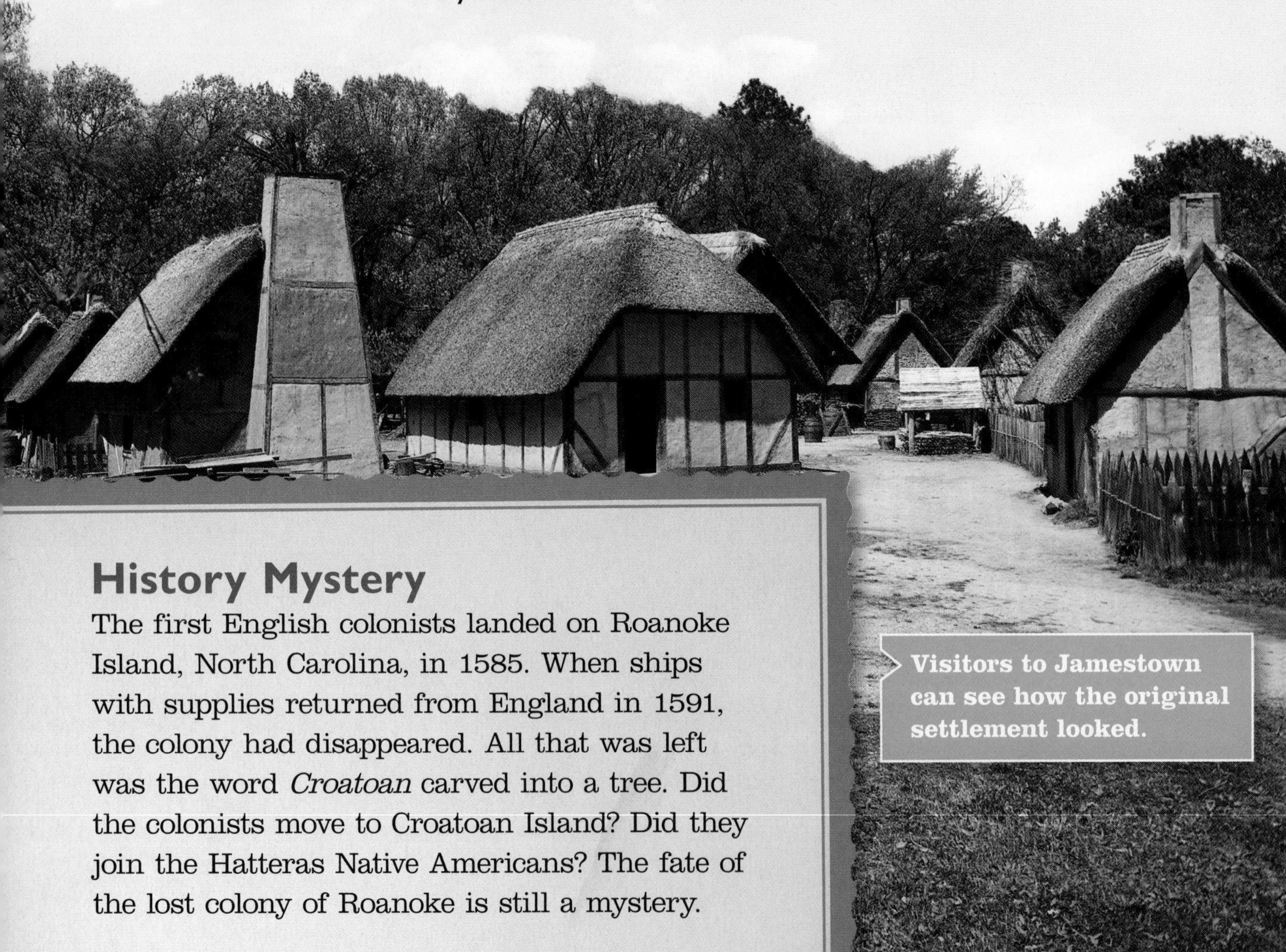

Visitors to Jamestown can see how the original settlement looked.

History Mystery

The first English colonists landed on Roanoke Island, North Carolina, in 1585. When ships with supplies returned from England in 1591, the colony had disappeared. All that was left was the word *Croatoan* carved into a tree. Did the colonists move to Croatoan Island? Did they join the Hatteras Native Americans? The fate of the lost colony of Roanoke is still a mystery.

Other colonies were formed. In 1663 the Carolinas were established by the Lords Proprietors, wealthy English nobility. Wars with Native Americans and crop failures prevented the colony from growing. When the wars ended and colonists learned to grow rice, the Carolinas flourished.

In 1732 the colony of Georgia was established by the Lords Proprietors. The proprietors created many rules that Georgia's colonists protested, such as forbidding slavery. Eventually the king of England took over both colonies.

During the Revolutionary War, George Washington (center) led American troops in an attack on British troops. The attack was one of the first significant victories in the war.

Thomas Jefferson

Thomas Jefferson was born in 1743 in Virginia. When he was thirty-three years old, Jefferson wrote the Declaration of Independence. In 1797 he became the second Vice President of the United States, and in 1801 he was elected the third President. He went on to found the University of Virginia, which continues to provide students with an excellent education. His home, Monticello, is visited by many people each year.

The South Atlantic Today

The South Atlantic States are an exciting place to be. You can see the history of the region in many of the older sections of its cities. Charleston, South Carolina, is known for its southern hospitality and the beautiful old homes along its waterfront.

Step back in time at Colonial Williamsburg in Virginia. You can experience village life as it was in the 1700s. See how people lived and worked, as actors play the parts of colonists going about their daily lives.

Charleston, South Carolina, was settled by English colonists in 1670.

Williamsburg was home to Virginia's first theater, newspaper, and paper mill. It was the cultural center of Virginia.

Visit Atlanta, the capital of Georgia, and you will see a modern, high-tech city that is a center of trade and manufacturing. Another place not to be missed is the Kennedy Space Center in Cape Canaveral, Florida. Here you can learn about the U.S. space program. You might even see a space shuttle launch!

Cape Canaveral launched the first U.S. manned flight into space as well as the first manned lunar landing.

Sum It Up

The Atlantic States

The Atlantic Coast is shaped by its geography, economy, history, and culture. The geography and natural resources of the Atlantic States still draw people today. The Atlantic Ocean and Appalachian Mountains support many kinds of work. The fertile lands around the Atlantic Ocean and the Gulf of Mexico are ideal for farming. The rivers and harbors in these regions make it easy to ship goods all over the world.

Many different people have settled along the Atlantic Coast. They have all added to the region's wonderful culture.

Henry and the Kite Dragon

BRUCE EDWARD HALL • *illustrated by* WILLIAM LOW

My name is Henry Chu. I am eight years old.

I live in a place called Chinatown in New York City. Chinatown is very small—pretty much just three tiny streets, all narrow and crooked, like a village in China would be.

老山東鍋貼

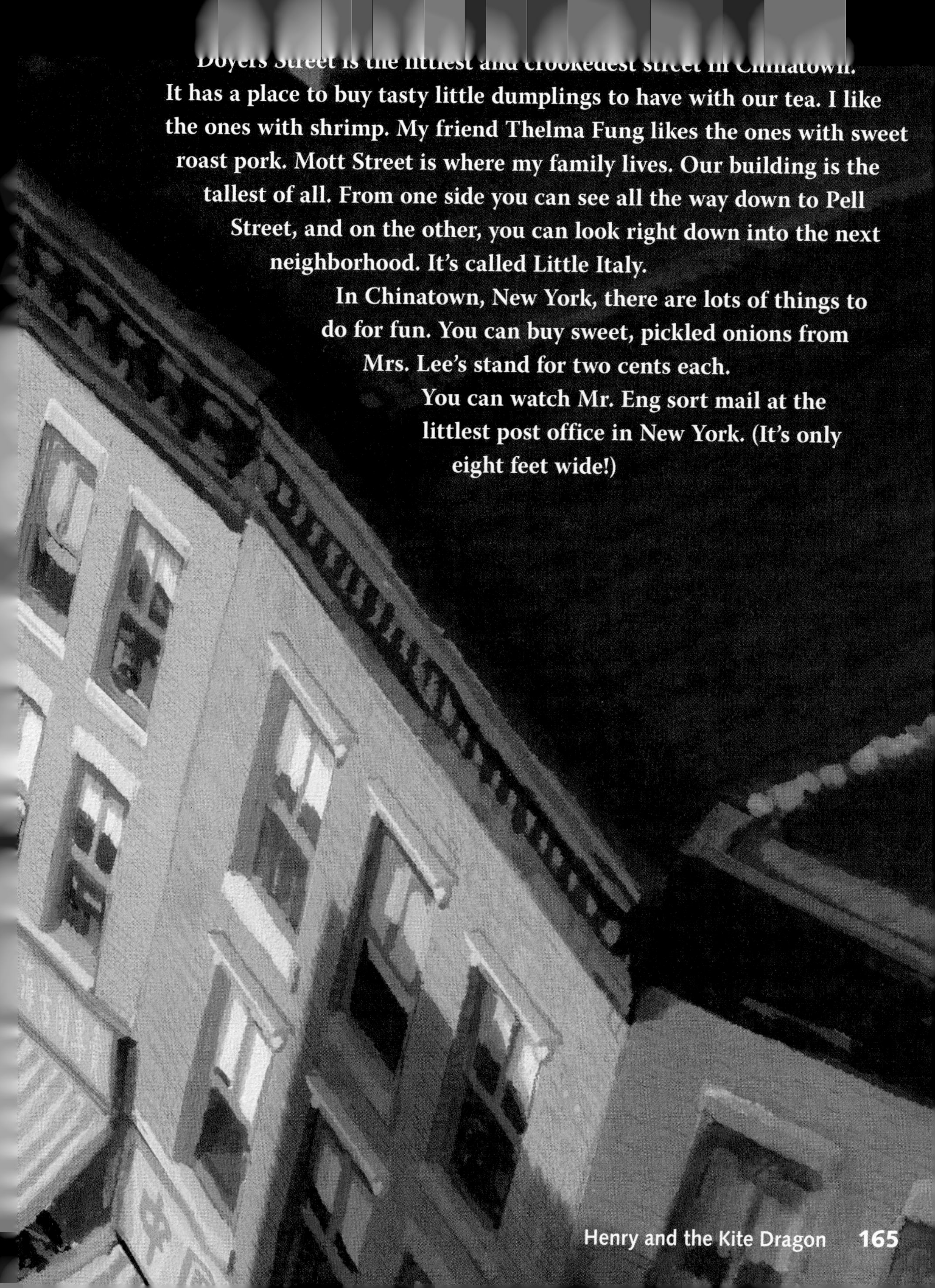

Doyers Street is the littlest and crookedest street in Chinatown. It has a place to buy tasty little dumplings to have with our tea. I like the ones with shrimp. My friend Thelma Fung likes the ones with sweet roast pork. Mott Street is where my family lives. Our building is the tallest of all. From one side you can see all the way down to Pell Street, and on the other, you can look right down into the next neighborhood. It's called Little Italy.

In Chinatown, New York, there are lots of things to do for fun. You can buy sweet, pickled onions from Mrs. Lee's stand for two cents each.

You can watch Mr. Eng sort mail at the littlest post office in New York. (It's only eight feet wide!)

But my favorite thing to do in Chinatown, more favorite than anything, is—fly kites!

And on the top floor of my building lives a man who makes the best kites of all, the best kites in the whole wide world. His name is Mr. Chin, but we kids call him Grandfather. It's a sign of respect for his age.

When he was a kid in China, everyone made kites. But his kites were the biggest and the prettiest, flew the highest, and always won first prize in all the contests. He is little and old now, and always wears a sweater with holes and worn-out brown slippers. But he still likes to climb the stairs to the roof to fly one of his famous kites shaped like a butterfly, or a caterpillar, or his specialty, a big, beautiful dragon.

My friend Thelma Fung and I get to help Grandfather Chin make them.

One time we made a butterfly from broken-up packing crates. The body was made from cardboard. We used the big pot of rice paste that Grandfather Chin boiled on the stove to stick on sheets of newspaper to make wings.

Grandfather Chin painted on bright orange stripes and deep purple spots and glued on glittery gold foil and blue polka dots.

Thelma Fung and I thought it was the best, most wonderful butterfly we'd ever seen!

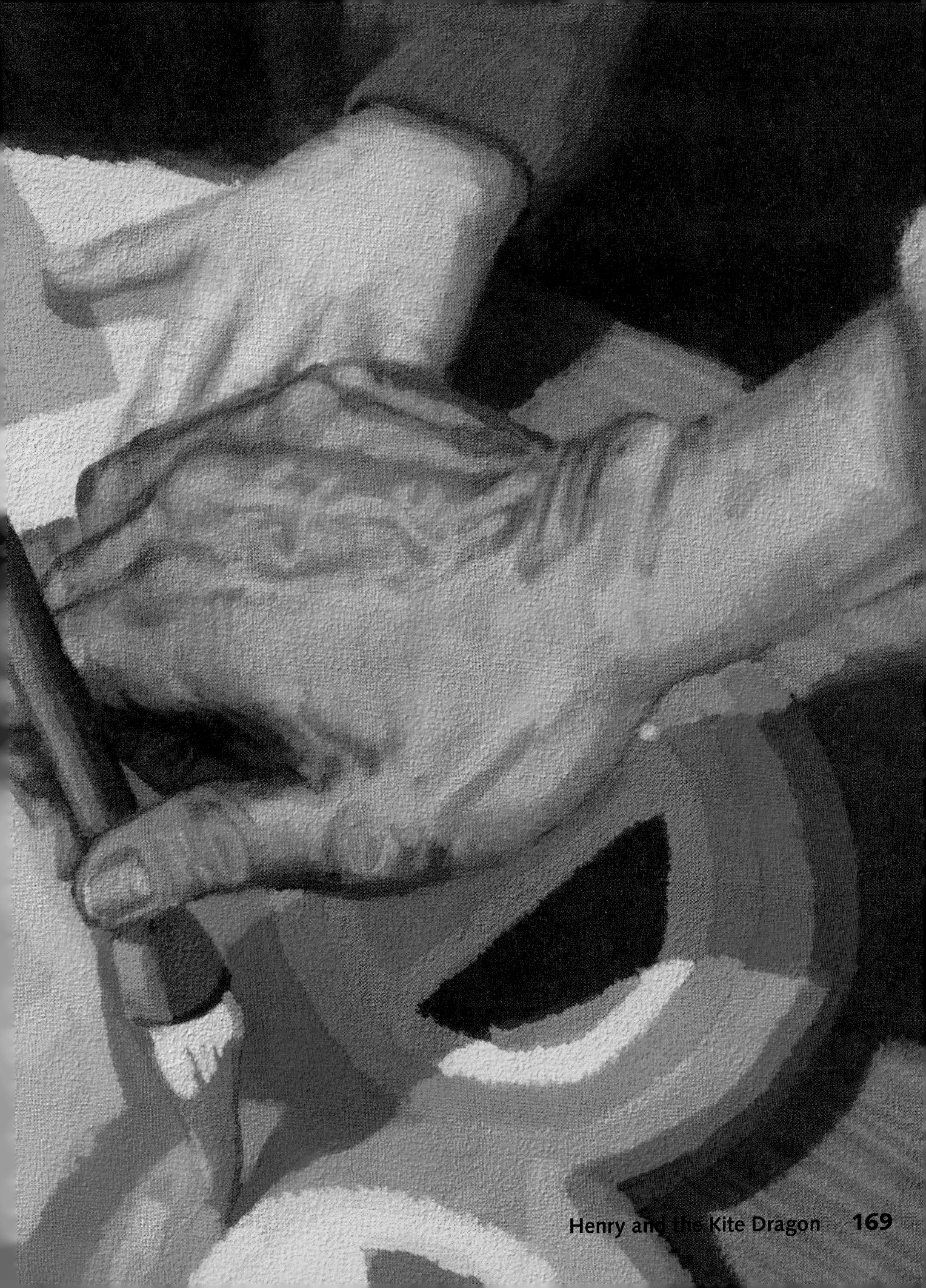

Up on the roof, it was a perfect kite-flying day. A brisk breeze, not too cold, and sunshine broken up by clouds skipping across the sky.

But Grandfather Chin was not only a great kite maker, he was a great kite flier. Slowly, he let the butterfly rise up—and out—and over—until it caught the wind and just took off!

He made the butterfly do swoops. He made it do swirls. He made it do loop-the-loops and reverse curls.

Our butterfly seemed alive!

A pigeon flew by, and in a flash, Grandfather Chin made the kite chase the little bird, as if our big, beautiful butterfly were going to eat him up! The pigeon flew away as fast as his wings could carry him. Our new friend, the butterfly, sailed over the building behind us and paused over the park in Little Italy, a block away.

But then, something happened.

A kid named Tony Guglione (that's goog-lee-ON-ee) saw our kite.

WHIZZ! A rock flew past our beautiful butterfly. WHOOSH! ZING! Two more went by, one of them just nicking the wing. Then—

SMASH! CRASH! RIP! A whole hail of rocks and pebbles tore through the butterfly's wings. Trembling as if in pain, the wonderful butterfly sank slowly to the ground, right into the park.

Tony and his friends tore the kite to bits. They ripped it and stomped on it and shook their fists.

Tony always made trouble for us Chinese kids. And that's why we never went into the park when he and his friends were there.

Grandfather Chin just watched, never uttering a word. Finally, he turned to Thelma Fung and me and said, "Well, we'll just have to go and make another one."

The next day, we three made a caterpillar kite. It was long and sleek, painted bright yellow with red spots, and had a face that made it look like it was surprised to be flying in the clouds at the end of a string.

The sky was overcast, and there was the smell of rain in the air. Grandfather Chin made the caterpillar chase its own tail. He made it wave like the ocean. He made it squiggle and spiral. This time, two pigeons appeared, and Grandfather Chin sent the giant caterpillar racing after them. They were terrified, and shot away from the kite.

But then, it happened again.

WHOOSH! went a rock. ZING! went another. Then Tony Guglione tied a long string to a stone and threw it right over the caterpillar's string, like a lasso. Now Tony and his friends reeled in our beautiful caterpillar, and once again our kite was stomped to pieces.

"Let's go beat them up!" I shouted. "Let's get all our friends and go down there and fight them!"

But Grandfather Chin just shook his head. "I have a better idea. But yes, get all of your friends."

Oh, good, I thought. Tony and his friends will leave us alone once and for all!

Soon, all our Chinatown buddies were climbing the stairs to Grandfather Chin's apartment—Everett Sing, Frances Eng, Walter Hom, Constance Ling, and others. But when we got there, we couldn't believe our eyes! Pots of paste boiled on the stove. Old wooden crates were everywhere, and so were stacks of colorful rice paper. "Come on! Come on!" Grandfather Chin said. "We have a kite to make!"

Make a kite? Now? But what could we do? After all, it was Grandfather Chin. So we rolled up our sleeves.

That day's kite was a dragon. It was huge, stretching from one end of the kitchen to the other and back again—who knew how long it was! It was covered in dazzling red rice paper and had two six-foot-long streamers for a tail. They were made of gold rice paper.

At last the dragon kite was ready. It was so long, it took all of us to carry it to the roof.

"This kite is so big and so beautiful that they wouldn't dare throw rocks at it!" Grandfather Chin said. "Everyone respects dragons! You'll see!"

There was another pigeon flying around, just one lonely bird, all by himself. We wanted the kite to chase it, but before we could even get the dragon in the air, Tony and his friends started throwing rocks again.

That's when I got really mad.

"Come on!" I shouted, and led my friends down eight flights of stairs and out onto the street, leaving Grandfather Chin and the giant dragon kite on the roof, alone.

"Wait!" Grandfather Chin called after us. "Where are you going?"

But we kids just kept on walking, right down Mott Street, making a right turn at the Catholic church, and marching one short block into the park where Tony and his friends were waiting. Chinese kids never went into the park when Tony Guglione was there.

But we did that day.

At first, Tony and his friends just stood with their mouths open. There was silence for a minute. Then Tony spoke.

"Get out of our park!" he sputtered.

"No, you get out!"

"No, you!"

"YOU!"

"We were here first!"

We were all lined up, breathing hard, ready to start swinging, when all of a sudden, the sky went dark.

A big splash of color seemed to stretch across the entire sky. It was so big, it blotted out the sun like a giant cloud.

Grandfather Chin had launched the dragon by himself.

For a moment, everyone in the park was quiet as the gigantic creature hung in the air above our building—and then it started to dance.

It made a slow curve. Everyone said, "Oooh!"

It made a majestic swing. Everybody said, "Ahhh!"

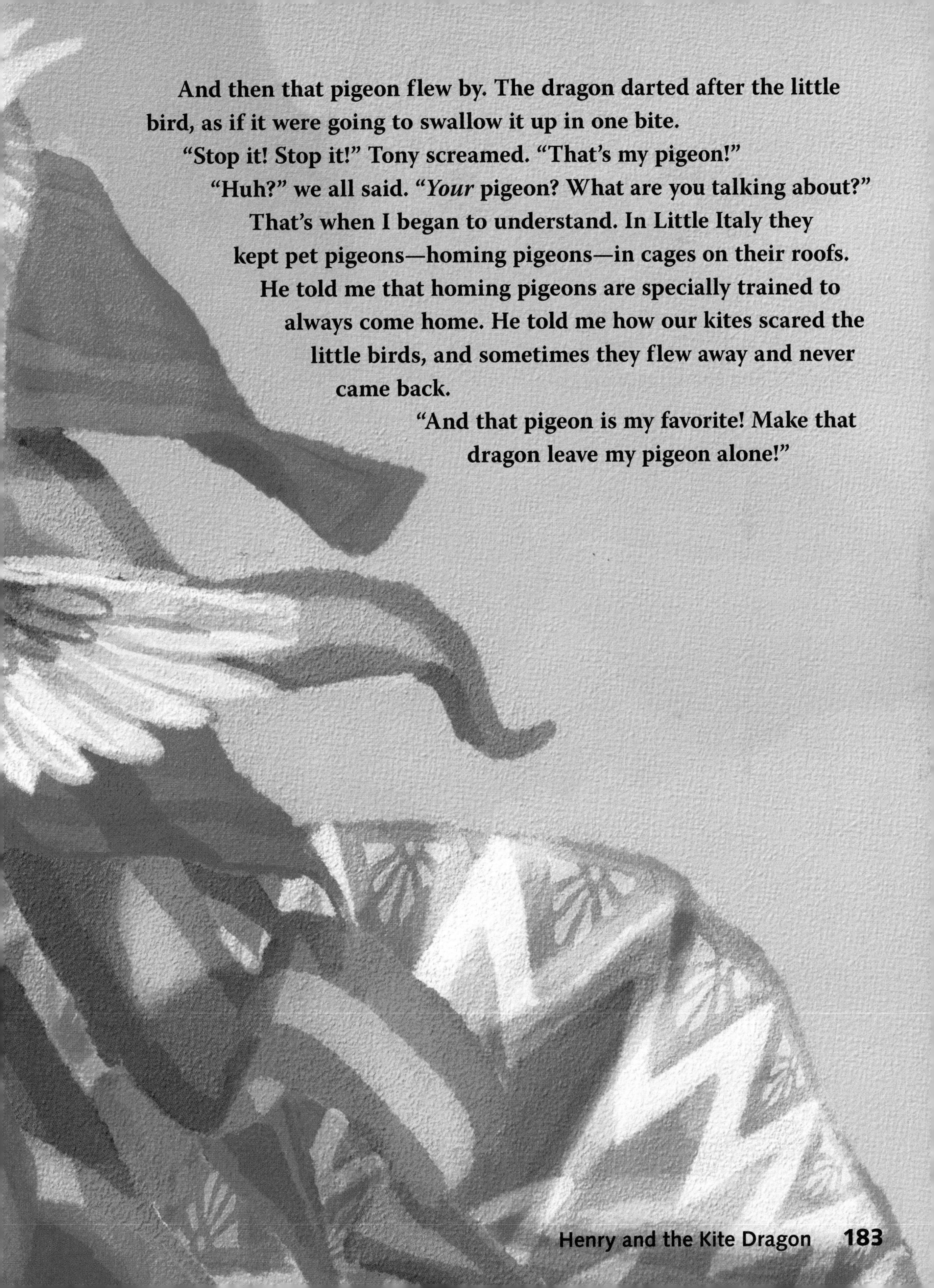

And then that pigeon flew by. The dragon darted after the little bird, as if it were going to swallow it up in one bite.

"Stop it! Stop it!" Tony screamed. "That's my pigeon!"

"Huh?" we all said. "*Your* pigeon? What are you talking about?"

That's when I began to understand. In Little Italy they kept pet pigeons—homing pigeons—in cages on their roofs. He told me that homing pigeons are specially trained to always come home. He told me how our kites scared the little birds, and sometimes they flew away and never came back.

"And that pigeon is my favorite! Make that dragon leave my pigeon alone!"

Then great big Tony Guglione actually started to cry.

I didn't know what to say. Thelma Fung didn't know what to say. Everett Sing, Frances Eng, and Constance Ling didn't know what to say. We all just stood there, too surprised to move.

And then I got an idea. "Grandfather Chin! Stop!" I shouted up to the rooftop.

Frances Eng, Walter Hom, and Constance Ling joined in.

Then even Tony and his friends started shouting, "Grandfather—Grandfather—(what's his name?) —Grandfather Chin! Stop!"

All at once we started running up the hill to Mott Street, the Chinese kids, Tony Guglione and his friends—everybody—running and shouting, “Grandfather Chin! Stop! Stop!”

We ran right up to our building, dashed through the door and up the stairs, still shouting, “Grandfather Chin! Stop! Stop!” By the time we got there, we were all out of breath.

“Grandfather . . . stop . . . pigeon . . . pet . . . Tony’s . . . please . . . oh.”

Grandfather Chin just looked at me. Then he looked at Tony. Then he looked at my friends, and Tony’s friends.

Finally he said, “Are you all crazy?”

When we told him about Tony's pet bird, Grandfather immediately reeled in the big, beautiful dragon. My friends and I watched as the poor, frightened homing pigeon made a couple of big, graceful circles and flew off to a cage we could see on the roof of a building a couple of blocks away. Everyone let out a sigh of relief.

And then, for the first time, Tony took a good, hard look at our dragon kite. "Where did you buy it?"

We laughed and told him how we made kites out of packing crates and rice paper and how Grandfather Chin painted on the faces.

"I guess I'm sorry we threw rocks at them." He paused. "It was our pet birds we were worried about . . . ."

We Chinese kids were sorry, too, and we said so, one by one.

Then we had another idea. From that day on, the Chinese kids fly kites in the mornings. The Italian kids fly their birds in the afternoons.

The really great thing about this is, now we can admire their birds, and they can admire our kites.

And everybody can go to the park whenever they want.

The next kite Grandfather Chin made was a brand-new specialty. It was big. It was silvery. It was all shiny and shimmery. The kite he made was a giant pigeon. And now, when the kids in the park see it, all they say is

"Ooooh!"

UNIT 4

Patterns in the Sky

Why do people study space?

Focus Questions

What patterns and cycles do we find in space?

How did people of the past explain objects in the night sky?

How do people view space today?

How might space be a part of our future?

Exploring Space

by Jeanette Bagnasco

Unit 4

Contents

Introduction

The Sky

Did you ever look up at the night sky? Did you notice that the moon seems to rise and set each night? Did you notice that it seems to change shape from week to week? Did you notice that the tiny stars seem to twinkle?

Today we know that the moon, sun, and other stars are far from Earth—in space. We know that the moon does not really change shape or rise and set. We know that stars are not so tiny. We also know that they do not twinkle. Technology, such as the **telescope**, helps us learn about stars and other objects found in space. A telescope is a tool that makes things appear closer and larger.

Long ago, people also looked up at the sky and noticed many things in space. These people had only their eyes or simple tools to see with. They wondered about the seasons, the stars, the tides, the moon, and the sun. In the future, people may wonder about the places in space we cannot see yet.

In this unit you will read about

- movements of the moon, Earth, and planets,
- stories from the past that helped to explain objects in space,
- technology that helps us learn about space, and
- space exploration and its future.

Chapter 1

Moving in Space

The moon is Earth's closest neighbor in space. It **revolves**, or moves, around Earth. It makes one complete orbit, or trip, around Earth about every 30 days.

Similar to Earth, the moon has **gravity**. The moon's gravity pulls slightly on the Earth. This is the main cause of high and low tides on Earth. Tides are the daily rising and falling of Earth's oceans.

As the moon revolves around Earth, we see different shapes, or phases, of the moon. But the moon does not change shape. It is always a sphere. So why do we see different shapes?

The sun shines on the moon. Some light **reflects**, or bounces, off the moon to Earth. We see this reflected light at night. As the moon revolves around Earth, part of the moon is lit up by the sun's light, and the other part is dark. The lighted parts of the moon are the phases we see. The phases repeat about every 30 days.

Phases of the Moon

Last-Quarter Moon

The moon is one-quarter of the way around Earth.

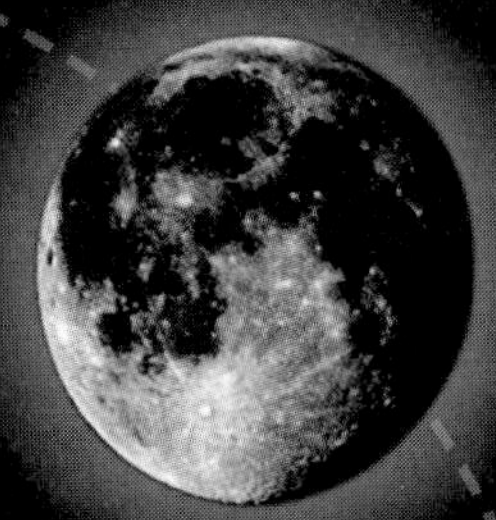

Waning Gibbous Moon

You begin to see less of the lighted side again.

Full Moon

You see the moon's entire lighted side.

Waxing Gibbous Moon

You see nearly all of the lighted side.

First-Quarter Moon

The moon is three-quarters of the way around Earth.

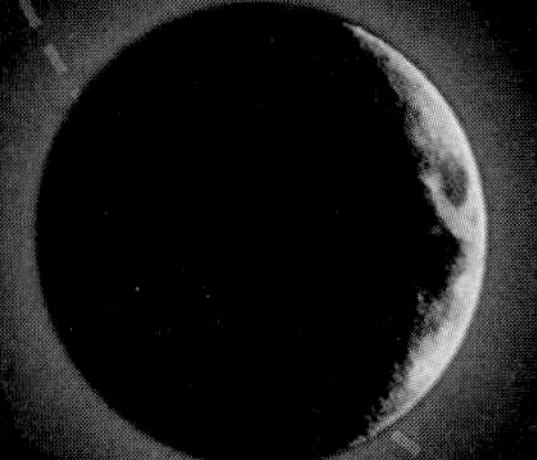

Waxing Crescent Moon

You see a small part of the moon's lighted side.

New Moon

You cannot see the moon's lighted side.

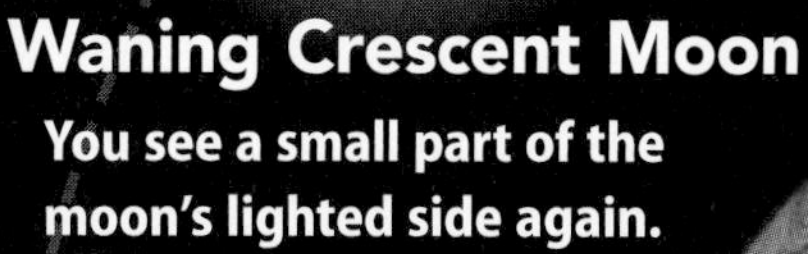

Waning Crescent Moon

You see a small part of the moon's lighted side again.

Earth's Movements

You do not feel it, but Earth moves. It **rotates** around an axis, which is an imaginary line through the center of Earth. It takes 24 hours, or one day, for Earth to rotate one time. As Earth rotates, half of it faces the sun and has day. The other side has night. As Earth continues to rotate, the light side becomes dark. The dark side becomes light. The cycle of day and night repeats every 24 hours.

As Earth rotates, it also revolves around the sun. Because Earth's axis is tilted, the sun hits Earth at different angles. Each of Earth's hemispheres, or halves, gets different amounts of sunlight. The tilt of Earth's axis and Earth's revolution around the sun cause the four seasons.

Fast Fact

What moves at about 66,700 miles (107,000 kilometers) an hour but feels like it's standing still? Earth! That's how fast Earth revolves around the sun!

Earth's Seasons

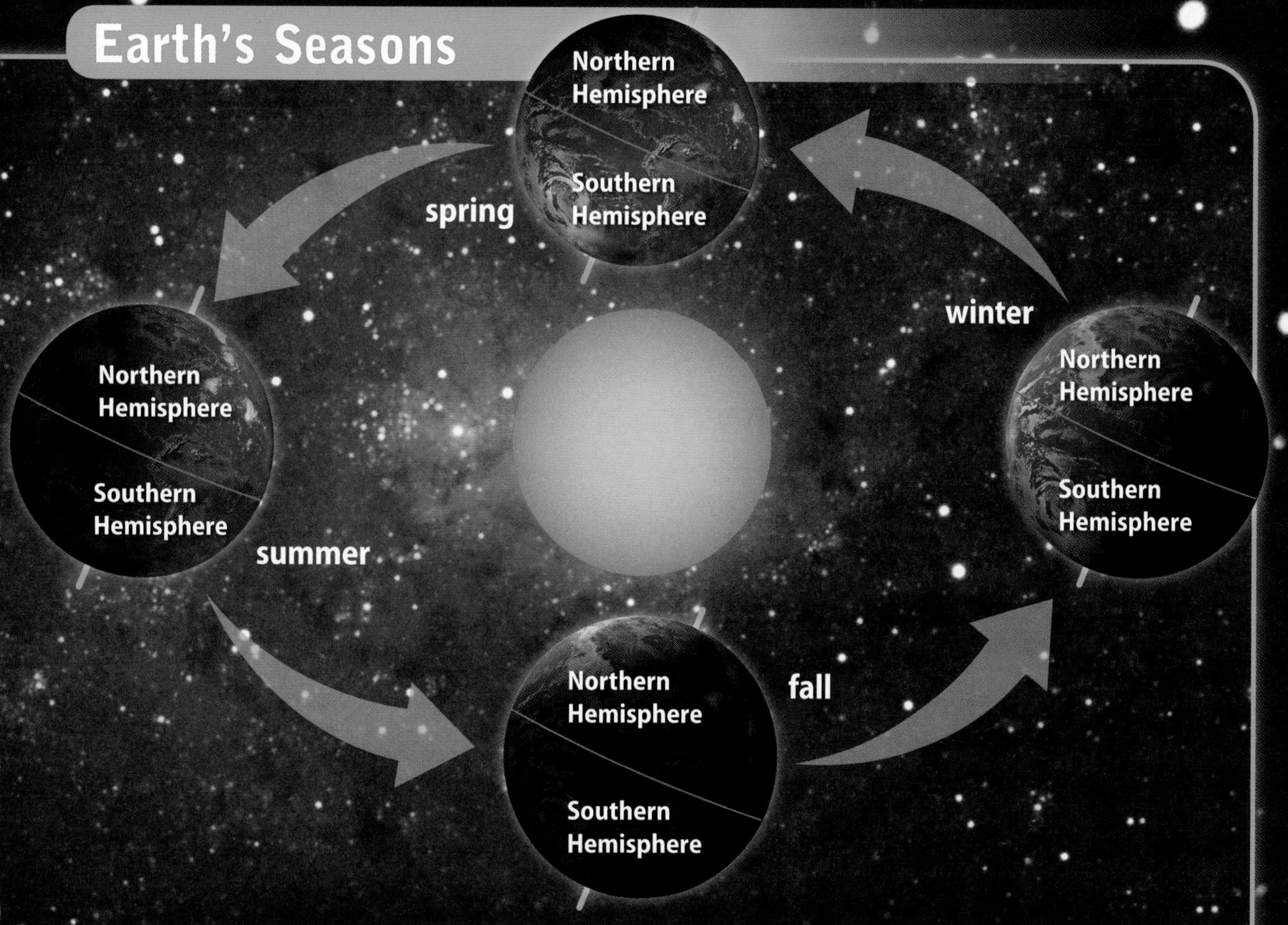

As Earth rotates on its tilted axis around the sun, Earth's hemispheres get more or less sunlight. In June the North Pole tilts toward the sun and the South Pole tilts away from it. It is summer in the Northern Hemisphere and winter in the Southern Hemisphere. In December the North Pole tilts away from the sun and the South Pole tilts toward it. It is winter in the Northern Hemisphere and summer in the Southern Hemisphere.

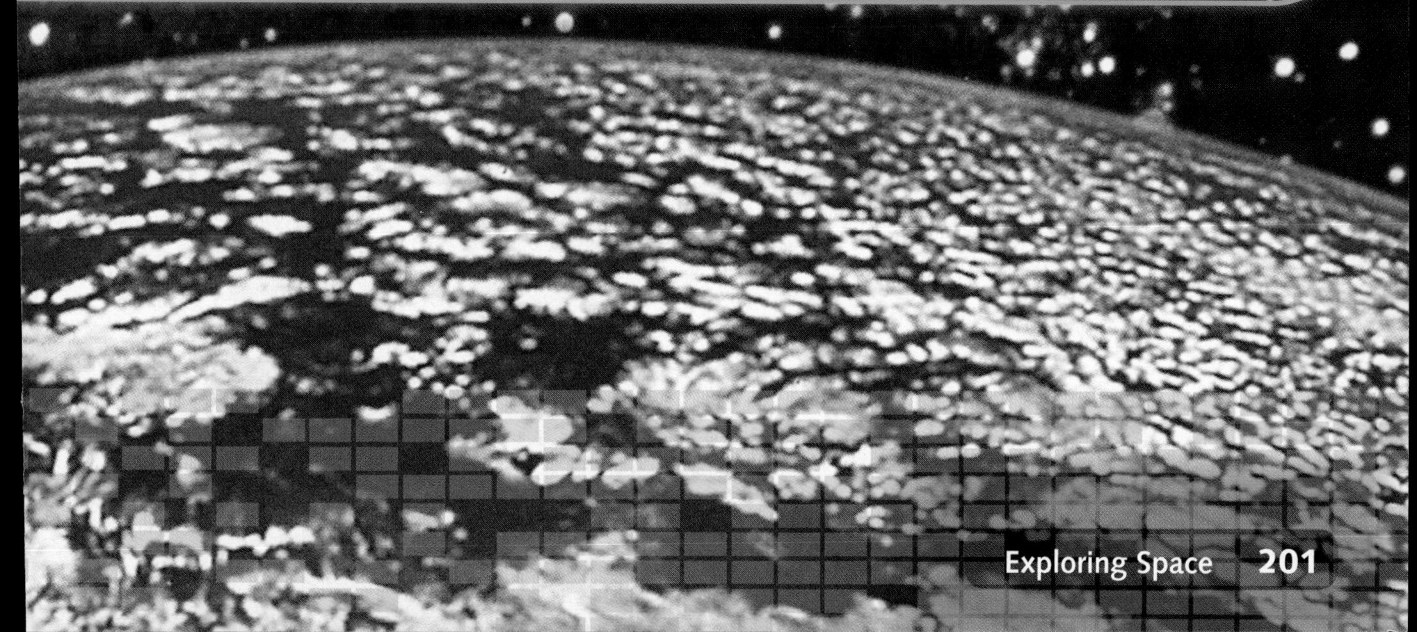

The Solar System

Earth and the moon are not the only objects revolving around the sun. Other planets do too. A planet is a large, round object that revolves around a star.

A solar system is made up of a star and all the things that revolve around it. At the center of our solar system is the sun, a star. Eight planets, their moons, asteroids, dwarf planets, and comets revolve around the sun. The planets in our solar system are all different in size and distance from the sun. Some are made mostly of rock. Others are made mostly of gases. Each planet rotates as it revolves. The sun rotates too. Everything moves in space!

Our solar system is only a tiny part of the Milky Way galaxy. A galaxy is a large system of billions of stars. Each galaxy has its own shape. Our Milky Way Galaxy has a spiral shape and contains about one hundred billion stars. Like other galaxies, the Milky Way rotates and moves through space.

Earth
Mars
Jupiter
Saturn
Uranus

Average Distance of Planets From the Sun
Distance in millions of kilometers
5,000
4,500
4,000
3,500
3,000
2,500
2,000
1,500
1,000
500
58
108
150
228
778
1,427
2,871
4,497
Mercury
Venus
Earth
Mars
Jupiter
Saturn
Uranus
Neptune
Planets
Source: UC Berkely Cosmology Group

Chapter 2

Stories of the Sky

The Big Dipper is part of the constellation Ursa Major. Lines have been added to show how this group of stars forms the shape of a dipper.

The moon's craters were made by meteoroids that crashed into it. Meteoroids are small, solid objects that travel through space.

Do you look up at the stars? Do you think they form pictures? Many ancient people thought so. People have looked at constellations for thousands of years. A constellation is a group of stars that seems to form a picture.

Today we know that stars are large; in fact, they are much bigger than our moon. They look tiny because they are far away. Unlike the moon, stars make their own light. Like the sun, all stars are made of glowing gases.

What do you see when you look at the full moon? Some of the moon's dark and light parts look like a face. The moon's dark areas are large plains called *maria*. The moon's lighter areas are highlands with many craters. A crater is a hole, or pit.

Today most scientists think that a huge object hit Earth long ago. The crash sent rocks into space. After a long time these rocks formed the moon.

Long ago, people wondered about things that happened in nature. What caused the seasons? Why were the stars in the sky? What caused the tides? How did the moon, sun, and Earth's oceans come to be? Those people had very few tools to give them answers. Ancient stories explained the patterns they saw in nature and in the sky.

The Navajo believed a goddess caused the seasons. According to Navajo legend, the goddess becomes young again each spring, and the seasons pass to winter as she gets older.

the constellation Cancer

Greek Stories

One ancient Greek myth tells how the constellation Cancer came to be. This myth tells about a hero named Heracles who was fighting a hydra, or a water beast with many heads. While Heracles was fighting, his enemy Hera sent a crab to pinch him on the heels. Hera wanted the crab to make Heracles lose the battle. But Heracles crushed the crab and won the battle against the hydra.

In Latin, *cancer* means "crab." Hera placed Cancer in the sky as a reward for its bravery and help.

Greek Stories

The word *myth* comes from the Greek word *mythos.* It means "word" or "story."

Killing the hydra was one of 12 battles that Heracles was challenged by.

Tsimshian Stories

"How Raven Made the Tides" is a story told by the Tsimshian (sihm SHEE an) people. It tells how the tides came to be. Raven, a bird, knows people need low tide to gather food along the beaches. But an old woman holds the tide line and won't let it go. So the tide stays high. Raven tricks the old woman into letting go of the tide line. Raven gets the old woman to agree to let the tide go in and out twice each day. That is why there are two high tides and two low tides each day.

The Tsimshian are Native Americans who live in the Pacific Northwest. They catch salmon and other kinds of seafood along the beach at low tide.

Nigerian Stories

"Water, Moon, and Sun" is a story from Nigeria in Africa. In the story the Moon and Sun live together on Earth. They miss their friend, Water, and invite him to visit. When Water visits he brings so many sea friends along that Moon and Sun's home becomes too crowded. Moon and Sun leap into the sky to escape. That is why Earth is covered by water, and the moon and sun shine above it.

Chapter 3

Technology and Space

You have learned that people used to make up stories to explain why things in space move and change the way they do. These stories reveal what people thought long ago. Now people have more advanced technology to help them study and understand space.

In the 1600s a man named Galileo built a telescope that let him watch objects in the sky that nobody had seen before. In those days people thought that everything in the solar system revolved around Earth. But Galileo demonstrated, or showed, that the planets, including Earth, revolve around the sun. The telescope changed the way people thought about our solar system.

People used to think that the moon's surface was smooth, but Galileo used a telescope like this to show that its suface was uneven.

The Kitt Peak National Observatory near Tucson, Arizona, has more than 20 telescopes! This observatory is also home to the world's largest solar telescope.

Today's telescopes are much larger than Galileo's. Many telescopes are on mountaintops, far from city lights, so people can see more clearly. Others are in deserts where there are few clouds.

These huge telescopes let us observe space and learn new things about it. As we learn new things, we may also change the way we think about space.

Technology Above Earth

The gases in Earth's sky make it hard for us to view space. So scientists use technology to study space *from* space.

One kind of technology they use is a satellite. A satellite is any object in space that revolves around something else in space. A satellite can be natural, such as comets, asteroids, and planets. Or, a satellite can be human-made, such as a piece of technology.

Some human-made satellites revolve around the moon, while others revolve around Earth or other planets. The Hubble Space Telescope, a human-made satellite launched in 1990, was designed to revolve around Earth.

The Hubble Space Telescope

The Hubble Space Telescope was sent into space. Why? Space is the best place for a telescope. Space objects are viewed more clearly there. For years the Hubble Space Telescope has been taking thousands of pictures of galaxies and other objects never seen before. It has sent the most amazing pictures back to Earth.

Astronauts and people with special training live and work in space on the *International Space Station*, or ISS. Many science experiments are performed there.

There are many human-made satellites, each with a different job. Some are used to help people stay in touch and learn things from one another. Others are used to help us study space.

A space probe is another tool used to study space from space. Some probes are sent to planets and land there. They get information that is sent back to Earth. Other probes don't land anywhere, but just fly around space collecting data.

Space Technology

You may wonder why people study space. There are many reasons. Some people are just interested, like people were long ago. Some people want to learn about space and what's in it. New ideas in space technology make this possible.

Everyday life has been changed in many ways by space technology. Because of space technology, there have been big changes in computers, telephones, and medicine. We have found new ways to move around, to stay safe, and to have fun!

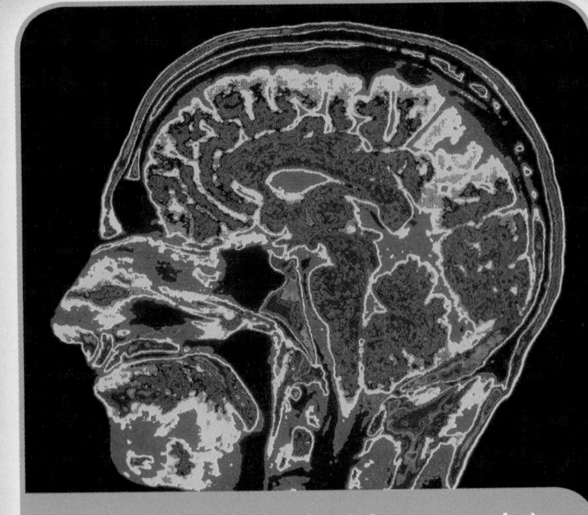

A CAT (computerized axial tomography) scan can reveal problems in the body without using surgery. NASA made big improvements to this technology.

Satellites orbiting Earth relay cell phone messages all over the world.

Solar power was first developed for use in spacecraft. Many things, such as this calculator, use solar energy today.

You may not even know that you are using space technology. Many things that people own were first made for space, but are now used commonly on Earth!

For example, space capsules need small, light computers. As a result, space technology turned old, large computers into the small ones people use today. Also, a material first made for moon boots was later used to improve the athletic shoes people wear when they play sports.

More than 1,300 products today have grown from space technology. Ribbed swimsuits for swimming faster, some fire-resistant materials, and improved brakes are just a few!

NASA developed many uses for Mylar. Today, Mylar can be found in several forms. Mylar blankets are given to marathon runners after a race because they reflect heat back to the body, keeping runners warm.

Chapter 4

Space and Our Future

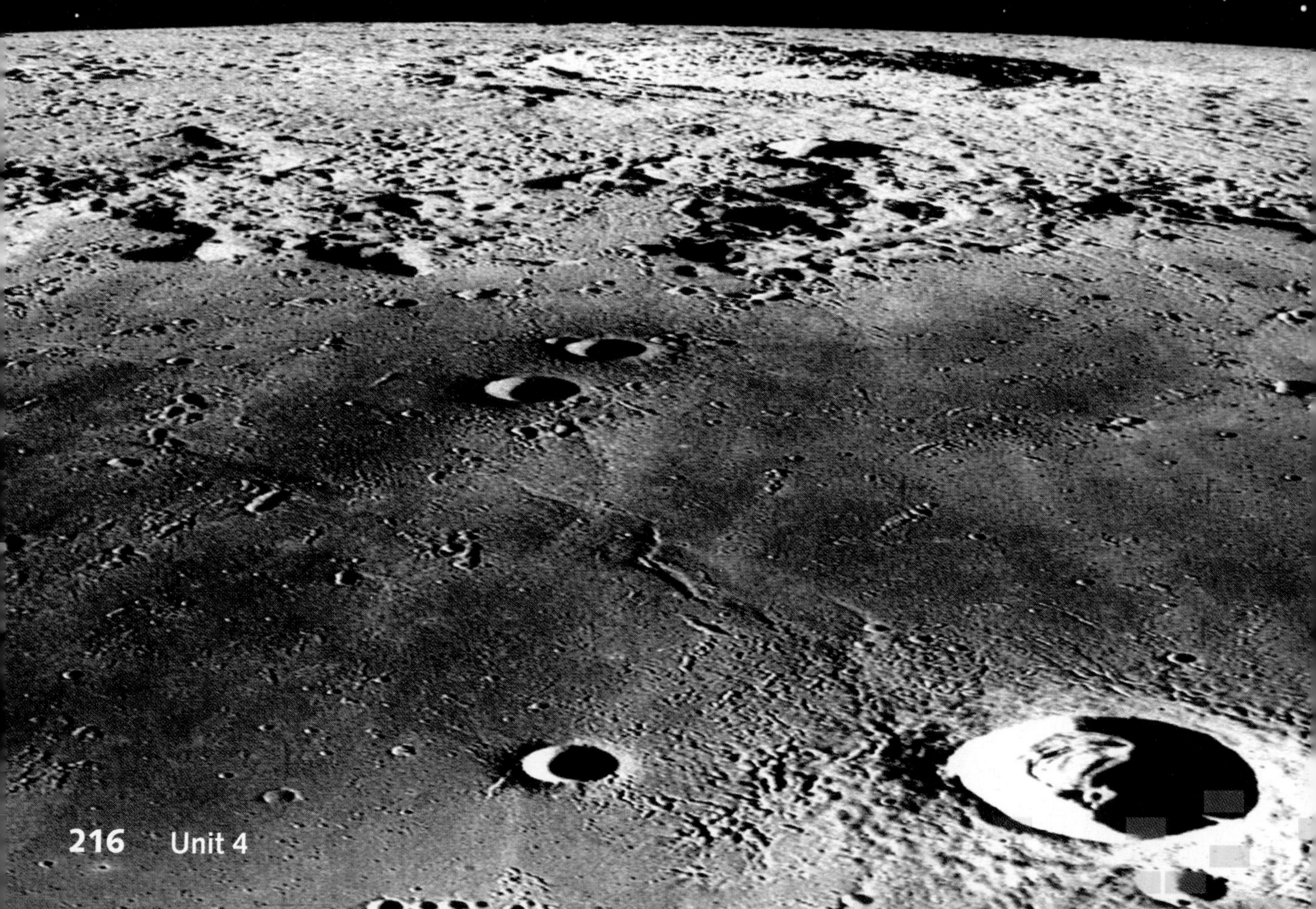

The Apollo 11 mission made Neil Armstrong and Edwin Aldrin, Jr. (pictured here) the first people to step foot on the moon.

The *Cassini-Huygens* probe sends pictures of Saturn never seen before. This color-enhanced image shows one of Saturn's rings.

Maybe in the future, people will live on the moon. Maybe life will be found on other planets.

No one knows when or if these things will happen. But some people think that we will wind up living in space. Why? Our planet may one day have too many people, and our natural resources may get used up. Also, many people love discovering new places.

NASA

In 1958, NASA (National Aeronautics and Space Administration) was started. One of NASA's first goals was to get people to the moon. On July 20, 1969, two Americans became the first people to walk on the moon. Moon, or **lunar**, landings continued, and a total of 12 Americans have walked on the moon.

NASA has sent out many space probes too. In the early 1970s scientists launched probes to study Jupiter and Saturn. In 1977 *Voyagers 1* and *2* were sent to study our solar system. Many probes continue to be sent into space.

These explorations have taught NASA much about space. This information allows NASA to continue discovering even greater things in the future.

A Future on the Moon?

NASA is focused on the moon again. The *Lunar Reconnaissance Orbiter*, or LRO, is NASA's first step back to the moon. The LRO has several tasks including mapping out safe landing sites, looking for frozen water, and studying how the sun affects people. Why? People need to know about these things before they can live and work on the moon.

We need to know a lot of other things too. There is little gravity on the moon, and living with little or no gravity affects our bodies.

Solar radiation may also cause trouble in space. Solar radiation is the radiation that comes from the sun. The radiation on the moon is much greater than on Earth. The moon does not have a thick layer of gases surrounding it to keep out the sun's harmful rays. Too much solar radiation can make people very sick. Scientists on Earth and on the *International Space Station* are trying to find ways to keep people healthy in space.

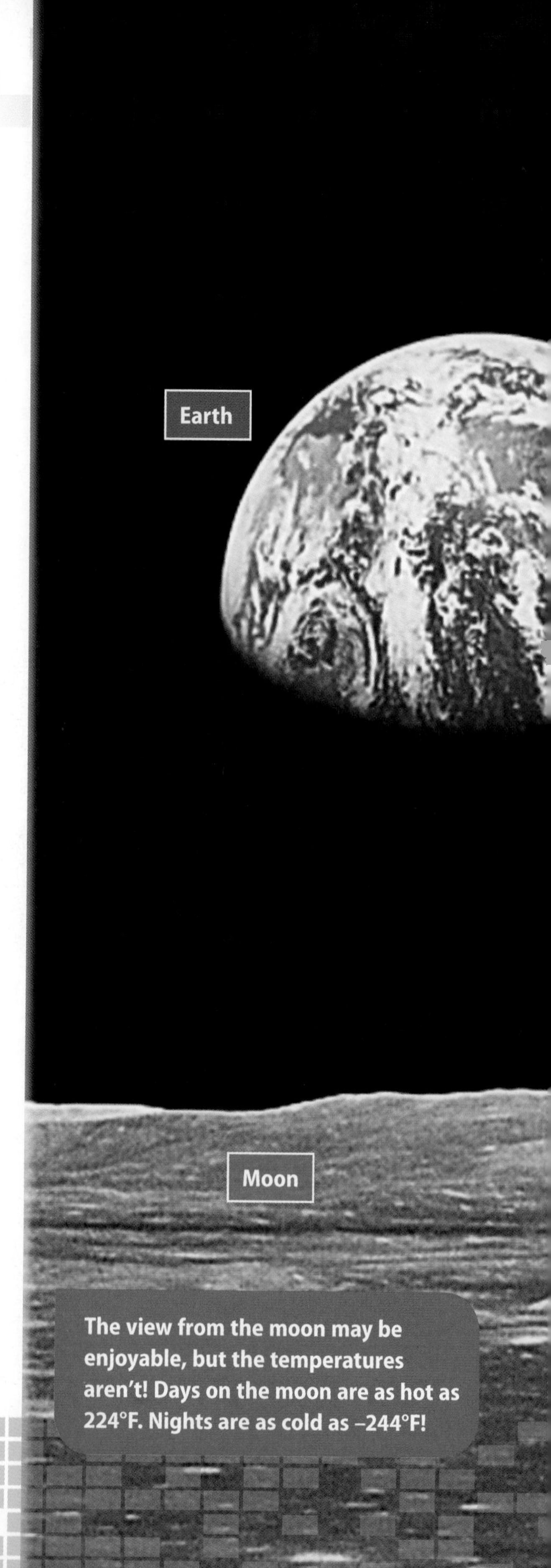

The view from the moon may be enjoyable, but the temperatures aren't! Days on the moon are as hot as 224°F. Nights are as cold as –244°F!

The LRO was launched in 2009 to orbit the moon for one year.

Astronauts perform many tests on the *International Space Station*.

A Future on Mars and Other Planets?

Two solar-powered rovers, or moving machines, named *Spirit* and *Opportunity* landed on Mars. They discovered minerals that usually occur where there is water. This discovery demonstrated that long ago Mars probably contained water.

This is not a scene from a space movie. It is a view of Columbia Hills on Mars taken by NASA's rover, *Spirit*.

In late 2008 the *Mars Reconnaissance Orbiter*, or MRO, sent radar images of Mars. They showed a mountain of ice buried under rocks and soil. Some scientists now think that Mars was once similar to Earth.

Machines have gone even farther than Mars. In 2004 the *Cassini-Huygens* probe entered Saturn's orbit. It studied Saturn's rings and moons. It found that water vapor and ice erupt from Enceladus, one of Saturn's moons. Some of Saturn's other moons are coated with ice too.

Why is it so important that water was found on Mars and on some of Saturn's moons? Living things need water, so there could be simple life forms in these places. It also means that these places could support human life in the future. Maybe one day your address will be on Mars!

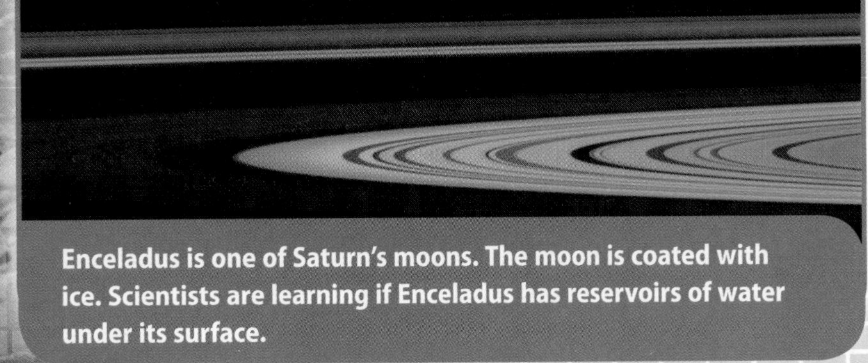

Enceladus is one of Saturn's moons. The moon is coated with ice. Scientists are learning if Enceladus has reservoirs of water under its surface.

The Big Ideas

- Everything moves in space—the sun, the moon, Earth, the planets. Even galaxies move.
- People have always wondered about the sky. Long ago they told stories to explain what they saw.
- Today, technology helps us understand the movements of Earth and the moon. It also helps us find out more about things in space.
- People will continue to explore space. Technology can help us discover if there are places beyond Earth where human beings can live.

Jeanne K. Pettenati
Illustrated by Paolo Rui

Galileo's Journal 1609–1610

Galileo lived in Italy 400 years ago. He was very curious and liked doing experiments to test his ideas. This book imagines what he might have written in his journal from July 1609 through March 1610. In those nine short months, Galileo made some of the most amazing discoveries in history.

July 30, 1609, Venice

This morning I said good-bye to my students for the summer. As soon as they left, I hurried home to grab my bags. Then I hopped on a boat to Venice. Luna was so excited she barked all the way there.

Later I ate dinner at my friend Paolo's house. Paolo told me he had heard about an amazing new invention: a tube for seeing things far away. The tube has eyeglass lenses inside it, and it makes far-off things look like they are right in front of you. The Dutchman who invented this thing calls it a spyglass.

I wish I could try a spyglass for myself.

August 1, 1609, Venice

I struck several sour notes on my lute this morning. I couldn't stop thinking about that spyglass. I'm going to try to make one.

I need a long tube, to focus my eye on a faraway object without distractions. I also need glass lenses to go inside the tube.

How long should the tube be, I wonder? How many lenses do I need?

August 3, 1609, Padua

I arrived home yesterday and went right to work on my spyglass.

I began with just one curved lens in the tube. That didn't work. A concave lens makes objects look smaller. A convex lens makes objects look larger, but they are blurry and out of focus.

Then I tried using two lenses together. I put a concave lens close to my eye and a convex lens at the far end of a tube. There it was! Trees, houses, people, and animals all leaped toward me.

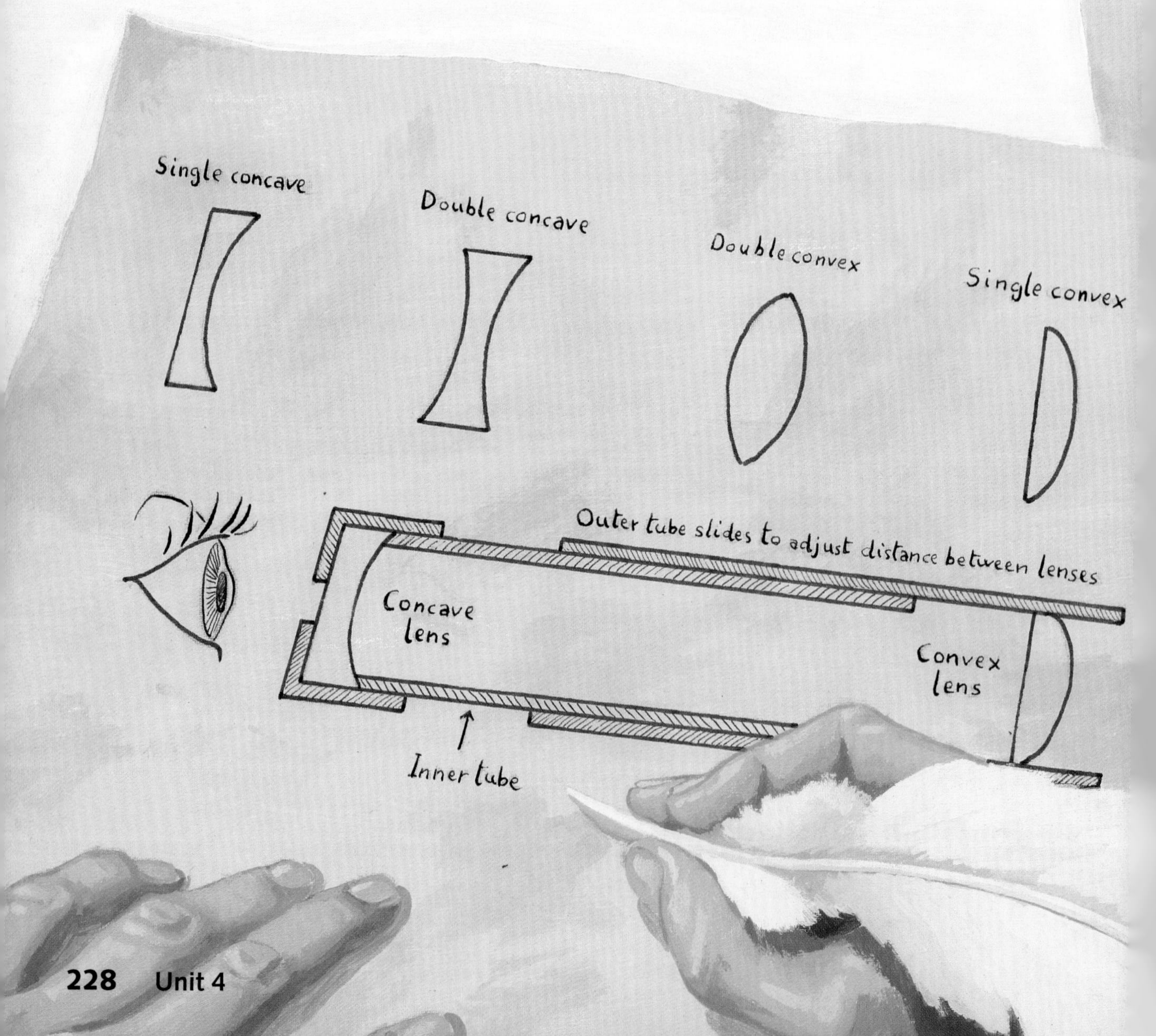

My spyglass makes things seem three times closer and nine times bigger. When I looked down into my garden, I saw two rabbits eating my lettuce! Where is that Luna when you need her?

August 19, 1609, Padua

Today I made my spyglass stronger by increasing the curve of the lenses. Distant objects now seem 60 times larger.

I am returning to Venice tomorrow. Luna can't come because I will be too busy. I am going to show my spyglass to the senators of the city!

August 21, 1609, Venice

This morning I took the senators to the top of St. Mark's tower, the highest point in the city. They looked through the spyglass at a tower in the town of Padua, 35 miles away. Then they looked across the water to an island and saw tiny people marching into a church. Finally, they spotted two ships far off at sea. Through the spyglass, the ships seemed close enough to touch.

"Extraordinary!" one senator cried. "Are they real?"

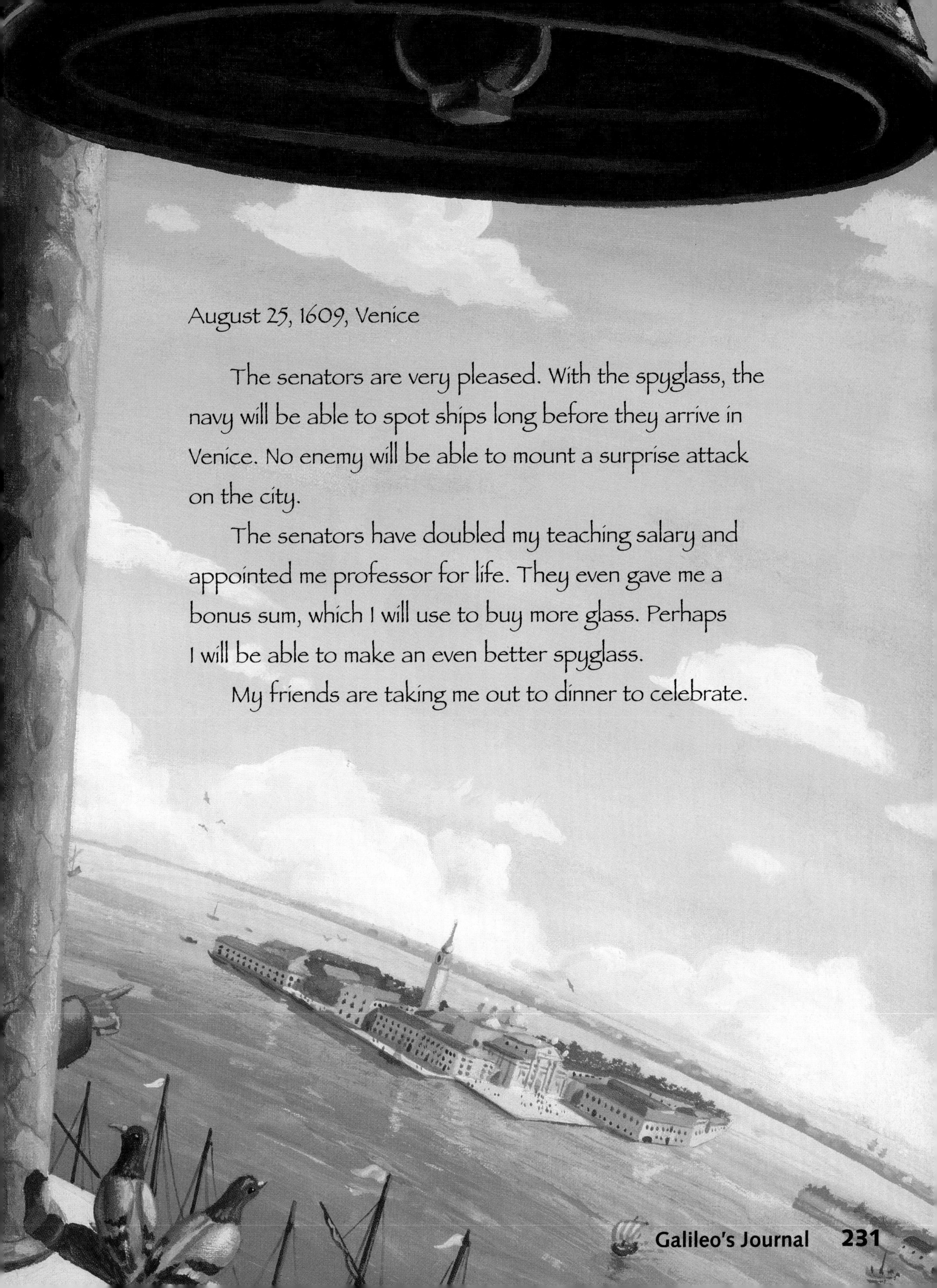

August 25, 1609, Venice

The senators are very pleased. With the spyglass, the navy will be able to spot ships long before they arrive in Venice. No enemy will be able to mount a surprise attack on the city.

The senators have doubled my teaching salary and appointed me professor for life. They even gave me a bonus sum, which I will use to buy more glass. Perhaps I will be able to make an even better spyglass.

My friends are taking me out to dinner to celebrate.

August 28, 1609, Padua

After a week of excitement, I am home again. Luna missed me.

September 15, 1609, Padua

My afternoons are filled with students, who come for their lessons AND to see the spyglass. Mornings and evenings I work on the spyglass—now it makes faraway objects seem 100 times larger.

With the spyglass, the navy can spot enemy ships. Sailors at sea can keep an eye out for pirates. But there must be other uses for this amazing tool. What could they be?

I tried looking at things up close, but that didn't work. All I saw was a blur.

September 18, 1609, Padua

After dinner Luna and I went out in the garden. The first stars of evening were beginning to shine. They looked so beautiful and so tiny. Luna began barking at the moon.

Suddenly I had an idea. I grabbed my spyglass and ran up to the rooftop.

I turned my spyglass to the moon, and my mouth dropped open.

People have always said that the moon is perfectly round, with a smooth surface like polished marble. Now I know the truth! The moon has mountains, valleys, and craters, just like Earth. I must be the first person ever to see them.

I watched the moon until it set. Now my arms are wobbly from holding the spyglass all night. I'm tired but too excited to sleep.

As a boy, I dreamed of walking on the moon. Tonight I traveled there!

October 15, 1609, Padua

Through the spyglass, the stars look brighter. There are many more stars than people think. Hundreds, maybe even thousands more.

With only my eyes, the Milky Way looks like a cloudy band of light stretching across the night sky. But the spyglass tells a different story. It shows that the Milky Way is made up of countless stars, so close to each other that their light blends together. I wonder why there are so many stars all grouped in harmony.

I am discovering so much, yet so many mysteries remain.

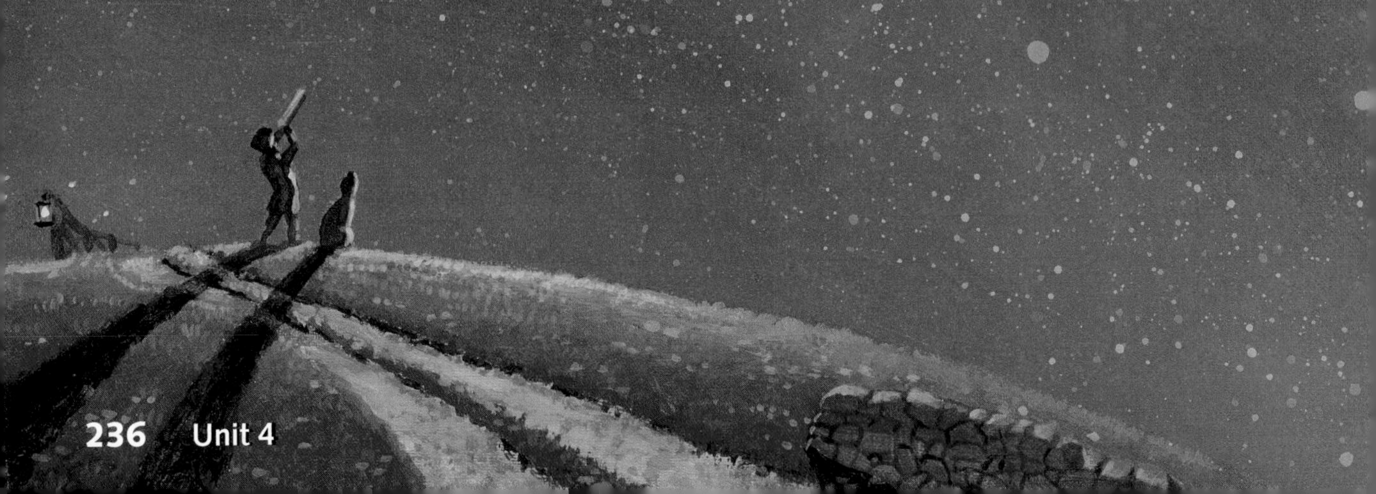

October 20, 1609, Florence

Prince Cosimo has invited me to his palace to show him my spyglass. I used to tutor the prince when he was a boy. Now young Cosimo is the ruler of all Tuscany.

October 21, 1609, Florence

At the palace, we sat down to a grand feast. The tables were filled with caviar, roasted meats, salted fish, baked pears, and almond pastries. I had more than a little of everything.

As soon as darkness came, we went to the courtyard to look at the night sky. Prince Cosimo **marveled** at all we saw. Without my spyglass, even a prince cannot see the millions of stars twinkling across the Milky Way.

November 28, 1609, Padua

News travels quickly in this day and age. Letters are arriving from people all over the world. Some call me a hero. Others say, "Galileo is a liar! His spyglass is a fake!" A few even say that I put little pictures inside my spyglass to trick people. Ha!

These people don't believe that I see mountains on the moon. They have looked at the same moon year after year and never seen such at thing.

Why are they afraid to see what's really there?

December 8, 1609, Padua

So many people refuse to listen to me. But I won't give up. I'll show them how incredible the night sky is.

Every day I think of some way to make the spyglass better. I built a stand to hold it steady. Now I can turn it to look at different parts of the sky. Bigger, better lenses also help—distant objects now look 1,000 times larger.

Over the last few nights, I have watched sunlight sweep across the moon, lighting up mountains and valleys. Observing the shadows and light, I used geometry to figure out that some of the moon's mountains are four miles high—higher than any mountains on Earth!

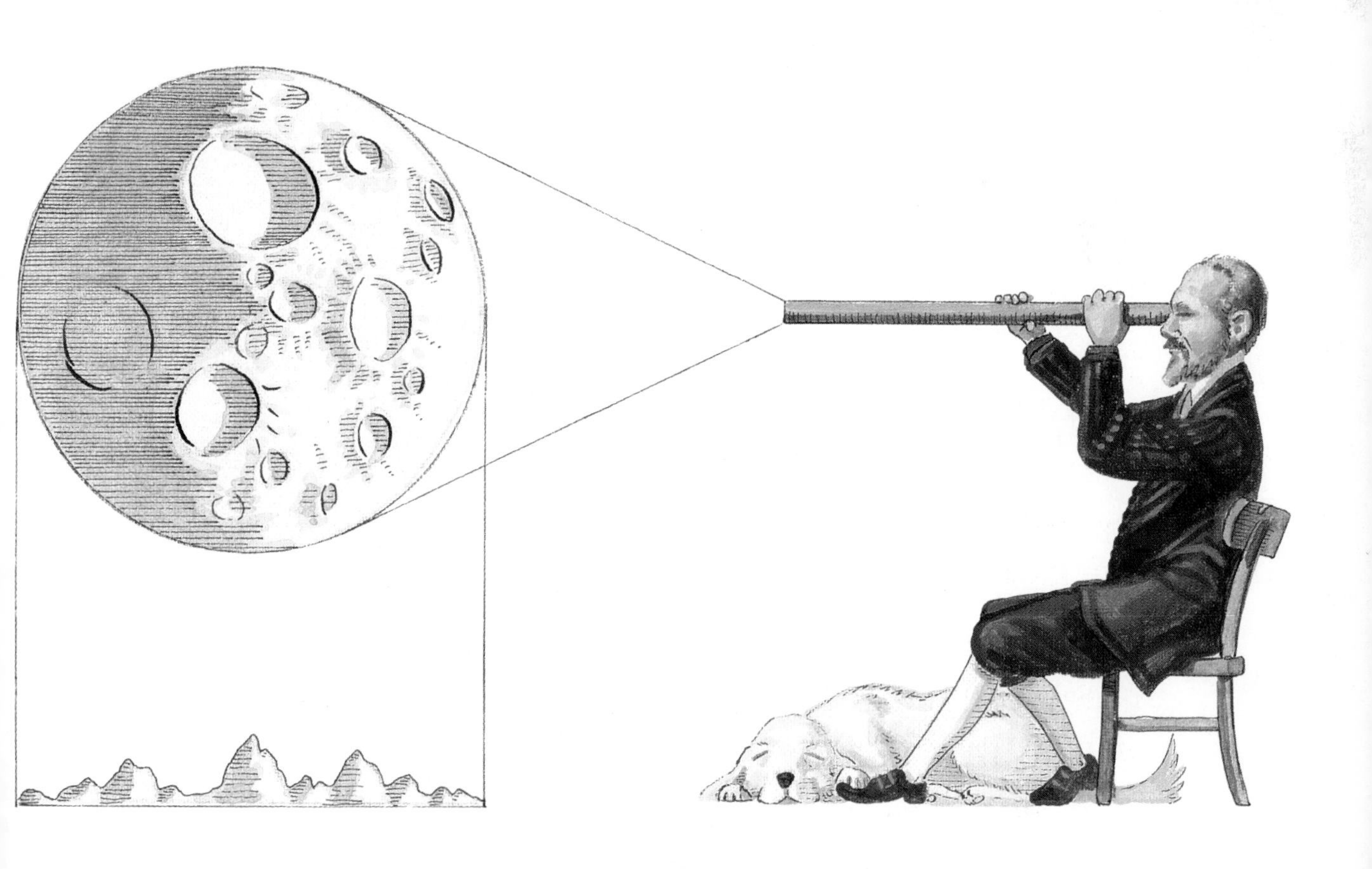

January 1, 1610, Padua

Happy New Year! Firecrackers are popping in the street. The smoke makes it hard to see the stars, so I'll just go outside and join the celebration.

Loud noises frighten Luna. She is hiding under my bed.

January 7, 1610, Padua

The new year brings a new mystery.

Jupiter is so bright tonight that I noticed it right away. Through the spyglass, I noticed something else. Three small, very bright stars are lined up with Jupiter. Two stars are to the east of the planet, and one star is to the west—all in a row. What an odd **formation**!

Tonight I am looking again at Jupiter and those three bright stars—but now all three stars are west of Jupiter!

East ● * * * West

How can this be? Jupiter moves westward from night to night against a background of stars. The planet should have moved to the west of the three stars. Yet there it is, to the east.

What is going on?

January 9, 1610, Padua

It is cloudy tonight. I cannot see Jupiter and that strange pattern of stars.

The changing formation from one night to the next puzzles me. Planets move in space, but stars do not. Are Jupiter and these stars connected in some way? How could they be?

My mind won't rest until I figure out this puzzle. But all Luna wants to do is go out and play.

January 10, 1610, Padua

Two of the bright stars are next to Jupiter tonight—but now both are to the east of the planet. Where is number three? Perhaps it is hidden from view behind the planet. Is that possible?

East * * ○ West

4:00 AM . . . Cannot sleep. Have been thinking—planets move and stars stay still . . . But these stars do not stay still . . . I wonder . . .

What if these stars and Jupiter are ALL moving? What if the stars move around Jupiter the way the moon moves around our Earth? Then what I see are not stars at all—they are moons!

I never thought another planet could have a moon. It doesn't seem possible that a planet could have three moons.

January 11, 1610, Padua East * * ● West

Tonight I can see only two "moons"—both east of Jupiter. I believe number three is behind Jupiter. If there are three moons again tomorrow, I'll know for sure that these moons go around and around Jupiter.

I have no patience—I can't wait for tomorrow night! Thank goodness for Luna. While other people and their dogs are sleeping peacefully, she is my constant companion. I take a deep breath and warm my hands in her fur. It helps me think more clearly.

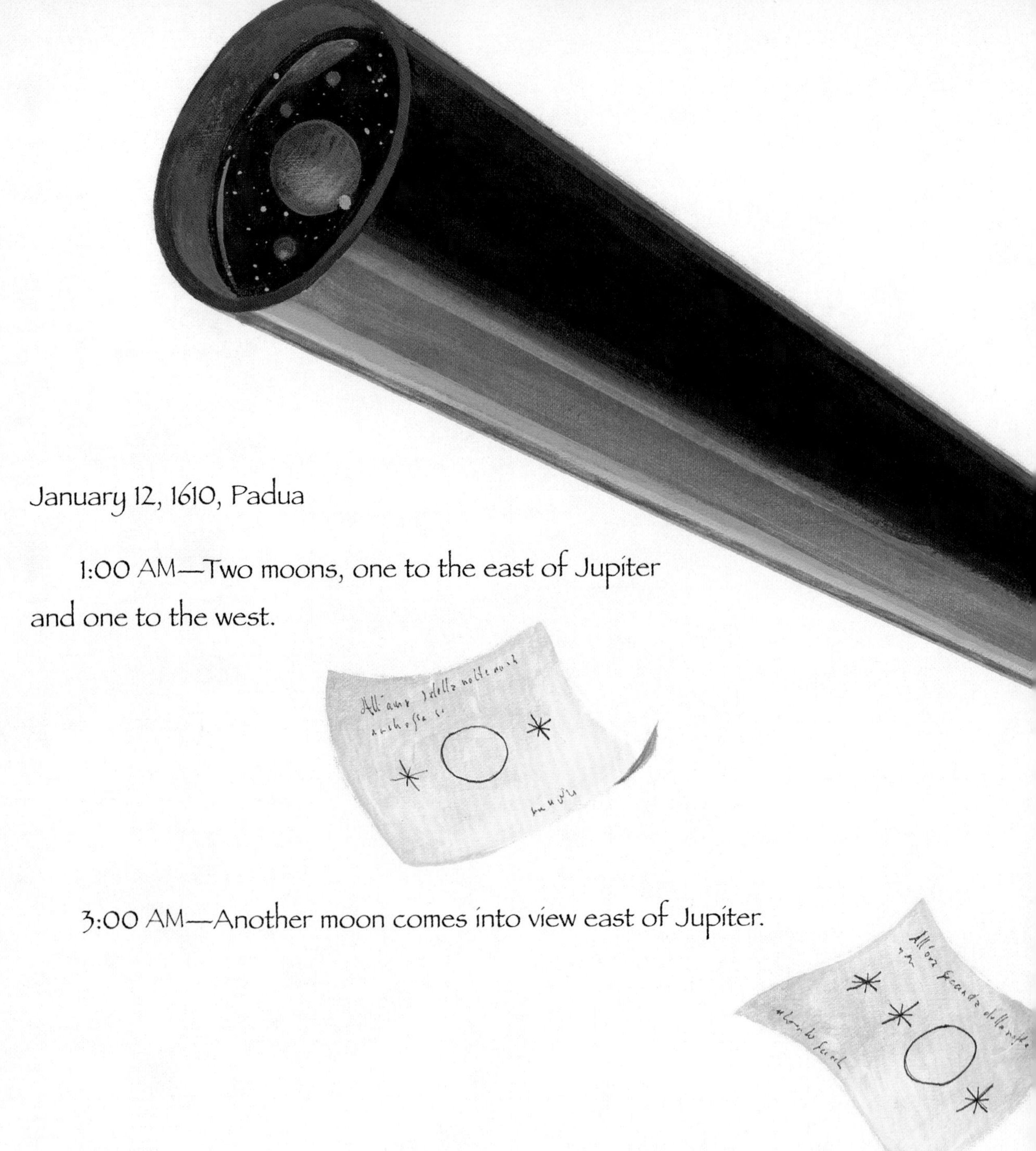

January 12, 1610, Padua

1:00 AM—Two moons, one to the east of Jupiter and one to the west.

3:00 AM—Another moon comes into view east of Jupiter.

Now I am certain—they are MOONS circling their planet!

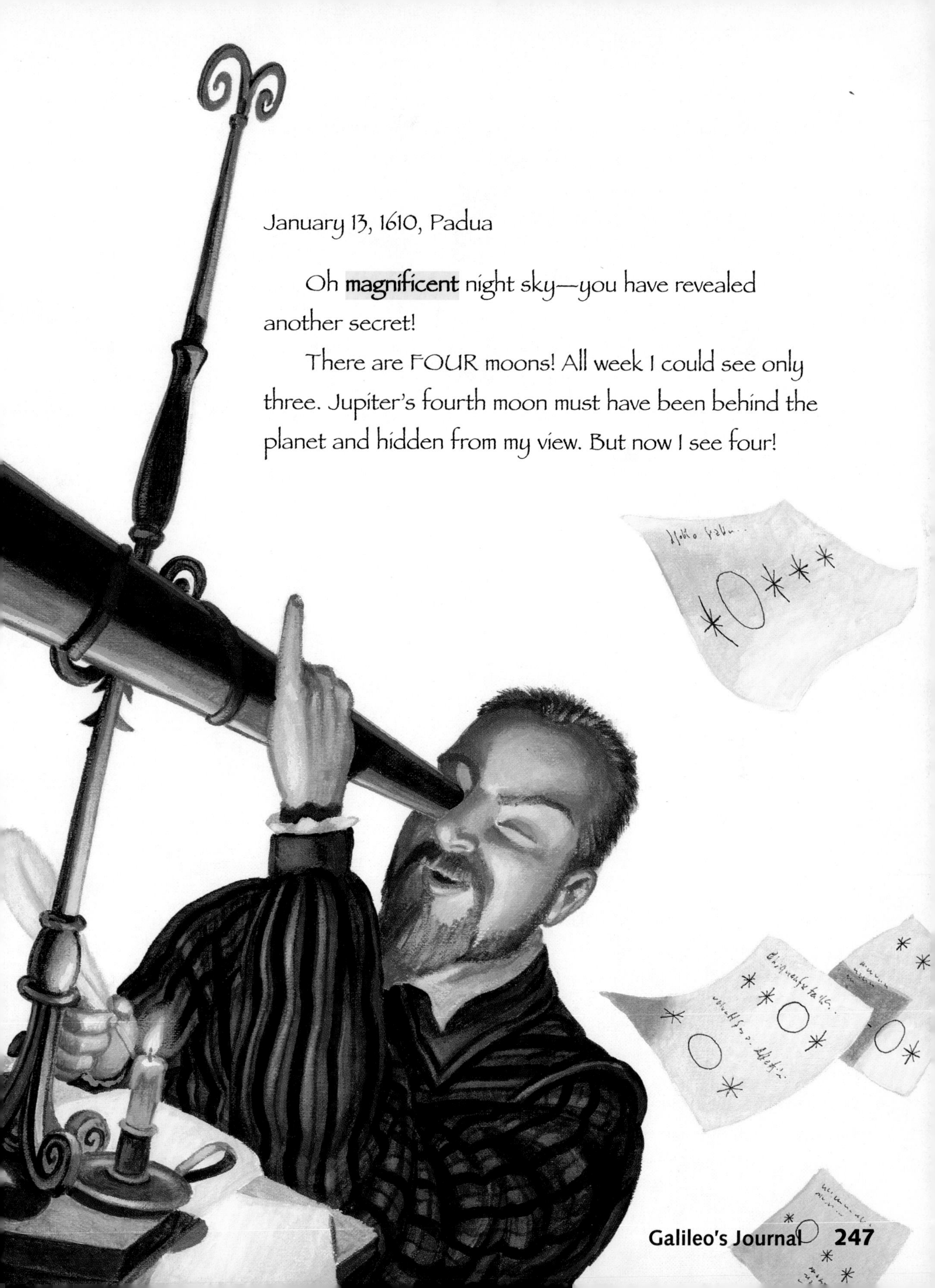

January 13, 1610, Padua

Oh **magnificent** night sky—you have revealed another secret!

There are FOUR moons! All week I could see only three. Jupiter's fourth moon must have been behind the planet and hidden from my view. But now I see four!

January 30, 1610, Padua

For weeks I have carefully observed Jupiter and its four bright moons. There can be no doubt about it. Jupiter has moons that orbit around it.

This changes everything!

Most people believe that the Earth is the center of the universe. They think that it stands still while the moon, sun, and planets move around it.

But the spyglass shows that the Earth is not the only center of motion in the universe. The Earth and Jupiter both have moons that travel around them.

Jupiter does not stand still—it moves as all the other planets do. If Jupiter can move in space with its moons, then so can Earth!

Here is evidence of what I have long suspected: all the planets, even Earth, move in space around the SUN.

January 31, 1610, Padua

The spyglass has helped me see what no one has ever seen before. I am writing a book to share my discoveries with the world.

I will call the book *The Starry Messenger*. As a messenger from the stars, I will tell everyone about the wonders I have seen.

March 13, 1610, Padua

The Starry Messenger is now published. Orders for my book are coming in every day. People near and far want to read the news for themselves.

When I first made my spyglass, I thought it would be useful for soldiers and sailors. I never imagined that it could bring people on Earth closer to the stars.

I still travel the starry sky every night with Luna at my side. With my spyglass, I'll continue to be a starry messenger. This is just the beginning!

The Life of Galileo

Galileo Galilei was born on February 15, 1564, in Pisa, Italy. At the age of 17, Galileo enrolled in the University of Pisa and began studying medicine and mathematics. Later, he became a mathematics professor and a private tutor. One of his students was Prince Cosimo de Medici II of the powerful and influential Medici family.

Galileo is considered the father of modern science. He performed experiments to see if an idea was correct. Today scientists do this all the time. But in Galileo's time, many scholars simply believed things because people had accepted them as true for centuries.

Galileo wrote about his discoveries with the spyglass (later called the telescope) in his first book, *The Starry Messenger* (1610). Many people were impressed by the ideas in the book, but some were furious. Galileo's discovery that Jupiter had four moons challenged the popular belief that everything in the universe moved around Earth. People accused Galileo of disturbing the order of things.

After publishing *The Starry Messenger*, Galileo continued to use his spyglass to see what had never been seen before. He discovered sunspots on the face of the sun and observed the phases of Venus.

In 1632 Galileo wrote a book entitled *Dialogue Concerning the Two Chief World Systems*. In this book, he showed with logic and humor that the astronomer Nicolaus Copernicus (1473–1543) was right: the sun is the center of the solar system, and all the planets orbit around it.

In 1633 religious leaders in Rome accused Galileo of teaching a forbidden view of the universe. Galileo was allowed to return to his home in Florence, but he was not allowed to travel or teach anymore. He continued working on his experiments and receiving visitors until he died on January 8, 1642.

Today scientists, historians, and religious leaders agree that Galileo unlocked many of the secrets of our universe. The four largest moons of Jupiter are called the Galilean moons in his honor.

Author's Note

Most of the things I write about in this book really happened. In 1609 Galileo lived in Padua, where he was a professor of mathematics at the university. He grew fruits and vegetables in his garden, played the lute, and invented things in his workshop. When he wasn't working, Galileo often visited his good friend Paolo Sarpi in Venice. Paolo told Galileo about the spyglass.

Galileo really did climb up to the top of St. Mark's tower to show off his spyglass to the senators. They were so impressed that they doubled his teaching salary. Galileo continued to make dramatic improvements to his spyglass over a short period of time.

One autumn night in 1609, Galileo became the first person to use a telescope to explore the night sky. He kept notes and sketches of his observations. The dates for his discoveries about the moons of Jupiter come directly from his book *The Starry Messenger.*

Galileo liked to eat well and had a sweet tooth. He also seemed to like animals. He kept a little mule, which he treated very well. I don't know if Galileo had a pet dog, but the Italian sheepdog was a pet in Italian households during his lifetime.

The settings and science in the book are factual. I used my imagination to create Galileo's thoughts and dialogue, based on Galileo's own works and the research I conducted in writing this book.

UNIT 5

America's Heartland

What makes the Central Region special?

Focus Questions

How are geography and economy connected in the Midwest?

How are geography and economy connected in the South Central States?

What is life like in the Midwest?

What is life like in the South Central States?

A Tour of the Central Region

by Lisa Lerner

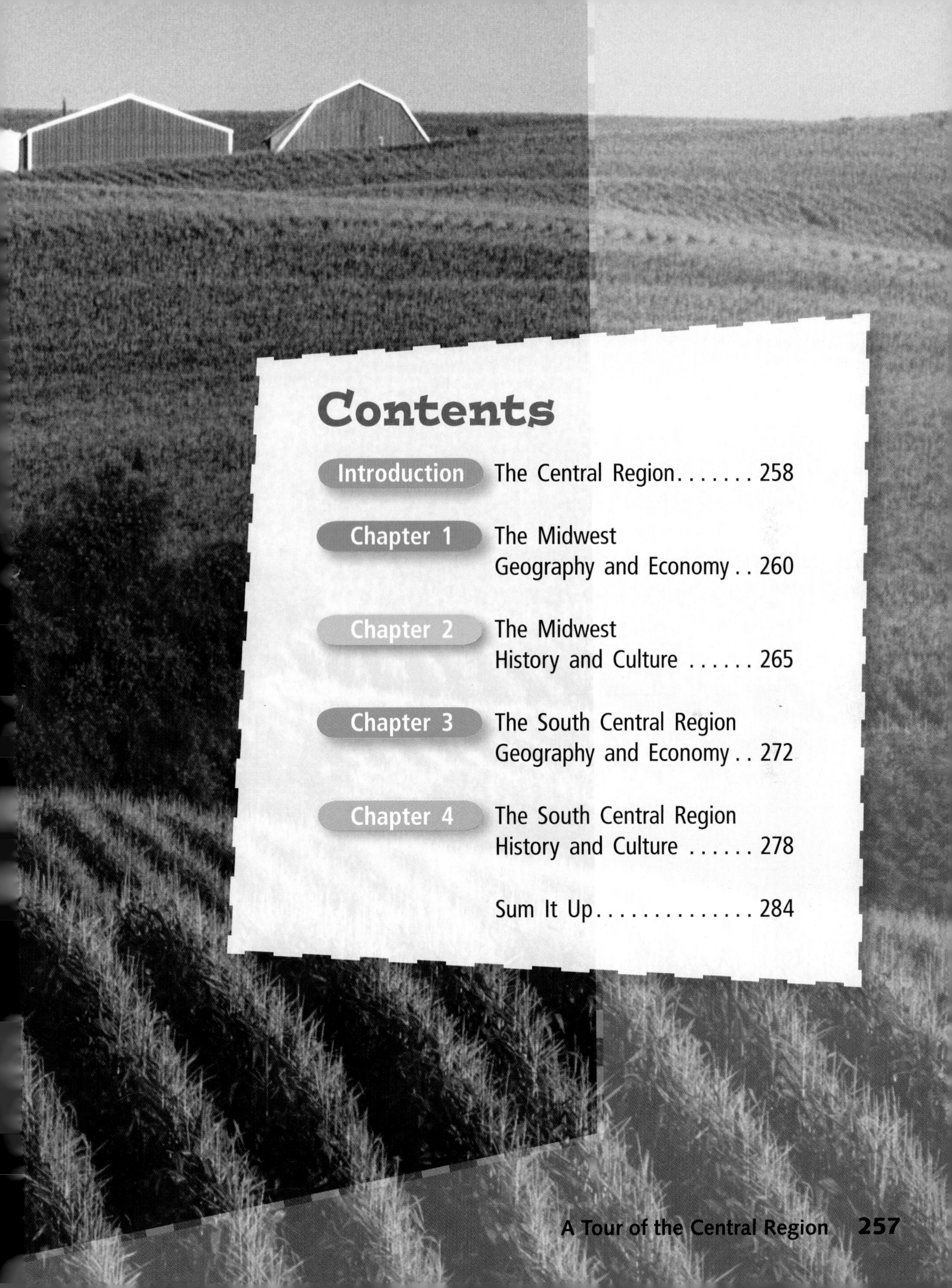

Contents

INTRODUCTION

The Central Region

The huge Central Region of the United States lies between the Rocky Mountains and the Appalachian Mountains. This large area of land is part of the Mississippi River Basin. A **basin** is low, bowl-shaped land that is drained by a river and its streams.

The mighty Mississippi River and the rivers that connect to it drain this basin. The Mississippi River Basin is more than 2,300 miles long. That's as long as about 40,480 soccer fields!

The Central Region is a big place and there are lots of interesting people and places here. We can learn about the Central Region by looking at its

- **geography**—land and water features,
- **economy**—how people make a living,
- **history**—how past events shaped the present, and
- **culture**—traditions, beliefs, and way of life.

THE CENTRAL REGION
CANADA
Lake Superior
Lake Michigan
Lake Huron
Lake Ontario
Lake Erie
MONTANA
NORTH DAKOTA
Bismarck
MINNESOTA
Minneapolis
St. Paul
SOUTH DAKOTA
Pierre
WISCONSIN
Madison
Milwaukee
MICHIGAN
Lansing
Detroit
WYOMING
PEN
Mississippi River
Missouri River
IOWA
Des Moines
Chicago
Cleveland
NEBRASKA
Lincoln
ILLINOIS
Springfield
INDIANA
Indianapolis
OHIO
Columbus
WEST VIRGINIA
COLORADO
KANSAS
Topeka
MISSOURI
Jefferson City
St. Louis
Ohio River
Frankfort
KENTUCKY
Nashville
TENNESSEE
APPALACHIAN
Arkansas River
Oklahoma City
OKLAHOMA
ARKANSAS
Little Rock
NEW MEXICO
Red River
Dallas
MISSISSIPPI
Jackson
ALABAMA
Montgomery
GEORGIA
SO CAR
LOUISIANA
Baton Rouge
New Orleans
TEXAS
Rio Grande
Austin
Houston
San Antonio
Gulf of Mexico
MEXICO
N
W
E
S
THE MIDWEST
THE SOUTH CENTRAL REGION
STATE CAPITAL

CHAPTER 1

The Midwest Geography and Economy

On a tour of the Midwest, you can see many **landforms**. The economy is connected to these landforms. You can see plains filled with waving grasses, which are good for raising farm animals. These flatlands have rich soil that is ideal for growing crops. Many waterways used for shipping products are located in this region. In South Dakota you can see rolling hills covered with forests, where loggers cut timber to build houses. The different geographic features of the Midwest have a lot to do with the way its people earn a living. Let's see how.

Mount Rushmore is located in the Black Hills of South Dakota. The heads of Presidents George Washington, Thomas Jefferson, Theodore Roosevelt, and Abraham Lincoln have been carved into the granite of the Black Hills.

Wisconsin ships some of its manufactured and agricultural products down the Mississippi River to the rest of the country and the world. The Mississippi River is important to the economy of the entire region.

The Great Plains—Great for Farming

The Great Plains is a large area of flat land that runs through the middle of the United States. In the Midwest Region the Dakotas, Nebraska, and Kansas are part of the Great Plains. Here, the climate and rich soil make it ideal for farming. Winters are cold and dry. Summers are hot. This climate is good for growing crops. In the Dakotas and Kansas, farmers grow wheat. The Great Plains includes part of the Corn Belt. Most of the corn grown in the United States grows here. The Midwest uses its land well. How does it use its water?

Nebraska is called the Cornhusker State because of the great amount of corn it produces.

Waterways and Transportation

The Great Lakes are an important part of the Midwest. Ships carry goods on these lakes. A system of man-made canals called the Saint Lawrence Seaway connects the Great Lakes to the Atlantic Ocean. The Saint Lawrence Seaway allows goods grown or made in the Midwest to be **transported**, or sent, to the rest of the world. Cities such as Chicago, Illinois, and Cleveland, Ohio, benefit because of shipping on the Great Lakes.

The Mississippi River is also an important waterway in the Midwest. Beginning in Minnesota, the Mississippi River flows south to the Gulf of Mexico. Goods from the Midwest, such as iron ore from Minnesota, are shipped down the Mississippi River.

Ships transport goods to and from the Midwest. The Great Lakes are important for trade with countries all over the world.

The Great Lakes

H-O-M-E-S

The Midwest has many lakes. Here's a tip for remembering the names of the most important lakes—the Great Lakes, the largest freshwater lakes in the world. Remember their initials: Huron, Ontario, Michigan, Erie, and Superior, H-O-M-E-S!

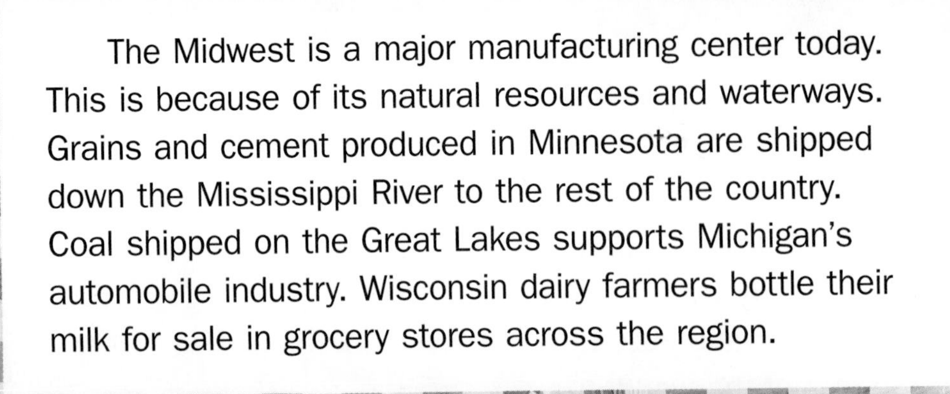

The Midwest is a major manufacturing center today. This is because of its natural resources and waterways. Grains and cement produced in Minnesota are shipped down the Mississippi River to the rest of the country. Coal shipped on the Great Lakes supports Michigan's automobile industry. Wisconsin dairy farmers bottle their milk for sale in grocery stores across the region.

In 2007 Michigan produced more automobiles than any other state.

The Birth of the Automobile in Detroit, Michigan

When automobiles were first invented, they were costly to produce. Few people could afford them. Henry Ford of Detroit, Michigan, found a way to make cars less expensive. In 1908 Ford invented the Model T, a reliable and affordable car. Because he mass-produced the Model T on assembly lines, he was able to sell them cheaply and many people were able to afford them.

Price of a Model T Ford

Year	Price
1911	$780
1912	$690
1913	$600
1914	$550
1915	$360

CHAPTER 2

The Midwest History and Culture

The history and culture of the Midwest connect in many ways to its geography. The first people to live in the Midwest were Native Americans. Some Native Americans farmed on the rich soil of the Great Plains. Others moved from place to place to hunt the bison, called buffalo, that grazed on the land.

Many Native Americans of the Great Plains used buffalo hides to build houses. In some areas they built homes out of dirt and trees from the forests. They survived by using the natural resources.

Native Americans such as the Lakota Sioux hunted buffalo on the Great Plains.

New Settlers to the Midwest

By the early 1600s Europeans began coming to the Midwest. Most were French and British. They explored the area and set up trading posts. They traded tools and weapons with Native Americans in exchange for furs. Later, Europeans built settlements in these areas.

In 1803 the United States bought a lot of land from France in an agreement known as the Louisiana Purchase. Most of the Midwest was part of the Louisiana Purchase. President Thomas Jefferson sent Meriwether Lewis and William Clark to explore the new area.

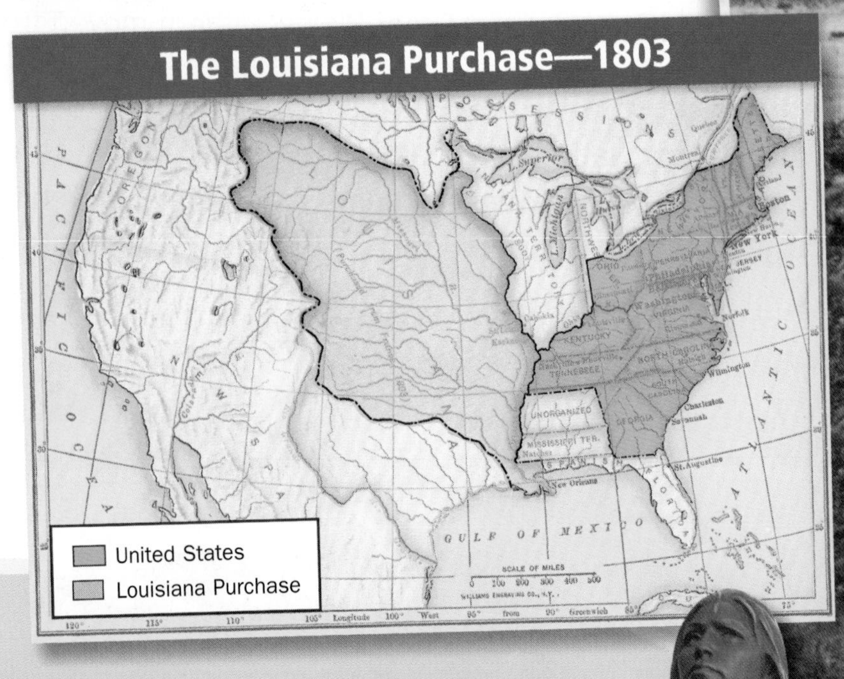

The Louisiana Purchase doubled the size of the United States.

Sacagawea Helps Lewis and Clark

Sacagawea, a Shoshone Native American, traveled thousands of miles with Lewis and Clark. She helped them communicate with her Native people, locate good travel routes, and determine which plants were safe to eat on their journey. She also sewed their moccasins and clothes. Once, when a boat almost tipped over, she rescued the team's important papers, books, and medicine from the water.

By 1900, homesteaders had claimed more than 80 million acres of land. Families, like this one in Iowa, built sod houses on their land.

More settlers moved to the Midwest. In 1862 the U.S. Congress passed the Homestead Act. This law offered free land in the Great Plains to settlers if they would farm it for five years. Settlers came from all over. The homesteaders came to make better lives for themselves.

Life was difficult for the homesteaders. The weather was harsh. There were few trees to build wood homes, so the homesteaders built sod homes. Sod is the top layer of soil that is held together by plant roots. Sod homes leaked. But at least the sod was free!

The Midwest Flourishes

The Midwest continued to **flourish**, or do well. More settlers pushed on to the Great Plains. The land near the Mississippi River was already settled, so the new settlers had to move farther west. From there it was hard for them to get their goods to market. When the railroads came that problem was solved. Small villages, such as Dodge City and Abilene in Kansas, became major railroad towns. Railroads connected the new settlers to these towns so they could sell their goods.

As more settlers farmed the Great Plains, better farming tools were invented. The Midwest began making farm equipment, such as the steel plow, using minerals that came from Minnesota and Michigan. Railroads carried the minerals to factories. They also carried the finished equipment to the rest of the country.

In 1879 Topeka, Kansas, was growing quickly. Settlers moved here to be near the railroads and to claim free land provided by the Homestead Act.

The Midwest Way of Life

The Midwest was prospering. People from many groups took part in settling the Midwest. They all made important contributions to the culture of the area.

People from all over the world still come to the Midwest for its culture. Great plays, art exhibits, dance, and sports draw tourists to the region. Culture, of course, is more than places and events. It's also how people honor their heritage and express themselves.

Today Topeka, Kansas, is still an important midwestern city. It is the capital of Kansas.

The culture of the Midwest is as unique as its geography and the people who live here. Early settlers and their descendents brought their art, literature, and music to the area. Many artists used the golden prairies, huge lakes, and green riverbanks as scenes for their paintings. Many writers told their stories set on the plains, on the banks of creeks, or in big cities. Jazz musicians often traveled to Chicago and many of the other big cities to play their music. This continues today.

Playhouse Square in Cleveland, Ohio, is home to many theaters, including the Allen, Ohio, State, Palace, and Hanna.

Art, literature, and music are just one part of midwestern culture. Sporting events, such as football and basketball, are also important. The Indianapolis 500, an automobile race, was first held in 1911. Today people come from many places to cheer their favorite drivers. People also come to see the buildings and monuments. The Gateway Arch in Saint Louis, Missouri, is the tallest monument in the United States. It is also known as the Gateway to the West.

The Gateway Arch was declared a National Historic Landmark in 1987.

Each year almost 400,000 people come to Indianapolis, Indiana, to watch the Indy 500.

CHAPTER 3

The South Central Region Geography and Economy

Like the Midwest, the South Central Region has many landforms. On a tour of this region, you can see high mountains and rolling hills. This is good land for growing trees for lumber. Beautiful river valleys have fertile soil that is excellent for growing crops. You can find mines filled with minerals here. You can also see raised, flat lands, called plateaus, in this region. Plateaus are ideal for raising animals.

South Central Region

Because of its warm climate, the South Central Region has a nine-month growing season. This growing season makes it possible to grow a variety of crops, such as cotton, peanuts, and rice. Let's take a closer look at the South Central Region's geography and economy.

Many resources can be found in the mountains of Tennessee, such as coal, copper, silver, and lead. Tennessee produces more zinc than any other state.

The Coastal Plains— Perfect for Cotton

In addition to a long growing season, rich soil is important to crops. The flat Coastal Plains that run along the Gulf of Mexico have very rich soil. And in Texas, Tennessee, Arkansas, Louisiana, and Mississippi, the moist soil is perfect for growing cotton. These states produce most of the cotton grown in the United States. Every year close to three million tons of cotton are produced here.

For many years, cotton was the most valuable product grown in Arkansas. Today farmers still grow cotton, but rice and poultry are the most important crops.

You Can Count on Cotton!

One bale of cotton weighs about 480 pounds. Can you guess what you can make from just one bale of cotton? Each of these is an example of what one bale of cotton can become—

- 215 pairs of jeans
- 249 bedsheets
- 690 bath towels
- 1,217 men's T-shirts
- 3,085 diapers
- 21,960 handkerchiefs!

Farming and Fishing

Like the Coastal Plains, the **delta** of the Mississippi River also has rich soil. The Mississippi River Delta is the flat, triangle-shaped area where the Mississippi River drains into the Gulf of Mexico. The mighty Mississippi brings millions of tons of rich mud to its delta each year. The Mississippi River Delta is about 11,000 square miles in area. Its rich soil makes it an ideal place for farming. Many crops grow here, such as peanuts, soybeans, and rice.

The port city of New Orleans, Louisiana, grew up on the Mississippi River in the delta region. New Orleans is a major shipping center. From this great port, peanuts, soybeans, rice, and cotton grown in the Mississippi River Delta are shipped to the rest of the world.

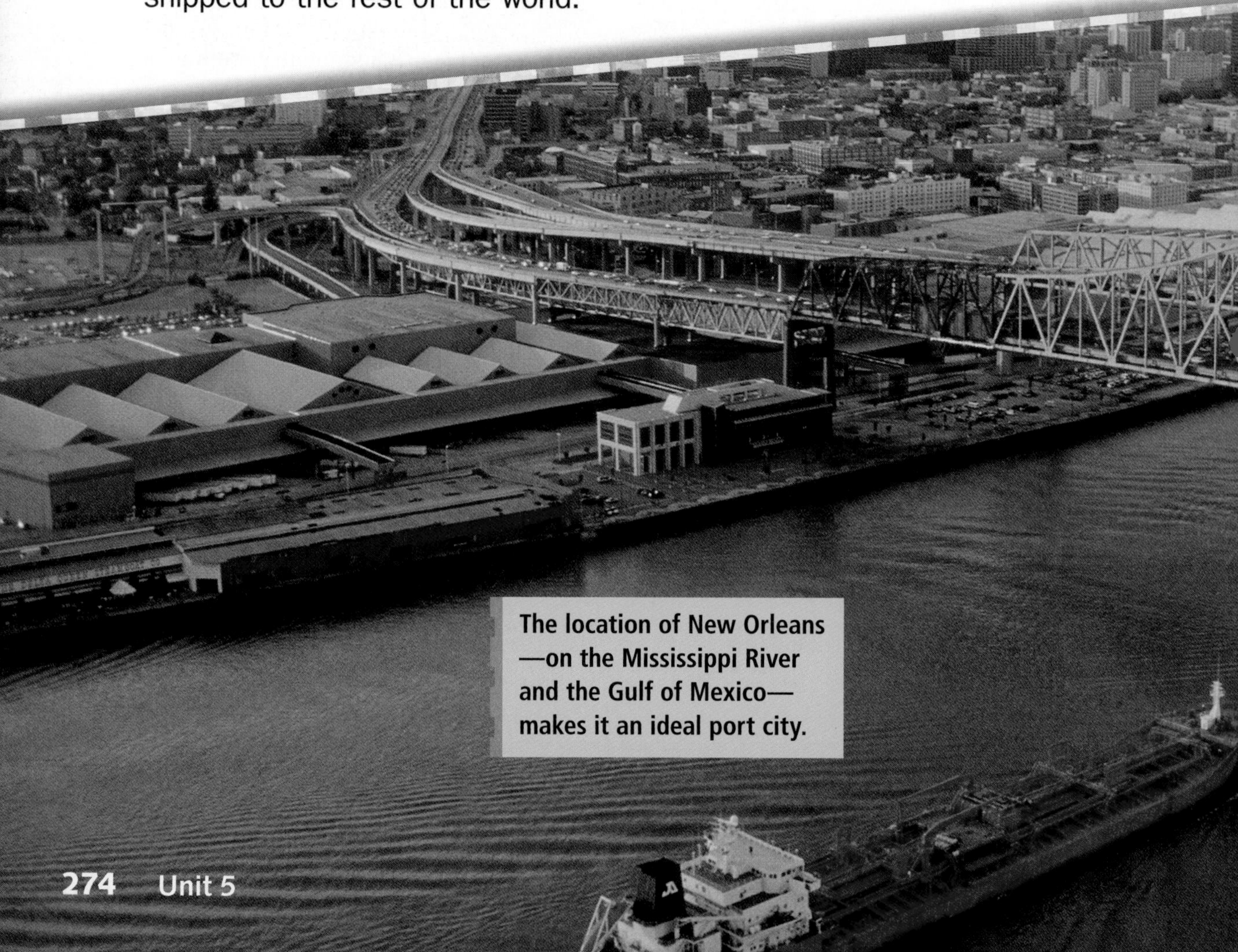

The location of New Orleans—on the Mississippi River and the Gulf of Mexico—makes it an ideal port city.

Commercial fishing is also a big business in this area. In Alabama, saltwater fish, such as shrimp and blue crabs, come from the Gulf of Mexico. Catfish, a freshwater fish, are raised on fish farms in the state. The catfish are raised in ponds and are fed grain. When the catfish farms began to produce fish, fish-processing plants became a part of the economy too.

Shrimp boats like this one are an important part of Alabama's economy.

Grasslands and Mountains

Huge grasslands cover many miles of the South Central Region. In Texas and Oklahoma these grasslands are home to grazing cattle. Ranching is a big industry in Texas. In fact, Texas raises more cattle and sheep than any other state.

Under these grasslands are huge amounts of oil and natural gas. Texas produces more crude, or raw, oil than any other state. Oklahoma is one of the leading producers of natural gas. These resources provide jobs for many people in the region. Workers here drill for oil and natural gas. They also build pipelines to transport the oil and gas.

Tornado Alley

Oklahoma's wide, flat land is often threatened by destructive tornadoes. Oklahoma is part of "Tornado Alley," which has the greatest occurrence of tornadoes in the country. Tornadoes are created when warm air and cool air meet, or converge. Strong winds develop, and the air begins to spin.

Oil can be found under two-thirds of the land in Texas.

The great amounts of coal found in Kentucky make it one of the nation's leading coal producers.

In contrast to the flat grasslands of Texas and Oklahoma are the mountain areas of Kentucky and Tennessee. The Appalachian Mountains are in the South Central Region. The mountains of Tennessee include many forests. From these forests come trees for construction and paper. In Kentucky the mountains also contain coal. Coal mining is an important part of Kentucky's economy.

CHAPTER 4

The South Central Region

History and Culture

The history of the South Central Region helped to shape its unique culture. Like the Midwest, Native Americans first settled the region. In the 1600s France claimed a large area of land, which included some of what is now the South Central Region. In chapter 2 you read about the Louisiana Purchase, and you know that the United States bought this land from France in 1803. Settlers who were drawn to the region's rich soil began moving here.

Spanish explorers claimed Texas and Mexico. Mexico became its own country in 1821 and assumed control of Texas. Stephen Austin, an American pioneer, led the fight for Texas's independence from Mexico. In 1845 Texas became part of the United States. Soon more settlers moved here.

The battle fought at the Alamo in San Antonio, Texas, was important in the war for Texas's independence from Mexico.

Settlers on the Move

In the early 1800s the U.S. government forced Native Americans living in the Southeast to move to what is now Oklahoma. This land was called Indian Territory. Then in 1889 the government opened some of the land in Indian Territory to settlers. Like the homesteaders in the Midwest, people had to be willing to live on it for five years. Some people rushed into the area early to claim land and were called Sooners. Today Oklahoma is called The Sooner State after these people.

In September of 1893 homesteaders rushed into Oklahoma to claim land. During this time nearly 50,000 people claimed land in Oklahoma.

Civil War and Civil Rights

In the 1800s many landowners in the southern states owned huge farms called plantations. A plantation was so big it needed many workers. Most landowners used enslaved Africans to work on their plantations.

In the northern and northeastern states, most people owned or worked in factories and were against slavery. In the 1860s some of the southern states broke away from the United States. They wanted to form their own country where slavery would be accepted. The United States was divided, and the North and the South fought the Civil War to settle their differences. The war lasted four years. After the war ended, a change to the Constitution set enslaved people free. The two sides came back together as people began the slow process of rebuilding the country.

During the American Civil War, the Northern Army won the battle at Vicksburg, Mississippi, which gave them control over the Mississippi River. This helped the North to win the war.

Although freed, many African Americans were not always treated fairly. Because of this, African Americans decided to fight for their equal rights. This long struggle became known as the civil rights movement. One of the movement's important leaders was Dr. Martin Luther King, Jr., an African American minister. He motivated African Americans to use peaceful ways to gain their equal rights. The civil rights movement quickly spread across the country. As a result, laws were passed that guaranteed equal voting and property ownership rights.

In 1965 Dr. Martin Luther King, Jr., (center left) and his wife, Coretta, led about 25,000 people to the Alabama State Capitol. Their purpose was to emphasize the unfair treatment of African Americans.

The South Central Way of Life

The culture of the South Central Region is **diverse** because of the many different people who settled its land. In Kentucky the culture of its early settlers is expressed through bluegrass music, a type of folk music. In Little Rock, Arkansas, the Arkansas Arts Center exhibits work that honors the culture of the state. In New Orleans, Louisiana, French and Spanish culture can still be seen in the food and the style of the buildings.

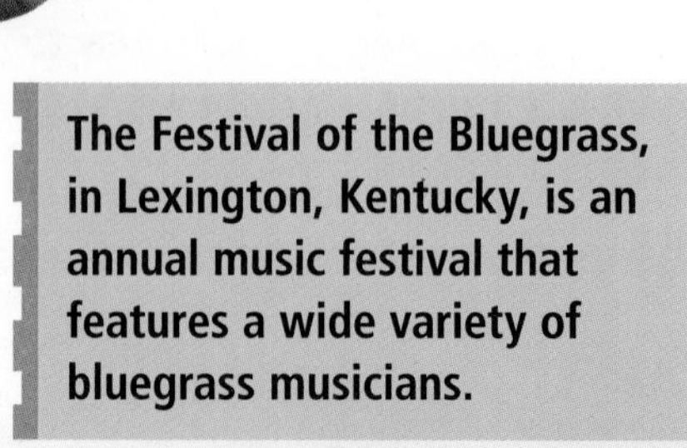

The Festival of the Bluegrass, in Lexington, Kentucky, is an annual music festival that features a wide variety of bluegrass musicians.

In Texas, Spanish culture can still be seen. Here you can see churches built in the Spanish style, called missions. The purples and yellows found in Texan paintings and pottery reflect the state's colorful landscape.

One way that African Americans express their heritage is through music. Jazz, gospel, and the blues are a few of the musical styles that are a part of this culture. There are many places you can hear this music in the region. The culture of this region is as diverse as the people who live in it.

Beale Street in Memphis, Tennessee, was an important place in the development of the blues. Today it remains an important part of Tennessee's culture.

Delicious Treats

Cultures often share similar delicious foods. Some of these foods are made from dough. Dough is a thick mixture of flour, liquid, and other ingredients. It can be baked, boiled, or fried. Some Native American groups use dough to make fry bread that is served with chili or cheese. In New Orleans, people remember their French heritage by frying dough to make a sweet, square doughnut called a beignet. Many people in Texas enjoy sopapillas, a fried Mexican dessert made from dough.

beignets

SUM IT UP

The Central Region

The Central Region of the United States is defined by its geography, economy, history, and culture. The region's geography plays a major part in the way people who live here earn a living. The region's land allows farmers to grow a variety of crops as well as raise farm animals. The land is also rich in oil and natural gas, which are valuable. Many waterways in the region allow for these goods to be shipped around the world.

The fertile soil, natural resources, and many waterways have also attracted a variety of people to the region. These people have contributed to the region's vibrant history and present-day culture.

Marven of the Great North Woods

WRITTEN BY
Kathryn Lasky

ILLUSTRATED BY
Kevin Hawkes

Influenza is spreading through the city of Duluth, Minnesota where Marven lives. To keep Marven safe, his mother and father decide to send him to a logging camp where most of the men speak French. Marven meets Mr. Murray after a long train ride across the cold and snowy landscape. The story continues as Marven enters the camp.

As they entered the camp, the longest shadows Marven had ever seen **stretched** across the snow, and he realized with a start that the shadows were the lumberjacks walking in the moonlight. He could smell hay and manure and saw the silhouettes of horses stomping in a snowy corral. From a nearby log building he heard the lively squeaks of a fiddle. It seemed for a moment as if the horses were keeping time to the music. Mr. Murray must have thought the same. "You want to watch the horses dance, or the jacks?" He laughed. "Come along, we'll take a look."

When they entered the building, the long shadows from the yard suddenly sprung to life. Marven stared. Immense men with long beards and wild hair were jumping around to the fiddler's tunes like a pack of frantic grizzly bears. They were the biggest and wildest men Marven had ever seen.

Marven could have watched the dancing all night, but Mr. Murray said, "Come on, Marven. We start early in the morning. I'll show you where you'll be living."

Mr. Murray took Marven to the small office where he would work and sleep. In Duluth, Marven had to share a bedroom with his two younger sisters and all of their dolls and toys, but this room was his—all his—and he liked it. A bed with a bearskin on it sat across from a woodstove; nearby, wood was stacked neatly. The big desk had cubbyholes for papers, envelopes, glue pots, and blotter strips. And on the desk there were blocks of paper and a big black ledger. There were pencils in a blue glass jar, as well as an inkwell. Marven hoped that somewhere there was a very good pen—a fountain pen.

"In addition to keeping the payroll," Mr. Murray said, " you have another job. The first bell in the morning is at four o'clock; second bell at four-fifteen. Third bell is at four-twenty. By four-twenty-five, if any jack is still in the sack, he's *en retard,* 'late.' So you, son, are the fourth bell. Starting tomorrow, you go into the bunkhouse and wake *les en retards.*"

"How?"

"You tap them on the shoulder, give 'em a shake, scream in their ear if you have to."

Then Mr. Murray said good night, and Marven was alone again.

It seemed to Marven he had just crawled under the bearskin when he heard the first bell. The fire was out and the room was cold and dark. He lit the kerosene lamp and pulled on his double-thick long underwear, two pairs of socks, two pairs of knickers, and two sweaters. Then he put on his cut-down overcoat.

After the second bell, Marven heard the jacks heading toward the eating hall. It was nearly time for his first job.

He ran through the cold morning darkness to the bunkhouse, peeked in, and counted five huge lumps in the shadows. Five jacks in the sacks. Marven waited just inside the door.

At the third bell, Marven was relieved to see two jacks climb out of the bed. Maybe the other three would get up on their own.

One lump stirred, then another. They grunted, rolled, and climbed out from under the covers. Their huge shadows slid across the ceiling.

One jack was still in the sack. Marven took a deep breath, walked bravely over to the bed, reached out, and tapped the jack's shoulder. It was like poking a granite boulder. The jack's beard ran right into his long, shaggy hair; Marven couldn't even find an ear to shout into. He cupped his hands around his mouth and leaned forward.

"Up!"

The jack grunted and **muttered** something in French.

"Get up," Marven pleaded.

Another jack pulled on his boots, boomed, *"Lève-toi!* Jean Louis. *Lève-toi,"* and shuffled out the door.

"Lève-toi! Jean Louis. *Lève-toi,"* Marven repeated.

Jean Louis opened one eye. It glittered like a blue star beneath his thick black eyebrow. He squinted, as if trying to make out the shape in front of him, then blinked and sat up.

"Bonjour," Marven whispered.

"Qui es tu? Quel est ton nom?"

"I don't speak French—just *bonjour, derrière,* and *lève-toi.*"

"That's all? No more?" the man opened his eyes wide now. "So what is your name?"

"Marven."

"Ah…Marven," Jean Louis repeated, as if tasting the sound of his name.

"Will you get up?" Marven asked anxiously.

Jean Louis growled and fixed him in the hard blue squint of one eye.

"Please." Marven stood straight and tried not to tremble.

Jean Louis grunted and swung his feet from beneath the covers. They were as big as skillets, and one of his huge toenails was bruised black and blue. Marven tried not to stare.

Marven and Jean Louis were the last to arrive at the breakfast table. The only sounds were those of chewing and the clink of forks and knives against the plates. At each place were three stacks of flapjacks, one big steak, eight strips of bacon, and a bowl of oatmeal. In the middle of the table were bowls of potatoes and beans with molasses, platters with pies and cakes, and blue jugs filled with tea, coffee, and milk.

Marven stared at the food in dismay. *It's not kosher*, he thought. In Marven's house it was against ancient Jewish law to eat dairy products and meat together. And never, ever, did a Jew eat bacon. Marven came to a quick decision. One day he would eat the flapjacks and oatmeal with milk. The next day he would eat the steak and the oatmeal without milk. And never the bacon.

After breakfast, as they did every morning, the jacks went to the toolhouse to get their saws and axes. Then, wearing snowshoes and pulling huge sleds piled with equipment, they made their way into the great woods, where they would work all day.

Marven went directly to his office after breakfast. Mr. Murray was already there, setting out Marven's work. A fresh pot of ink was thawing in a bowl of hot water on the woodstove. There were two boxes on the desk filled with scraps of paper.

"Cord chits," Mr. Murray said. "The jacks are paid according to the number of cords they cut in a pay period—two weeks. You figure it out. I'm no good as a bookkeeper and have enough other things to do around here. Each chit should have the jack's name—or, if he can't write, his symbol."

"His symbol?" Marven asked weakly.

"Yes. Jean Louis's is a thumbprint. Here's one!" He held up a small piece of paper with a thumbprint on it the size of a baby's fist. Marven blinked.

It was all very confusing. Sometimes two names were on one chit. These were called doublees; there were even some triplees. This meant more calculations. And sometimes chits were in the wrong pay-period box.

Marven sat staring at the scraps. "There is no system!" he muttered. Where to begin? His mother always made a list when she had many things to do. So first Marven listed the jacks' names alphabetically and noted the proper symbol for those who could not write. Then he listed the dates of a single pay period, coded each chit with the dates, and, with a ruler, made a chart. By the end of the morning, Marven had a system and knew the name or symbol for each man. There were many chits with the huge thumbprint of Jean Louis.

Every day Marven worked until midday, when he went into the cookhouse and ate baked beans and two kinds of pie with Mr. Murray and the cook. After lunch he returned to his office and worked until the jacks returned from the forest for supper.

By Friday of the second week, Marven had learned his job so well that he finished early. He had not been on his skis since he had arrived at camp. Every day the routine was simply meals and work, and Marven kept to his office and away from the lumberjacks as much as he could. But today he wanted to explore, so he put on his skis and followed the sled paths into the woods.

He **glided** forward, his skis making soft whisking sounds in the snow. This certainly was different from city skiing in Duluth, where he would dodge the ragman's cart or the milkman's wagon, where the sky was notched with chimney pots belching smoke, where the snow turned sooty as soon as it fell.

Here in the great north woods all was still and white. Beads of ice glistened on bare branches like jewels. The frosted needles of pine and spruce pricked the eggshell sky, and a ghostly moon began to climb over the treetops.

Marven came upon a frozen lake covered with snow, which lay in a circle of tall trees like a bowl of sugar. He skimmed out across it on his skis, his cheeks stinging in the cold air, and stopped in the middle to listen to the quietness.

And then Marven heard a deep, low growl. At the edge of the lake a shower of snow fell from a pine. A grizzly bear? Marven gripped his ski poles. A grizzly awake in the winter! What would he do if a bear came after him? Where could he hide? Could he out-ski a grizzly?

Marven began to tremble, but he knew that he must remain still, very still. Maybe, Marven thought desperately, the grizzly would think he was a small tree growing in the middle of the lake. He tried very hard to look like a tree. But concentrating on being a tree was difficult because Marven kept thinking of the bundle on the train platform—his mother, his father, his two big sisters, his two little sisters. He belonged in Duluth with them, not in the middle of the great north woods with a grizzly. The hot tears streaming down his cheeks turned cold, then froze.

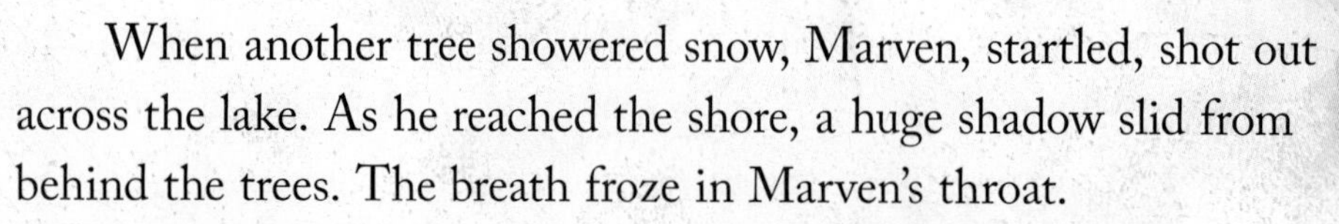

When another tree showered snow, Marven, startled, shot out across the lake. As he reached the shore, a huge shadow slid from behind the trees. The breath froze in Marven's throat.

In the thick purple shadows, he saw a blue twinkle.

"Aaah! Marven!" Jean Louis held a glistening ax in one hand. He looked taller than ever. "I mark the tree for cutting next season." He stepped closer to the trunk and swung the ax hard. Snow showered at Marven's feet.

"Ah, *mon petit*, you cry!" Jean Louis took off his glove and rubbed his huge thumb down Marven's cheek. "You miss your mama? Your papa?" Marven nodded silently.

"Jean Louis," he whispered. The huge lumberjack bent closer. "I thought you were a grizzly bear!"

"You what!" Jean Louis gasped. "You think I was a grizzly!" And Jean Louis began to laugh, and as he roared, more snow fell from the tree, for his laugh was as powerful as his ax.

As they made their way back to the sled paths, Marven heard a French song drifting through the woods. The other jacks came down the path, their saws and axes slung across their shoulders, and Marven and Jean Louis joined them. Evening shadows fell through the trees, and as Marven skied alongside the huge men, he hummed the tune they were singing.

In April, four months after Marven had arrived at the camp, the snow began to melt. Mr. Murray said to Marven, "I promised your parents I'd send you back while there was still enough snow for you to ski on. Every day it grows warmer. You better go before you have to swim out of here. I'll send your parents a letter to say you're coming home. But I don't know what I'll do for a bookkeeper."

So it was planned that Marven would leave on the last day of the month. When the day came, he went to the bunkhouse to find Jean Louis.

"Ah, Marven." Jean Louis tasted Marven's name as he had the first time he had ever said it, as if it were the most delicious French pastry in the world. "I have something for you, *mon petit*." He got up and opened the chest at the end of his bed.

"You are a woodsman now," he said, and handed Marven a brand-new ax. The head was sharp and glinting; the handle glistened like dark honey.

"*Merci*, Jean Louis. *Merci beaucoup*," Marven whispered.

Jean Louis went with Marven all the way to the train station. When the snow ran out on the banks of a muddy creek near the depot, he turned to Marven, grinned widely, and said, "Up, up. *Lève-toi,* Marven." The giant of a man swung the small boy onto his shoulders, skis and all, and carried him across to the opposite bank.

As the train pulled away, Marven waved at Jean Louis through the window, which had become foggy with his breath. "*Au revoir,*" he murmured. "*Au revoir,* Jean Louis."

Marven sat alone on the train and thought of his family. Who would be waiting for him at the station? He felt the edge of his new ax. It was so sharp, so bright. But it was good only for cutting wood. What could it do against the terrible flu that had sent him away?

With each mile the land slid out from under its snowy cover. When the train finally pulled into the station in Duluth, Marven pressed his face against the window, the glass fogging as he searched the crowd on the platform.

When Marven stepped down from the train he was still searching. Everyone looked pale and winter worn, and not a single face was familiar. Then suddenly he was being smothered with kisses and hugs. His little sisters were grabbing him around his waist, his big sisters were kissing his ears, and then all of them tumbled into Mama's and Papa's arms, and they were one big hugging bundle.

"The sickness is over," said Mama. "And you are finally home!"

A NOTE FROM THE AUTHOR

Marven Lasky was born in 1907 in Duluth, Minnesota. He is my father. He was the first child born in America to Ida and Joseph Lasky, who had emigrated from Tsarist Russia to escape the persecution of Jews. The story of their escape in 1900 was told in my novel *The Night Journey*.

Marven at age ten

In 1918 an influenza epidemic swept through the United States. The disease was the worst in the cities, among large populations. Old people and young children were the most vulnerable. Ida and Joseph believed that they might save at least one of their children if they could arrange for that child to go far from the city. Marven was not chosen because he was loved most; Joseph and Ida loved all of their children. Girls in that era, however, were never permitted to travel far from home by themselves—and the last place a girl would ever be sent was to a logging camp. Marven, therefore, was sent by himself on a train to a logging camp in the great north woods of Minnesota.

Marven in his late sixties

UNIT 6

Nature's Neighborhoods

How are living things connected?

Focus Questions

What roles do the parts of an ecosystem play?

Why do living things need each other?

What happens when there are changes to an ecosystem?

How do people play a part in ecosystems?

Balance in the Wild

by Sylvia Bergins

Contents

Chapter One

What Is an Ecosystem?

What does a hot, sandy desert have in common with a cold, snowy mountaintop? What about the bottom of an ocean and a sunny field full of flowers? What about a marsh and your own yard? All of these places are **ecosystems**.

Ecosystems are nature's communities. They exist everywhere in the world. Some are very large, filling a whole forest. Others are so tiny that they fit under a rock.

These photos show different ecosystems. Each has its own types of plants and animals that live there.

desert

field

yard

Every ecosystem is different, but all ecosystems have a few things that are the same. They all have living things, which include plants and animals. They all have nonliving things, such as rocks, soil, water, and air. All ecosystems need space, even if it is under a rock. This space is called a habitat. A habitat is a place where the plants and animals live.

Finally, every ecosystem can be changed by its climate. What might happen to an ecosystem with green rolling hills if it did not rain for many months? Plants would not be able to grow. There may not be enough food for the animals in that ecosystem. This would become a big problem for the living things in that ecosystem.

Living or Nonliving?

Think of a living thing. Did you picture an animal? A plant? A person? All of these are living things. They need food, water, and air to live, and they all grow.

What about nonliving things? Some nonliving things used to be alive. Logs used to be part of a tree. Some nonliving things, such as rocks and water, never were alive.

One amazing thing about an ecosystem is that each and every thing in it is important, even the dirt! Each part of an ecosystem does a certain job. Each job helps living things meet their basic needs, such as finding food and shelter. All living and nonliving things are connected to each other by the jobs they do in their ecosystem. Living things depend on each other to meet their basic needs. They depend on nonliving things too. This is called **interdependence**.

Think about a bicycle. It has many different parts that are connected. All the different parts work together to get you from one place to another. There are two wheels, two pedals, a seat, a set of handlebars, and many other parts. Now, what if your bicycle didn't have any handlebars? How would you steer? What if the pedals were taken away? How would you move the wheels? If a bicycle is going to work, it needs all of its parts. Just like a bicycle, an ecosystem has different parts that need one another to work.

A tree provides shelter for these birds. The young birds in this ecosystem wait for food from their mother.

The bee and the flower are interdependent. The flower provides nectar for the bee to drink. The bee moves pollen from one flower to another, helping new flowers grow.

Eco-*what*?

The word *ecosystem* comes from the Greek words *oikos*, which means "house" and *systēma*, "to place together."

An *ecosystem* is the way that the living and nonliving things in the same habitat are connected and work together.

The word *ecological* comes from the Greek words *oikos* and *logikos*, which means "the science of reasoning." *Ecology* is a kind of science that looks at the connections between living things and their surroundings.

The parts of ecosystems are all connected. Each separate part is important to the whole ecosystem. Here is a picture of some living and nonliving things in an ecosystem in the Rocky Mountains. How do you think they are connected?

Trees need nonliving things like the sun, the air, and water to grow. Animals large and small use the trees for shelter. Even when a tree dies, insects will make a home inside the dead wood.

Black bears mostly eat vegetation, such as twigs, buds, leaves, grasses, nuts, roots, fruit, berries, and new plants. Animals, such as insects, are a small part of what they eat. How do black bears find these tiny insects? They tear apart rotting logs that lie on the ground. Inside the logs are insects, such as beetles, ants, and crickets.

Sometimes a bear will climb a tree to escape from danger. You can see why this ecosystem is a good home for the black bear.

The black bear gets everything it needs to live in the Rocky Mountain ecosystem.

The orange shaded area shows approximately where the Rocky Mountains are located in the United States.

Chapter Two

The Food Connection

All living things need energy to **survive**. Where do they get that energy? From their food! The parts of an ecosystem are connected by food chains and food webs.

Food Chains

A food chain shows how energy flows from one living thing to another in an ecosystem. Just as in any chain, each link is connected to the next one. Each link in a food chain is a living thing. The order of the food chain shows what each living thing eats to survive.

Plants are the first link in the food chain. Did you know that plants use nonliving things to make their own energy? They use air, water, and the energy from the sun to make their own food. Plants are called producers because they produce, or make, their own energy.

Animals like this mule deer are consumers in a food chain.

Food Chain

At each link of the chain, the energy becomes part of the next living thing. The arrow shows which way the energy moves.

Animals cannot make their own energy as plants do. They must eat, or consume, food to get energy. Animals are called consumers. Herbivores, carnivores, and omnivores are types of consumers. Animals that eat only plants are called herbivores. Herbivores follow plants in a food chain. The mule deer is one of the herbivores that lives in the Rocky Mountains.

Plants are producers in a food chain.

Carnivores and omnivores follow herbivores in a food chain. Carnivores eat meat. A snake is one example of a carnivore. It eats worms, caterpillars, frogs, mice, fish, and small birds. Omnivores eat both meat and plants. A small bird eats insects, spiders, and the seeds of plants.

How do animals know what to eat? Some animals are taught by their parents. Mammals, such as lions, bears, and wolves teach their young how to hunt for food. Their eating habits are learned. Other animals are born with knowledge about what to eat. Most reptiles, such as turtles, snakes, and lizards, find their own food as soon as they hatch from an egg. Their eating habits are inherited.

Types of Consumers

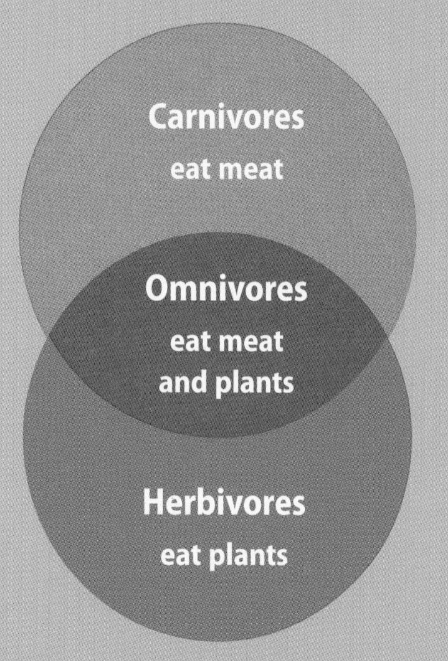

Carnivores and omnivores are predators. They live by hunting and eating other animals. The animals they hunt are called their prey. A predator can also be the prey for a larger predator. For example, a lizard hunts insects, but some birds hunt lizards. Top predators, such as mountain lions, are not prey. They are at the top of the food chain.

The mountain lion is a top predator. Few animals would hunt a mountain lion.

Food Webs

The links in a food chain do not always follow a straight line. Sometimes they branch out in different directions, like a spiderweb. This is called a food web. A food web shows the various food chains in an ecosystem. In a food web, living things are connected in many ways. Energy spreads out like a web.

Food webs show that consumers eat different kinds of food. In this food web, lizards eat rabbits, but they also eat small birds. This means that the lizard is connected to everything that a rabbit eats *and* everything that a small bird eats.

Sometimes two different consumers eat the same kind of food. Rabbits eat plants, but so do small birds. The plants are a part of both food chains.

From a web, you can also tell what kind of consumer an animal is. In this food web, there is no arrow pointing from the plant to the lizard. This means that the lizard does not eat plants. The lizard is a carnivore. The rabbit only eats plants. It is an herbivore. The bird eats plants and ants. It is an omnivore.

lizard
Lizards eat rabbits.
Lizards eat small birds.
bird
Small birds eat ants.
Small birds eat the seeds of plants.
ants

Chapter Three

A Food Balancing Act

Food chains and food webs show us that living things in an ecosystem are connected by the food that they eat. Did you know that the *amount* of each thing matters too? In order for this system to work, there needs to be enough food to keep the chain going. Ecosystems should be balanced. Each ecosystem should have the right number of each species, or type of living thing, to keep it balanced. It also should have the right amount of food for each species.

Energy Pyramid

This pyramid shows one food chain in the Rocky Mountain ecosystem. There is a good balance among the plants, deer, and mountain lions.

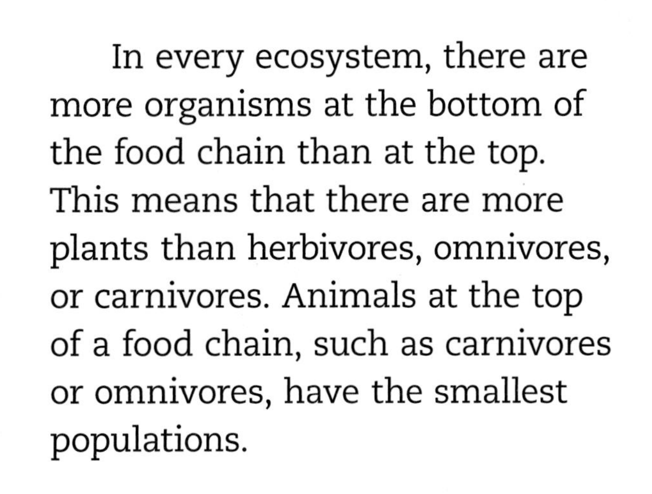

In every ecosystem, there are more organisms at the bottom of the food chain than at the top. This means that there are more plants than herbivores, omnivores, or carnivores. Animals at the top of a food chain, such as carnivores or omnivores, have the smallest populations.

In the Rocky Mountains, there are more plants than deer. That means that herbivores, such as deer, have enough to eat. Deer don't have to **compete** with each other to find food. There also are more deer than mountain lions, so there is enough food to go around. The pyramid on these pages shows how energy moves through that food chain.

Chapter Four

Tiny, but Mighty

We have explored an ecosystem from bottom to top—almost. The food chain does not end with the biggest predators. It ends with the tiniest members. Most of them are too small to see! They are the decomposers. They link the end of the food chain with the beginning.

Decomposers, such as bacteria and fungi, are an ecosystem's recyclers. Humans recycle bottles and newspapers and turn them into new things. Decomposers recycle things that once were alive and turn them into things that are useful for the ecosystem. Decomposers break down dead leaves, animal waste, and dead insects and other animals on the habitat floor. These nonliving things become a part of the soil that plants use to grow. All of this is happening right under your nose!

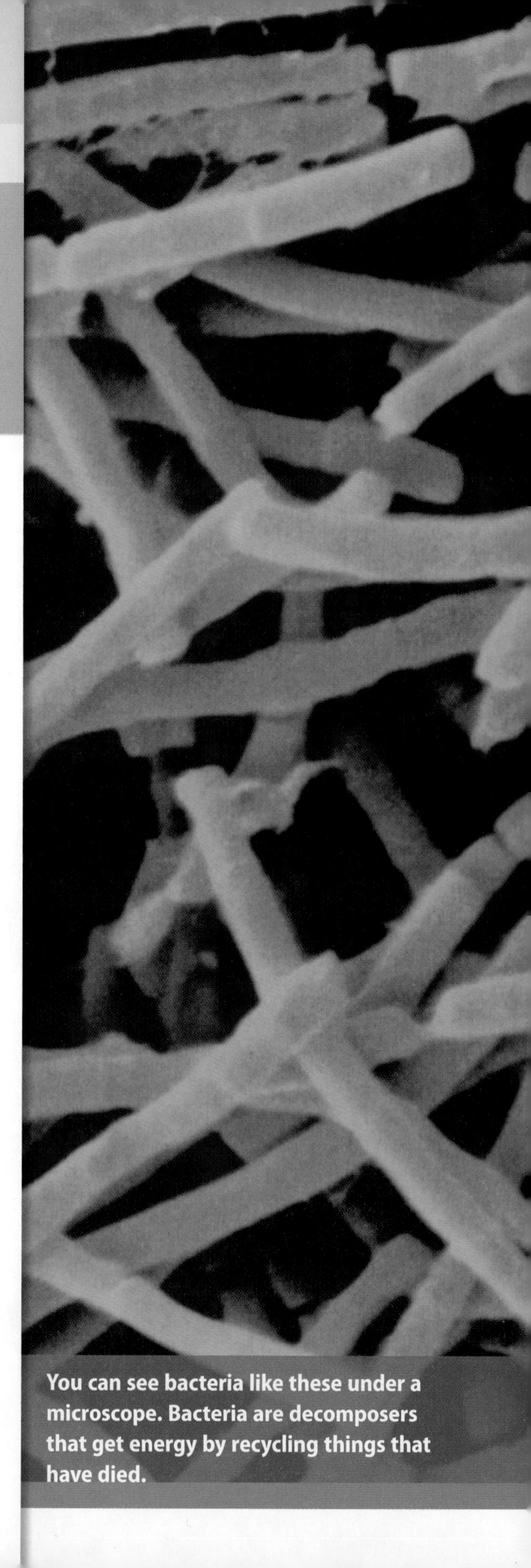

You can see bacteria like these under a microscope. Bacteria are decomposers that get energy by recycling things that have died.

Fungi are also decomposers. In this picture, they are breaking down a rotting tree.

Many decomposers are too small to see. But if you take a walk through the woods, you may see a lot of dead tree trunks on the ground. Some of them will have fungi on them. The fungi are decomposing the dead wood. Even the dead trees are eventually turned into fungi food!

Scavengers

Scavengers are animals that look for dead animals or plants to eat. As scavengers eat, they break down the dead animals and plants into small bits. Houseflies, cockroaches, and earthworms are scavengers. Decomposers such as bacteria then break down the small bits that the scavengers leave.

Chapter Five

Creature Features

Living things have adaptations that help them survive in their ecosystems. Adaptations have different purposes. Some adaptations help living things find food. Others protect animals from predators or help predators hunt their prey. Some help living things survive in very hot, very cold, or very dry climates.

Adaptations can be features of the body, such as teeth or hooves. Mountain goats have split hooves with rough bottoms; the hooves hold on to rocky cliffs when mountain goats are looking for food. Behaviors, or ways of acting, also can be adaptations. In the fall, black bears will eat more to store fat in their bodies. This helps them to survive long winters with little food.

The mountain goat's thick white coat helps protect it from the cold.

Plants have adaptations too. Near the peaks of the Rocky Mountains, plants grow close to the ground. This adaptation helps them survive icy winds that rip across the mountaintops. If these plants grew tall, like pine trees, the wind would blow them down.

The shape and texture of a mountain goat's hooves help it to travel on steep and smooth surfaces.

Chapter Six

Changes in an Ecosystem

Think again about that bicycle without any handlebars. Like a bicycle, an ecosystem needs every part in place. If one part of an ecosystem is missing or harmed, the entire ecosystem changes. A bicycle with a broken or missing part is easy to fix. A damaged ecosystem may be very hard to repair.

The pictures on these pages show a food chain in an African savanna. The grasses are a key producer in this ecosystem. There seems to be plenty of grass to feed the animals in this ecosystem. Herds of wildebeests graze on the grass. Lions prey on the wildebeests. As long as there is enough food for each living thing in the food chain, everything is in balance.

These grasses provide food for the animals in this ecosystem.

Changes to an ecosystem can **affect** the way that all the plants and animals meet their basic needs. Even the tiniest animal can cause huge changes. Think about this African savanna ecosystem and what might happen if the grasses **disappeared**. What would the wildebeests eat? What would the lions eat? What else would be affected?

Lions eat wildebeests to survive.

Wildebeests are one group of animals that eat the grasses.

A Change in the Habitat

A habitat is a place where plants and animals live. When a habitat changes, the plants and animals may have trouble surviving. Sometimes a habitat is changed just a little bit, but sometimes it is destroyed.

People can change a habitat when they turn land into farms or build towns with homes and stores. In China, for example, logging and farming have destroyed some of the giant panda's habitat.

Habitats also are changed by natural causes, such as wildfires, volcanic eruptions, or hurricanes. On Macquarie Island, near Australia, landslides destroyed part of a habitat where penguins lived. The landslides were caused by rabbits grazing in the area.

Farms like this one have changed the Chinese countryside in recent years.

Fires can destroy many plants in a habitat. Animals that depend on these plants may not have enough food to survive.

Habitats give plants and animals a place to sleep or hide. Habitats are where animals find food and water, and a place to stay warm or cool so they can survive. It is very hard for a species to survive when its habitat cannot provide even one of these things.

Many birds live in trees. They would have to move to other areas if trees were destroyed by fire.

A New "Neighbor"

Sometimes, a new species moves from one habitat to another. When these species cause big changes in their new "neighborhood," they are said to have *invaded* the habitat. These invasive species take over the new habitat and throw everything off balance.

Invasive species travel to new habitats in different ways. Sometimes people grow plants from different habitats in their backyard. They do not think that the species may become invasive.

Invasive species are most dangerous when they have big appetites and no predators. Wild pigs are a problem in the southern United States because they eat just about anything. They eat so much that there isn't enough for the other animals. Predators in the area don't hunt pigs, so the number of wild pigs keeps growing.

Wild pigs eat so much food in a habitat that other animals can go hungry.

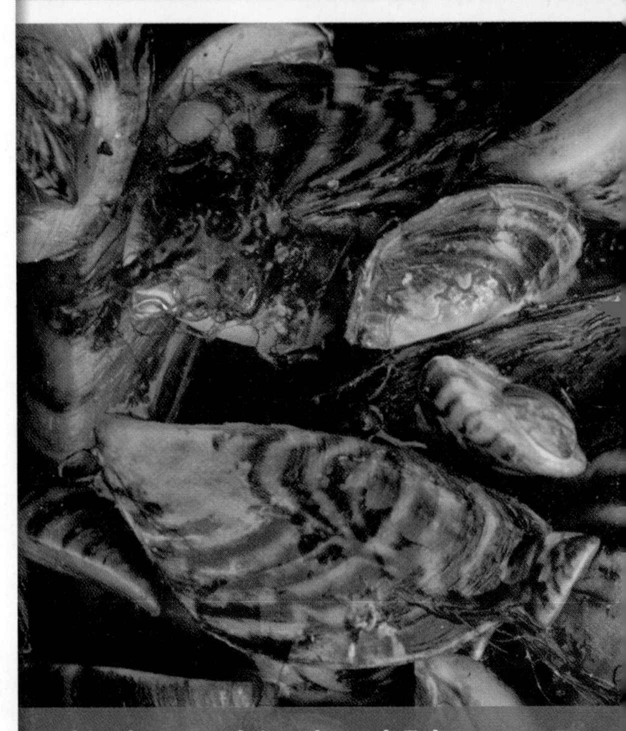

This photograph is enlarged. Zebra mussels are the size of a fingernail. This invasive species has caused problems for fish and other animals in the Great Lakes.

Zebra mussels are another invasive species. They are sea animals from the Caspian Sea in Western Asia. Somehow they traveled by ship to the Great Lakes in the United States. Zebra mussels may benefit freshwater ecosystems in Western Asia. But they do not fit into the ecosystem of the Great Lakes. They eat the food that other living things need to survive.

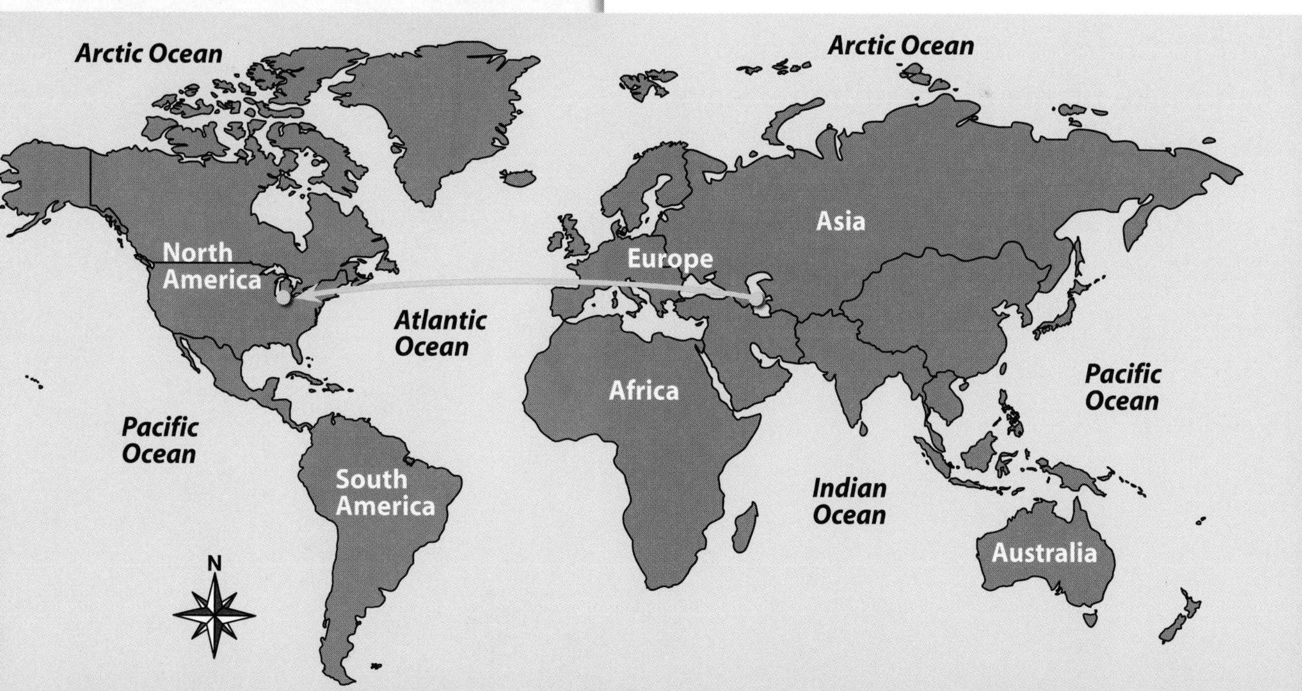

Zebra mussels came to the United States from Western Asia.

Losing a Link

Remember that all the living and nonliving things in an ecosystem are connected. If one link in a food chain is missing, every other link is affected. For example, coyotes feed on pronghorns. If coyotes disappeared, the number of pronghorns would go up. The pronghorns would eat too many plants. There wouldn't be enough plants for smaller herbivores such as mice and insects. Soon, those animals might also disappear. Losing one species hurts all the other species in the ecosystem.

Ecosystems lose links in different ways. Some animals are hunted too much. Changes in the climate also can make plants die or animals leave an ecosystem.

Passenger pigeons were hunted to extinction. The last surviving one died in 1914. This figure of the bird is from a museum.

One way ecosystems change is by humans tearing forests down. This affects many living creatures that depend on the forest.

cotton

Cotton is used in fabrics that are made into clothing, towels, curtains, sails, and more!

Keeping Ecosystems Healthy

An ecosystem is an amazing part of the natural world. Sometimes an ecosystem can survive even if it changes. Often, however, a change causes it to break down. The plants and animals must struggle to meet their basic needs.

People also depend on healthy ecosystems to meet their basic needs. We eat plants and animals. Much of our clothing, such as things made of cotton and wool, comes from plants and animals. Homes are sometimes made from the wood of trees. We even get medicine from living things. We must keep ecosystems healthy for all living things.

Ecosystems: The Big Ideas

Ecosystems are communities of living things. Every part of an ecosystem is important.

- The living things in an ecosystem are interdependent. They need other living things and nonliving things to meet their basic needs.
- One basic need is food. The living things in an ecosystem are connected by a food chain. A food web shows different food chains.
- Plants are producers, and animals are consumers.
- Living things have adaptations that help them to survive.
- A change to even one part of an ecosystem can change the way the whole ecosystem works.

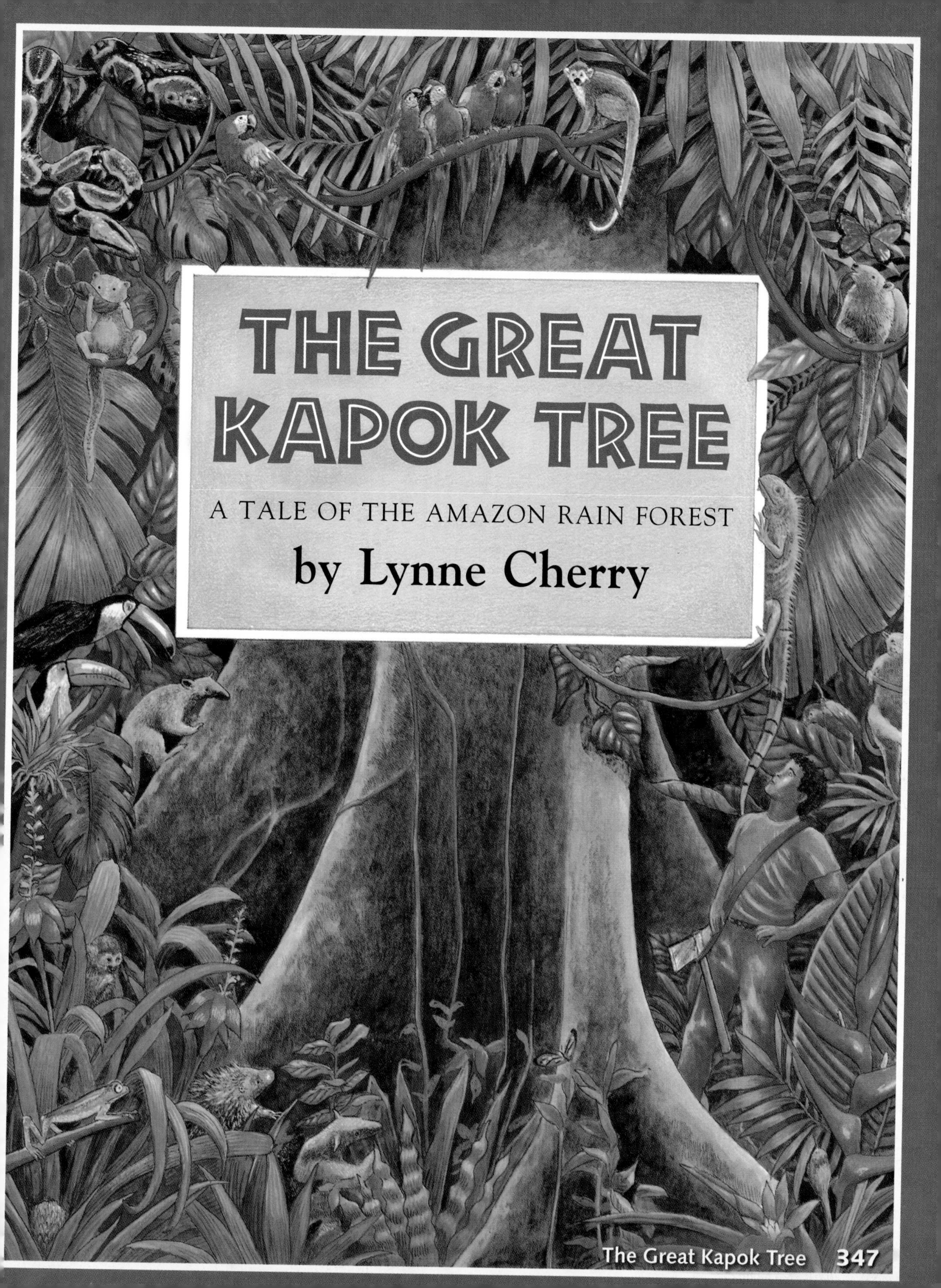
THE GREAT
KAPOK TREE
A TALE OF THE AMAZON RAIN FOREST
by Lynne Cherry

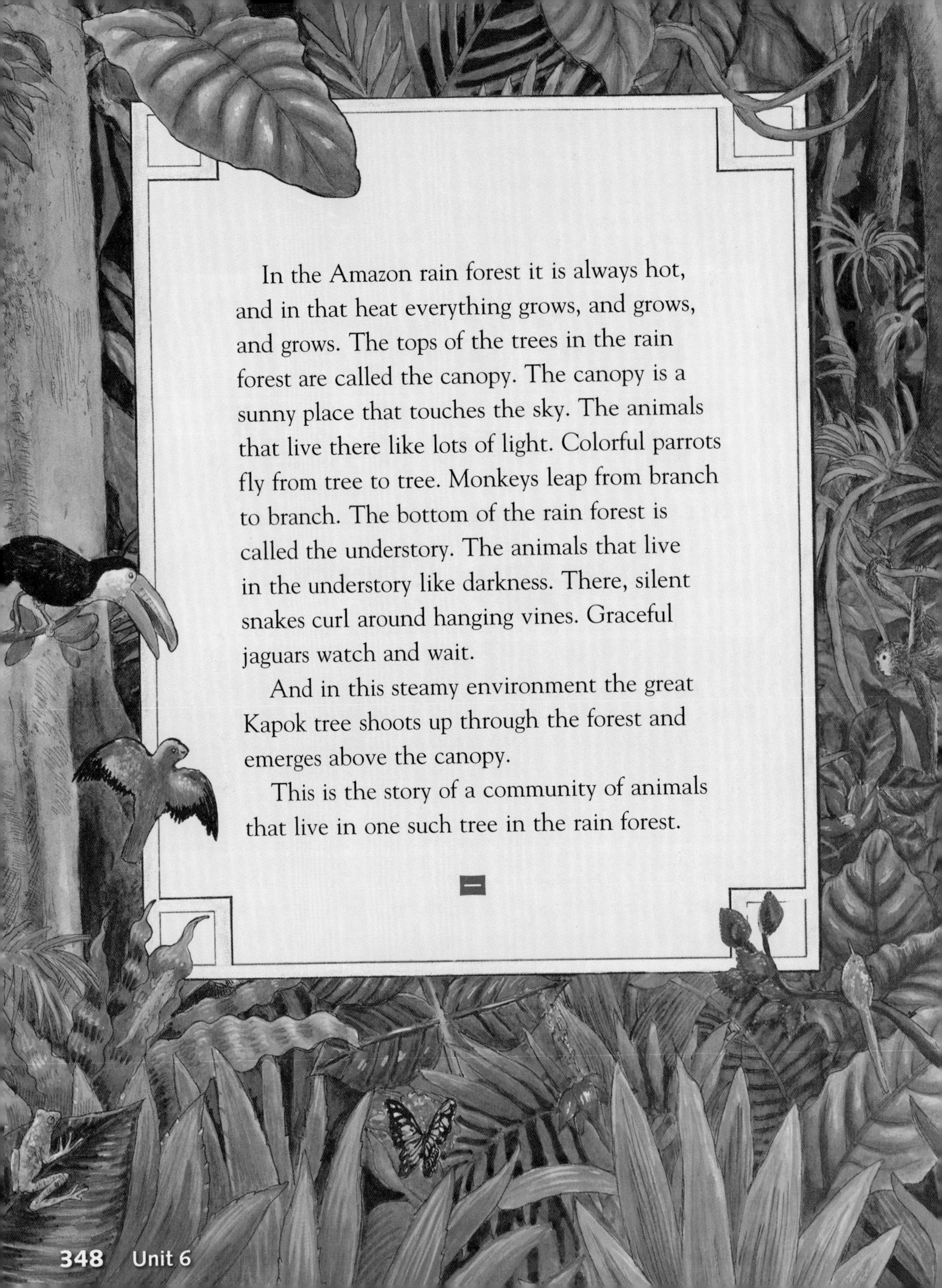

In the Amazon rain forest it is always hot, and in that heat everything grows, and grows, and grows. The tops of the trees in the rain forest are called the canopy. The canopy is a sunny place that touches the sky. The animals that live there like lots of light. Colorful parrots fly from tree to tree. Monkeys leap from branch to branch. The bottom of the rain forest is called the understory. The animals that live in the understory like darkness. There, silent snakes curl around hanging vines. Graceful jaguars watch and wait.

And in this steamy environment the great Kapok tree shoots up through the forest and emerges above the canopy.

This is the story of a community of animals that live in one such tree in the rain forest.

Two men walked into the rain forest. Moments before, the forest had been alive with the sounds of squawking birds and howling monkeys. Now all was quiet as the creatures watched the two men and wondered why they had come.

The larger man stopped and pointed to a great Kapok tree. Then he left.

The smaller man took the ax he carried and struck the trunk of the tree. Whack! Whack! Whack! The sounds of the blows rang through the forest. The wood of the tree was very hard. Chop! Chop! Chop! The man wiped off the sweat that ran down his face and neck. Whack! Chop! Whack! Chop!

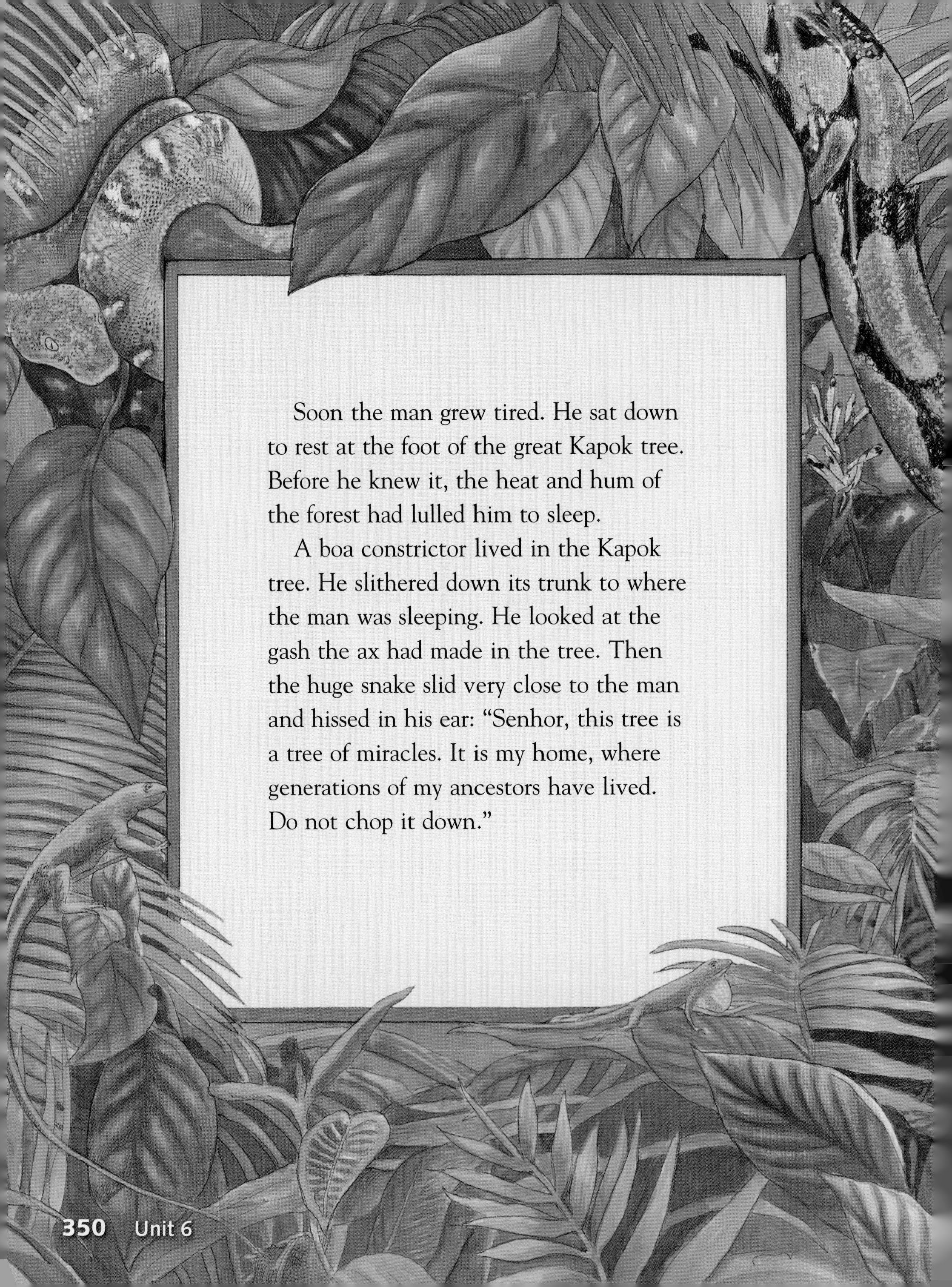

Soon the man grew tired. He sat down to rest at the foot of the great Kapok tree. Before he knew it, the heat and hum of the forest had lulled him to sleep.

A boa constrictor lived in the Kapok tree. He slithered down its trunk to where the man was sleeping. He looked at the gash the ax had made in the tree. Then the huge snake slid very close to the man and hissed in his ear: "Senhor, this tree is a tree of miracles. It is my home, where generations of my ancestors have lived. Do not chop it down."

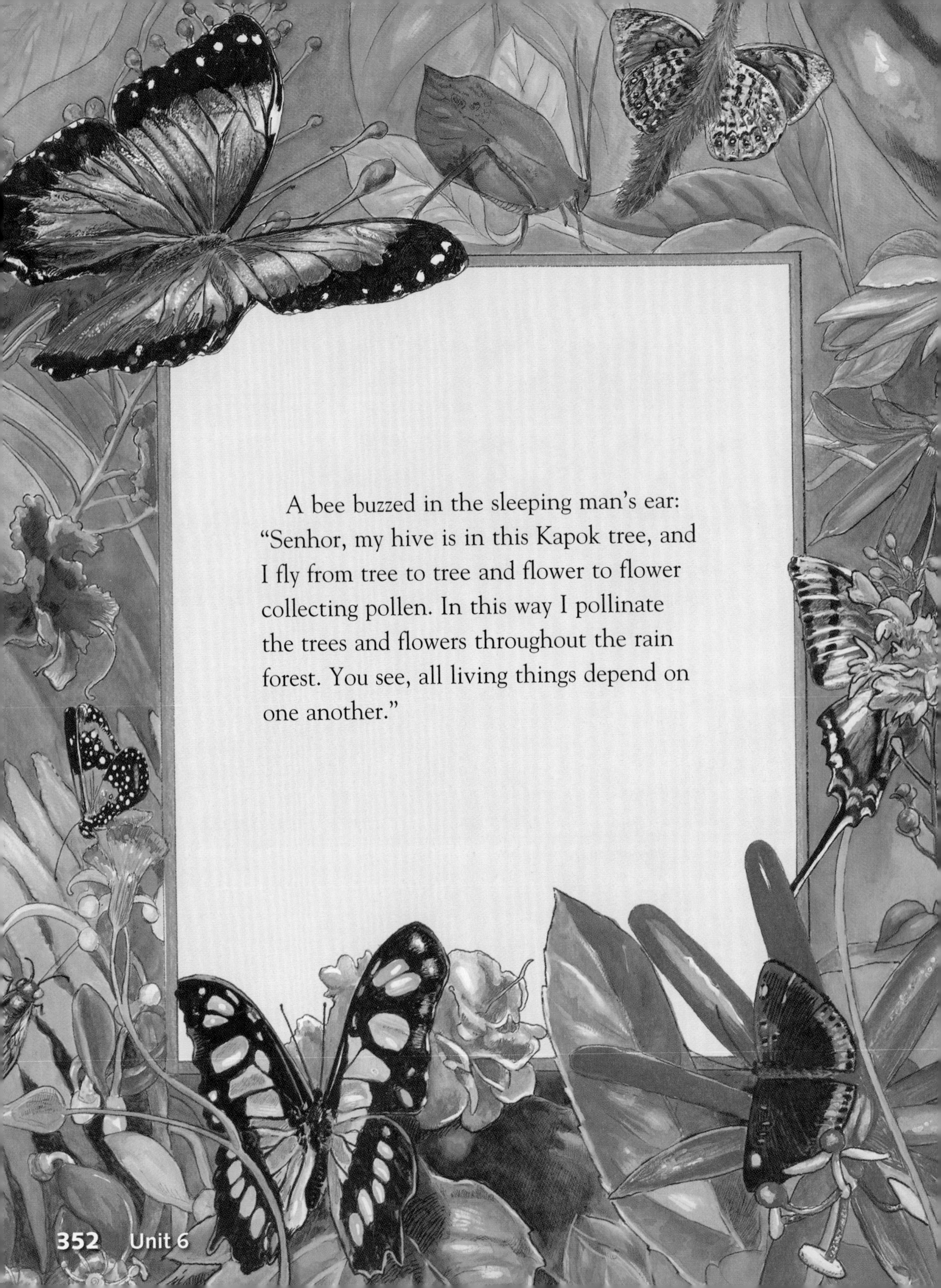

A bee buzzed in the sleeping man's ear: "Senhor, my hive is in this Kapok tree, and I fly from tree to tree and flower to flower collecting pollen. In this way I pollinate the trees and flowers throughout the rain forest. You see, all living things depend on one another."

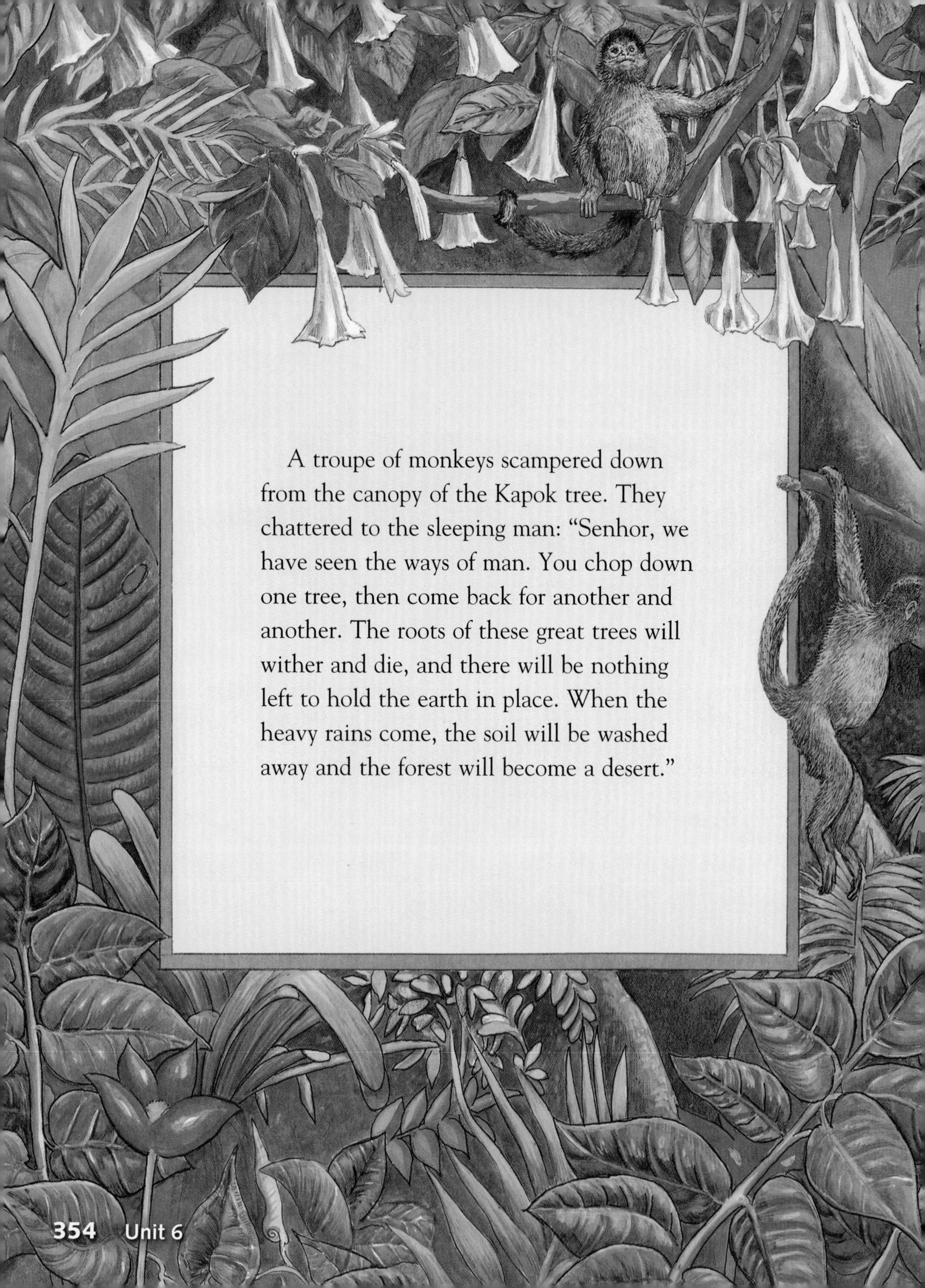

A troupe of monkeys scampered down from the canopy of the Kapok tree. They chattered to the sleeping man: "Senhor, we have seen the ways of man. You chop down one tree, then come back for another and another. The roots of these great trees will wither and die, and there will be nothing left to hold the earth in place. When the heavy rains come, the soil will be washed away and the forest will become a desert."

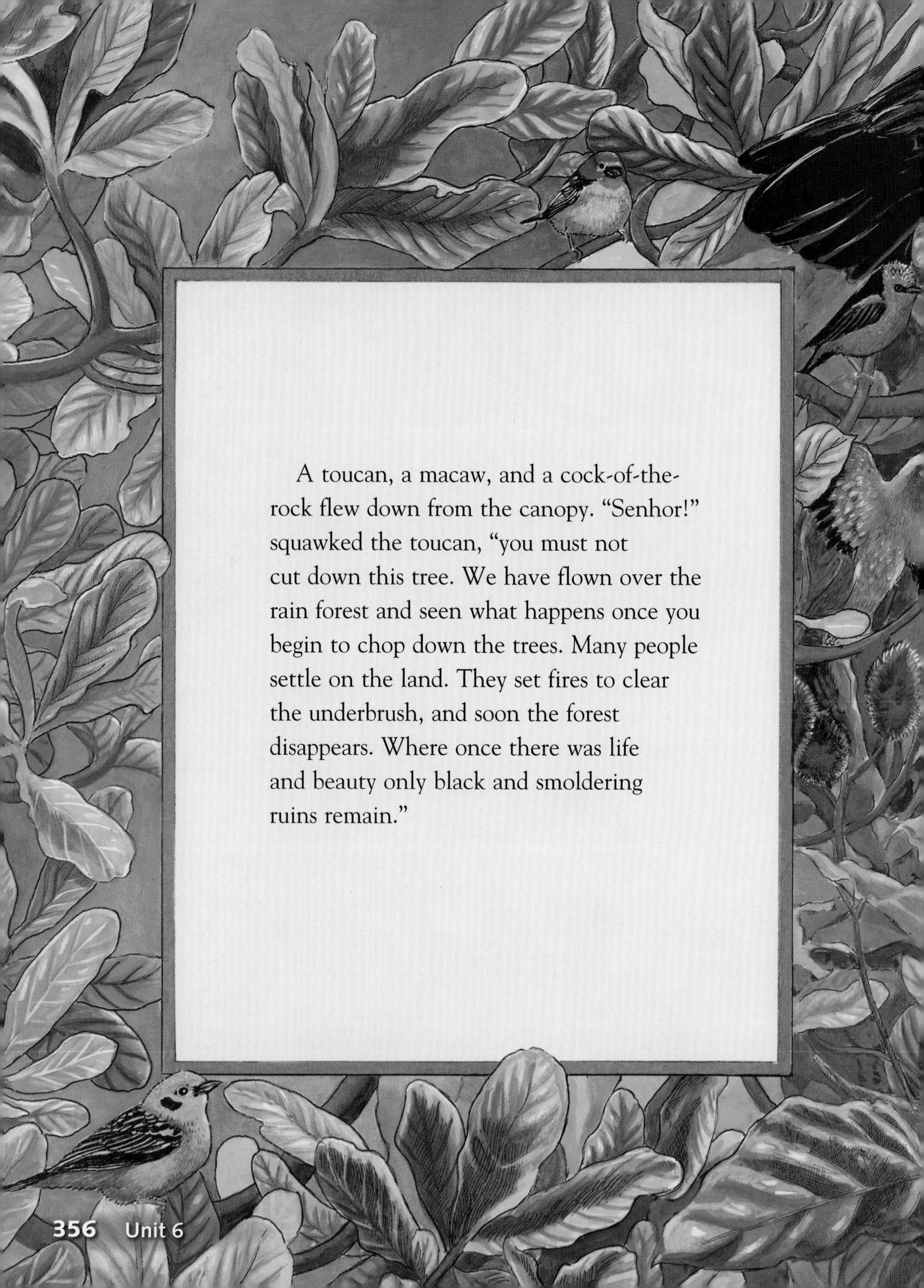

A toucan, a macaw, and a cock-of-the-rock flew down from the canopy. "Senhor!" squawked the toucan, "you must not cut down this tree. We have flown over the rain forest and seen what happens once you begin to chop down the trees. Many people settle on the land. They set fires to clear the underbrush, and soon the forest disappears. Where once there was life and beauty only black and smoldering ruins remain."

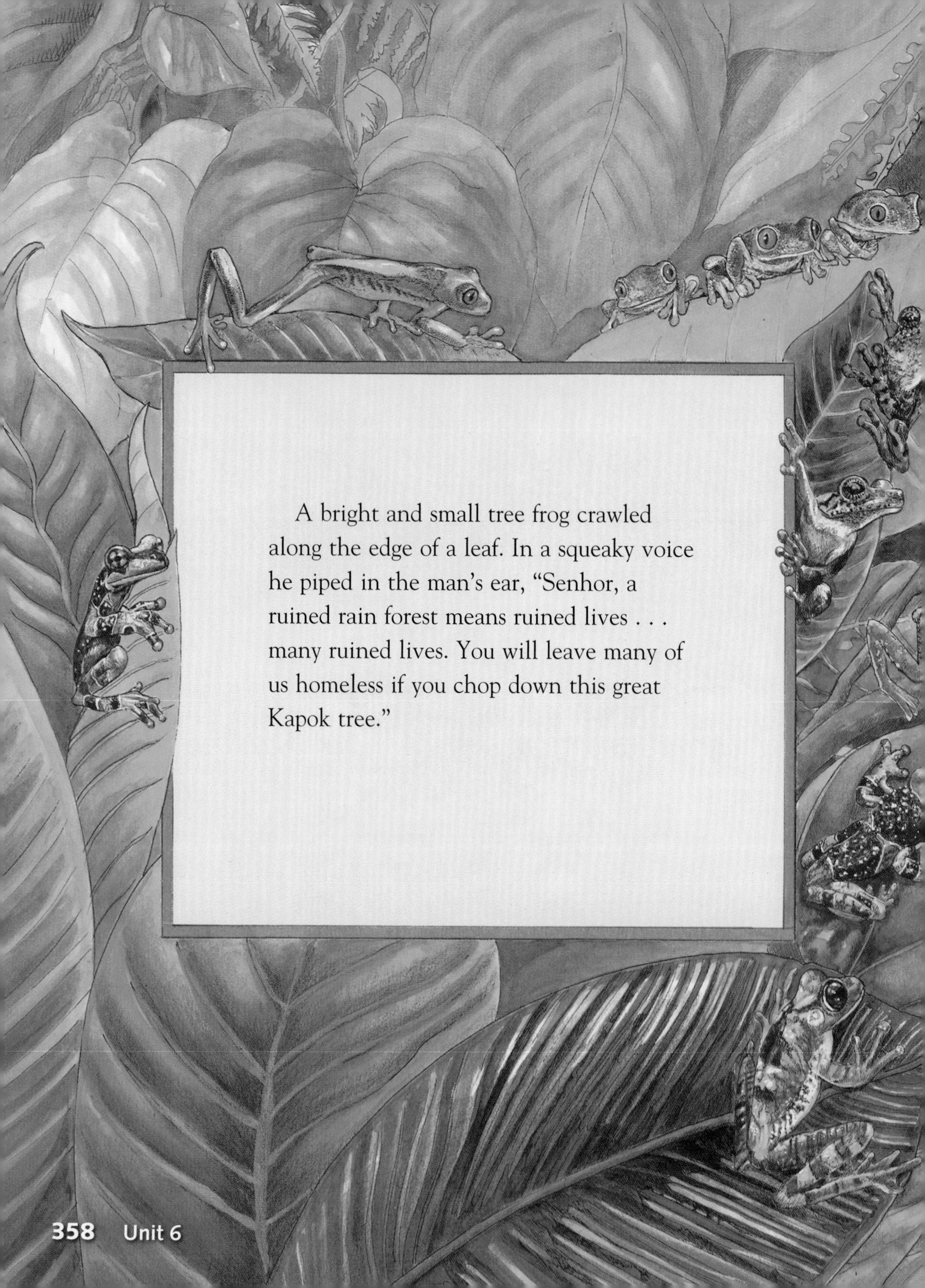

A bright and small tree frog crawled along the edge of a leaf. In a squeaky voice he piped in the man's ear, "Senhor, a ruined rain forest means ruined lives . . . many ruined lives. You will leave many of us homeless if you chop down this great Kapok tree."

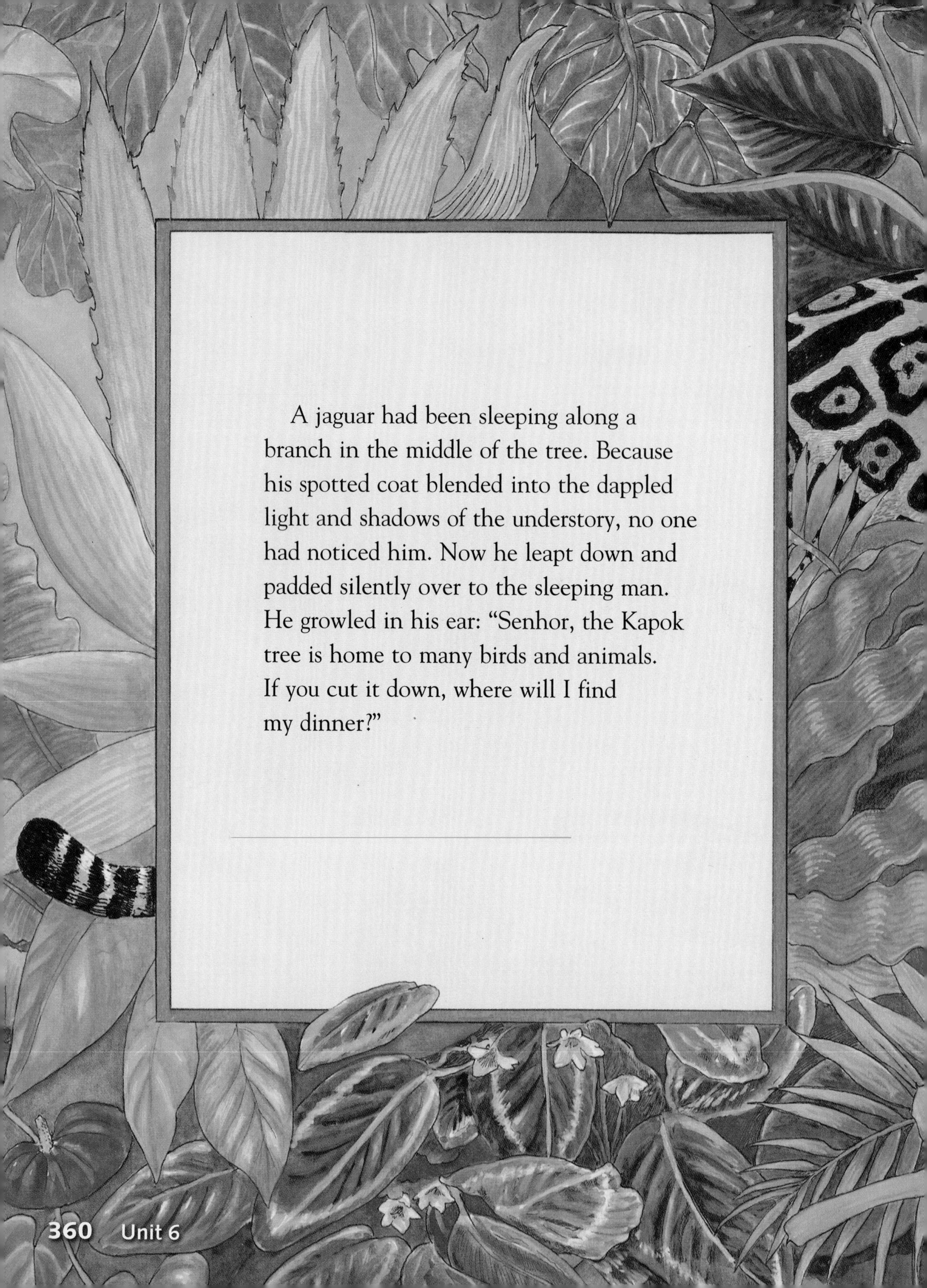

A jaguar had been sleeping along a branch in the middle of the tree. Because his spotted coat blended into the dappled light and shadows of the understory, no one had noticed him. Now he leapt down and padded silently over to the sleeping man. He growled in his ear: "Senhor, the Kapok tree is home to many birds and animals. If you cut it down, where will I find my dinner?"

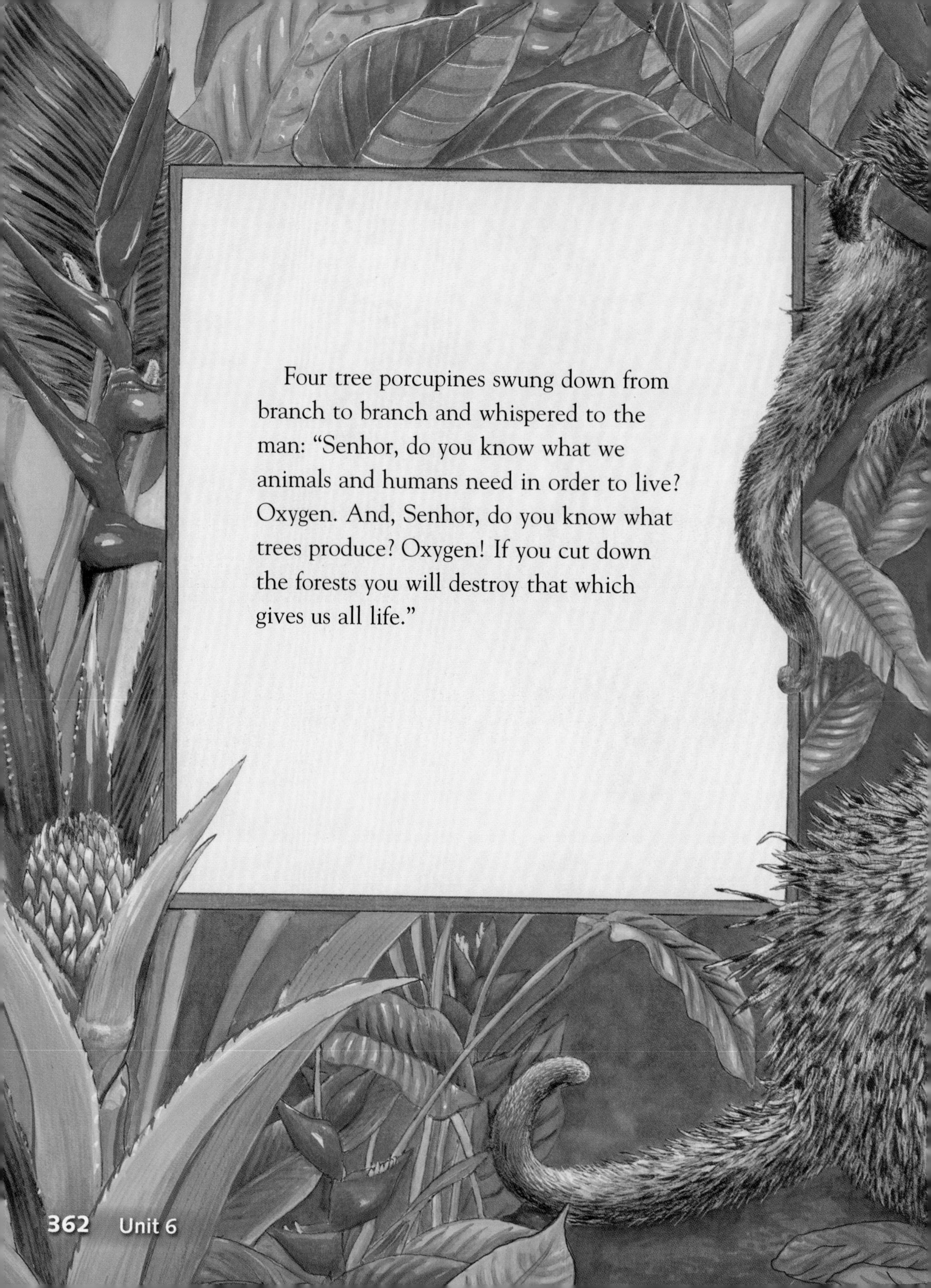

Four tree porcupines swung down from branch to branch and whispered to the man: "Senhor, do you know what we animals and humans need in order to live? Oxygen. And, Senhor, do you know what trees produce? Oxygen! If you cut down the forests you will destroy that which gives us all life."

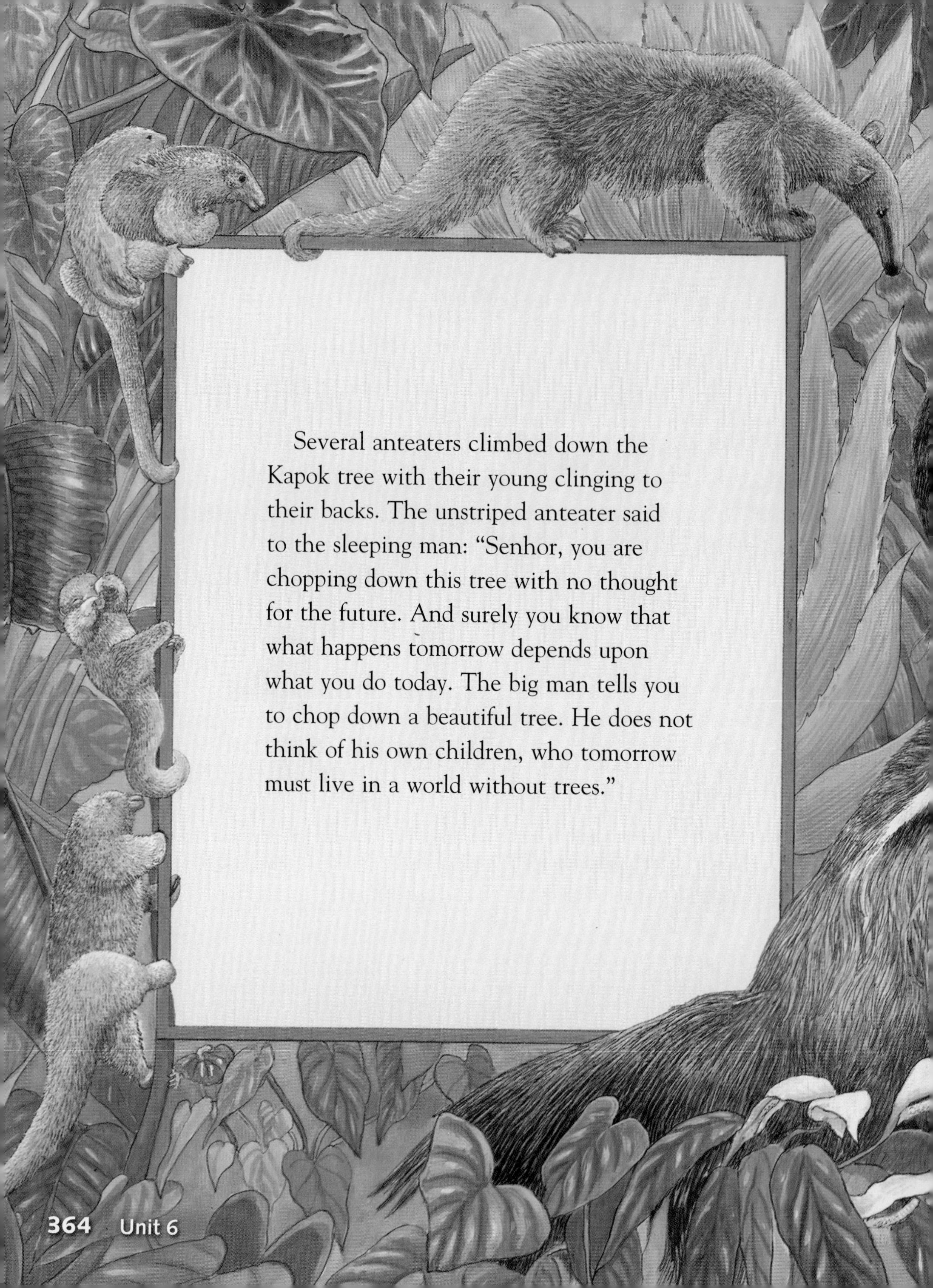

Several anteaters climbed down the Kapok tree with their young clinging to their backs. The unstriped anteater said to the sleeping man: "Senhor, you are chopping down this tree with no thought for the future. And surely you know that what happens tomorrow depends upon what you do today. The big man tells you to chop down a beautiful tree. He does not think of his own children, who tomorrow must live in a world without trees."

A three-toed sloth had begun climbing down from the canopy when the men first appeared. Only now did she reach the ground. **Plodding** ever so slowly over to the sleeping man, she spoke in her deep and lazy voice: "Senhor, how much is beauty worth? Can you live without it? If you destroy the beauty of the rain forest, on what would you feast your eyes?"

A child from the Yanomamo tribe who lived in the rain forest knelt over the sleeping man. He murmured in his ear: "Senhor, when you awake, please look upon us all with new eyes."

The man awoke with a start. Before him stood the rain forest child, and all around him, staring, were the creatures who depended upon the great Kapok tree. What wondrous and rare animals they were!

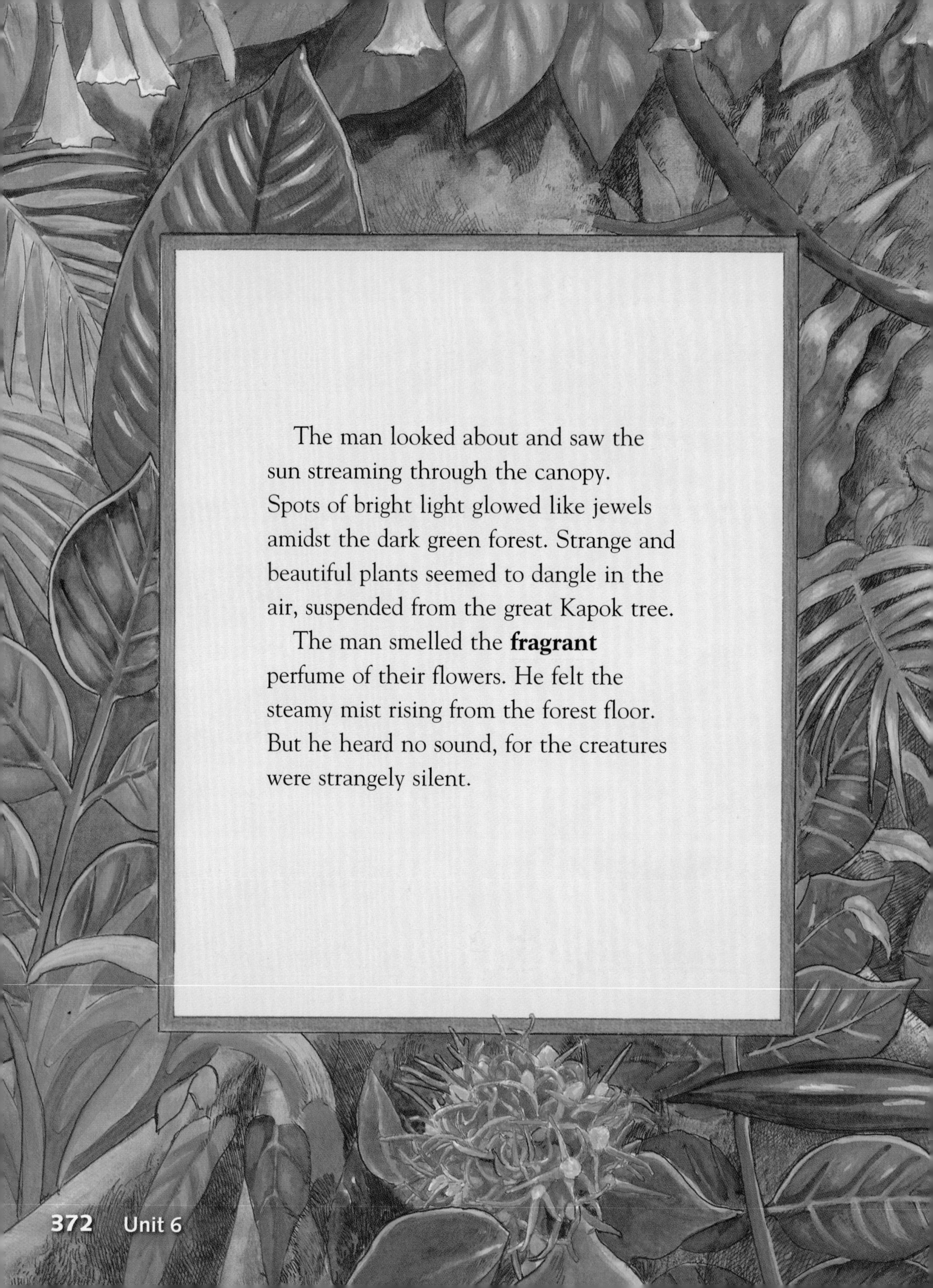

The man looked about and saw the sun streaming through the canopy. Spots of bright light glowed like jewels amidst the dark green forest. Strange and beautiful plants seemed to dangle in the air, suspended from the great Kapok tree.

The man smelled the **fragrant** perfume of their flowers. He felt the steamy mist rising from the forest floor. But he heard no sound, for the creatures were strangely silent.

The man stood and picked up his ax. He swung back his arm as though to strike the tree. Suddenly he stopped. He turned and looked at the animals and the child.

He **hesitated**. Then he dropped the ax and walked out of the rain forest.

UNIT 7

The Wide-Open West

What makes the West exceptional?

Focus Questions

How are geography and economy connected in the Mountain States?

How are geography and economy connected in the Pacific States?

What is life like in the Mountain States?

What is life like in the Pacific States?

A Tour of the Western Region

by Cate Foley

Contents

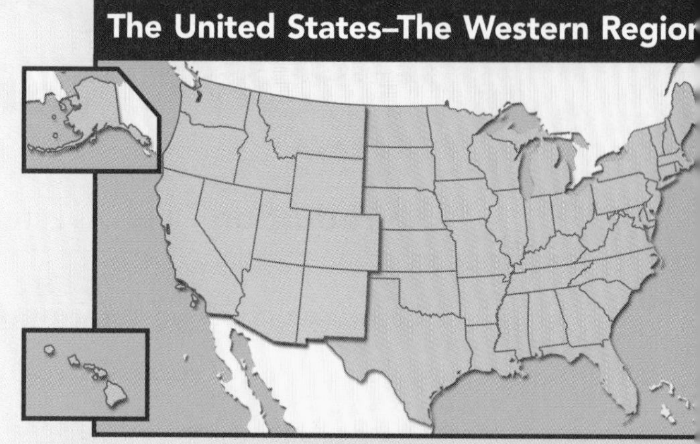

Let's visit the Western Region of the United States. From soaring mountains to rugged coastlines to hot, dry deserts, the western part of the United States is a region of **extremes**. We will visit its highs—Mount McKinley, with its elevation of 20,320 feet—and its lows—Death Valley with its elevation of 282 feet below sea level.

We will get to know the eight Mountain States. Afterward, we will move farther west to the Pacific States—California, Washington, and Oregon. We will even top off our trip by visiting our two newest states—Alaska and Hawaii.

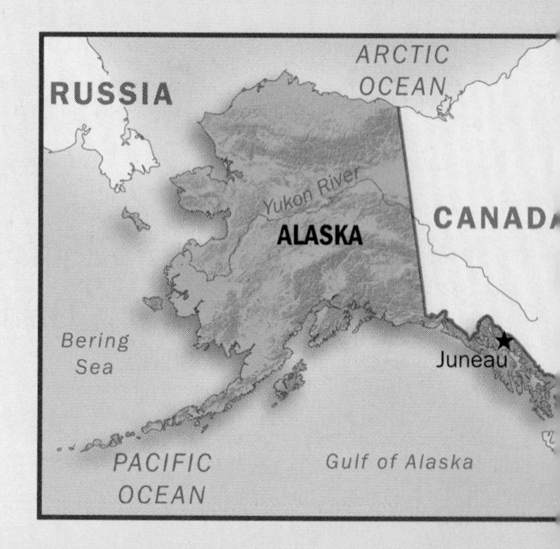

The Western Region is as diverse as the people who live here. We'll learn about it by looking at its

- geography—the land and water features of the region,
- economy—how people make a living in the region,
- history—how the events of the past shaped the present, and
- culture—the traditions, beliefs, and ways of life of the region.

So grab your pack and come along! We'll begin our visit to the Western Region by hiking through the Mountain States.

The Western Region
CANADA
WASHINGTON
Olympia
COAST RANGES
Columbia River
Salem
OREGON
IDAHO
Boise
ROCKY MOUNTAINS
Helena
MONTANA
Missouri River
Snake River
WYOMING
Cheyenne
NORTH DAKOTA
SOUTH DAKOTA
MINNESOTA
NEBRASKA
Platte River
IOWA
Missouri River
Sierra Nevada
Carson City
Sacramento
NEVADA
Salt Lake City
Salt Lake Desert
UTAH
Central Valley
CALIFORNIA
Denver
COLORADO
Colorado River
Arkansas River
KANSAS
Mojave Desert
Painted Desert
Santa Fe
OKLAHOMA
ARIZONA
Phoenix
NEW MEXICO
PACIFIC OCEAN
TEXAS
Brazos River
Rio Grande
N
W
E
S
MEXICO
PACIFIC STATES
MOUNTAIN STATES
STATE CAPITAL

CHAPTER 1

THE MOUNTAIN STATES

Geography and Economy

Are you ready for some extreme fun? The Mountain States are home to the Rocky Mountains. Visitors come year round to enjoy the Rockies. These mountains stretch from Canada down to New Mexico. This region is rich in forests and plains and also has many copper and silver mines.

We will visit the plateaus and canyons around the Colorado River. And no trip would be complete without a raft ride down the Colorado River itself. This "Lifeline of the Southwest" is a great water source for the farms and people of the region. This geographical feature of the Mountain States is the backbone for the many people who live and work here.

Red Rock Canyon is in the Mojave Desert in Nevada. Each year, around one million people visit the canyon.

Mining the Mountains

More than one hundred years ago, the promise of gold brought many people to the West. Mining soon became a way of life. That way of life is shared today by many people in the Mountain States. Copper, silver, and coal mines can be found in Idaho, Colorado, Montana, Wyoming, and New Mexico.

The mountains of Wyoming, Colorado, and Utah are also rich in oil shale. Oil shale is a rock that can be made into fuel by heating it. People estimate that there could be enough oil shale to make 800 billion barrels of oil!

Riding the Range

Cattle ranchers also live and work in the Mountain States. Cattle and sheep ranching is a way of life for many people of the plains and plateaus of Montana, Wyoming, Idaho, and Colorado. These states produce large numbers of sheep, cattle, and hogs. In Wyoming, sheep and cattle use as much as 70 percent of the state's land for grazing.

During the frigid winters in the northern Mountain States, the ranchers move their animals from mountain pastures and meadows to the lowlands to provide them with food.

Wyoming is often called the Cowboy State. Ranching is an important part of the state's culture.

Throughout eastern Montana, millions of cattle and sheep graze on the rolling hills.

A Land Rich in Farming

Some of the land in the Mountain States is also good for farming. When many people think of Idaho, they think of potatoes. There is good reason for this. The **irrigated** soil around the Snake River makes the land perfect for farming. When land is irrigated, water is carried to it by pipes or ditches. The water that is transported makes the once-dry soil rich for growing many crops.

In Arizona farmers grow a lot of lettuce. Chili peppers are an important crop in New Mexico. The people of the Mountain States use the land and water to provide the country with cotton, grains, fruits, and vegetables. Now let's take a look at the source of the water used in farming.

About one-third of the potatoes in the United States come from Idaho.

A Mighty River

The Colorado River is an important water source for the Mountain States. For about 1,450 miles, the Colorado River twists and turns its way through Colorado, Utah, and Arizona. It even forms part of the border between Arizona and Mexico.

The Colorado River flows from the forests and tundra in the upper elevations, through the plateaus, to the arid lands in the lower elevations. The river helps the economy of the cities and towns along its path.

The Four Corners

How would you like to stand in four states at once? Impossible, you say? Not if you visit The Four Corners. It is the only place in the United States where four states (Utah, Colorado, Arizona, and New Mexico) come together at one place.

Most of the water in Lake Mead comes from melted snow from Colorado, Utah, New Mexico, and Wyoming.

Engineers saw the benefit of the power that the Colorado River held. In the 1930s Hoover Dam was built. Hoover Dam is on the Arizona-Nevada border and spans the Colorado River. The building of Hoover Dam helped the economy of this **arid**, desert land in many ways. Water from Hoover Dam is used to make electric power. This electricity source allowed cities such as Las Vegas, Nevada, to prosper.

Another important feature of Hoover Dam is Lake Mead. Lake Mead was formed by water that was contained by Hoover Dam. It is the largest human-made lake in the United States. Las Vegas gets most of its water from Lake Mead.

The Hoover Dam was originally named the Boulder Dam. Later it was renamed in honor of President Herbert Hoover, who was instrumental in getting it built.

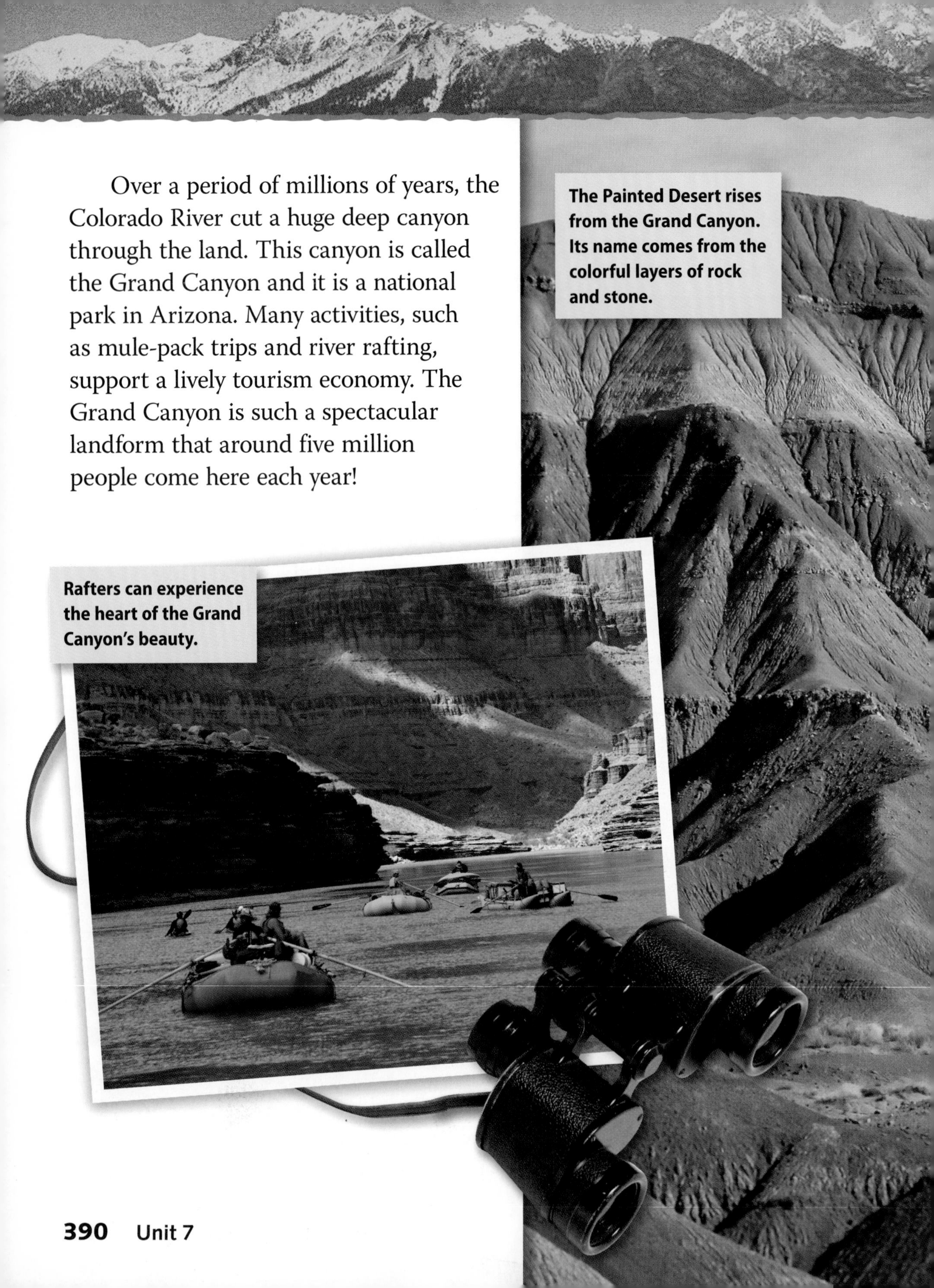

Over a period of millions of years, the Colorado River cut a huge deep canyon through the land. This canyon is called the Grand Canyon and it is a national park in Arizona. Many activities, such as mule-pack trips and river rafting, support a lively tourism economy. The Grand Canyon is such a spectacular landform that around five million people come here each year!

The Painted Desert rises from the Grand Canyon. Its name comes from the colorful layers of rock and stone.

Rafters can experience the heart of the Grand Canyon's beauty.

A Land of Beauty and Fun

Because there are so many interesting things to do here, tourism adds greatly to the economy of this region. We will continue our trip through the Mountain States by visiting some of the region's attractions. There are great places to ski all around Colorado and Utah. Wyoming, Montana, and Idaho are home to one of our country's most well-known parks, Yellowstone National Park.

Nevada is home to Lake Tahoe, with its blue waters. In Utah you can see Arches National Park. Many visitors also come to the desert states of Arizona, Nevada, and New Mexico to enjoy their warm weather and wonderful scenery.

The movement of an underground salt bed has created the sandstone formations in Arches National Park in Utah.

CHAPTER 2

THE MOUNTAIN STATES

History and Culture

Native Americans have inhabited the Mountain States for thousands of years. One of the first groups to live in this region is the Ancestral Pueblo, who lived in what is now known as Arizona, New Mexico, Colorado, and Utah. The earliest groups of Ancestral Pueblo lived in pithouses, shallow holes in the ground that were covered by earth and wood. These people hunted and gathered wild plants. They also began to grow vegetables, such as corn and beans.

Many years later the Pueblo farmed the same vegetables as their ancestors and also learned to grow cotton. They became skilled at building villages along cliffs. These cliff dwellings were made from adobe, or dried earth. Today many Pueblo people live throughout Arizona and New Mexico. In Taos, New Mexico, a group of Pueblo live in adobe homes that are more than six hundred years old!

The Ancestral Pueblo cliff dwellings in Mesa Verde National Park, Colorado, are about eight hundred years old.

Another Native American group is the Navajo. Originally from land that is now part of Canada, the Navajo moved to New Mexico, Arizona, and Utah, and learned how to farm like the Pueblo. The Pueblo people taught them how to weave baskets and paint pottery, and the Navajo later became known for making pictures with dry sand and weaving rugs. Today about 300,000 Navajo make up one of the largest Native American groups in the United States. Many of them can be found living in the areas their ancestors settled.

The Navajo of the Mountain States are known for their beautifully woven blankets and rugs.

A Changing Land

By the early 1800s the United States was expanding into the West. Meriwether Lewis and William Clark explored some of the Mountain States. They went through land that is now known as Montana and Idaho.

Other people moved west to explore this part of the country. Fur trappers set up posts here.

In 1847 Brigham Young led a religious group called the Mormons from the Midwest to land around the Great Salt Lake in Utah. The Mormons came here to set up a place where they could freely practice their religion. The Mormons moved into Utah and the surrounding areas.

The history of the Mountain States Region can be seen in its culture today. Montana is home to museums that preserve the state's way of life. Visitors can also learn about the region's Native Americans by visiting the many cultural events held throughout Montana.

In Idaho, mining towns, such as Kellogg and Wallace, grew rapidly because of the silver found in the area's mountains. Today tourists are attracted to these historical towns.

Santa Fe Opera House

silver

Silver is still a big part of the economy of Wallace, Idaho. The town's historic buildings and ski resorts also draw tourists.

Since 1957 the Santa Fe Opera House has continually drawn the world's best singers, conductors, and directors to New Mexico. The open-air theater allows audience members to view the region's beautiful landscapes.

A Short History of Utah

The first residents of Utah were Native American hunters and gatherers. Later, other groups of Native Americans moved into the area, including the Ute, for whom the state was named. Two Spanish missionaries discovered the area in 1776, but when "mountain men" James Bridger and Jedediah Smith arrived about 50 years later, they established trading posts and started a fur trade. In 1847 the Mormons began to arrive in large numbers, and by 1860 about 40,000 Mormons had established themselves in the state. They continued to prosper, and today Mormons make up almost 70 percent of Utah's population.

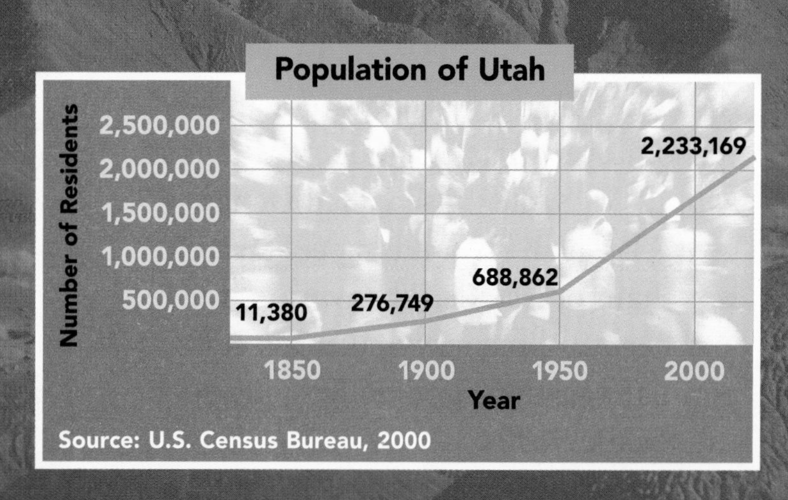

Geography and Economy

Are you ready to get wet? Now we will visit the Pacific States. Water greatly affects the economy and the people who live here. Parts of Washington and Oregon have many days of precipitation. This makes some areas of the region ideal for farming. California has more than 1,000 miles of coastline. The coastline, climate, and size of California help make it the biggest state economy in the United States.

We will even step off the mainland to visit Alaska and Hawaii. In Alaska, the coldest state, frozen water can be seen all over! Glaciers and snow-capped Mount McKinley, also called Denali, give Alaska an icy landscape. Hawaii is a chain of islands. The warm climate and beautiful scenery make this state a popular vacation spot. So let's check out the Pacific States!

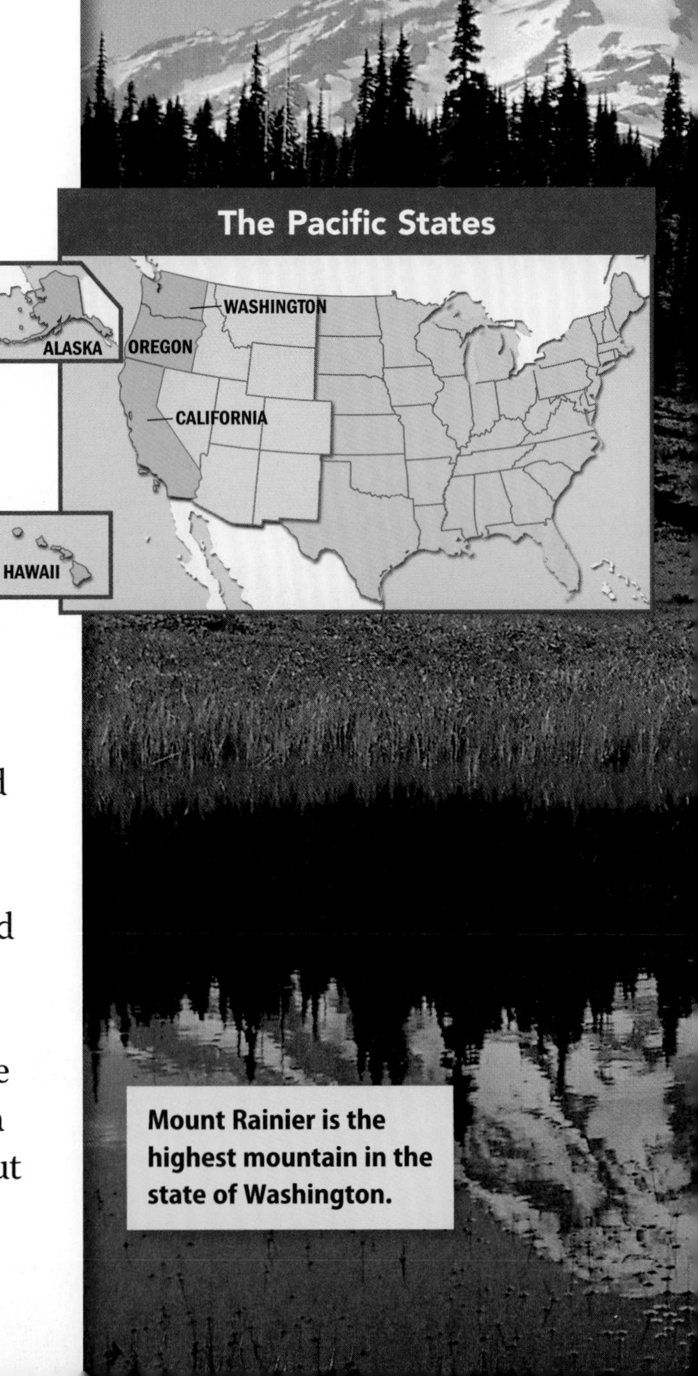

Mount Rainier is the highest mountain in the state of Washington.

The Pacific Northwest

The Pacific Northwest mostly includes the states of Oregon and Washington. Wheat, strawberries, and cherries are just some of the crops grown here. Dairy farms play an important role in both states' economies. Using metal from the region's mines, airplane manufacturing in the Seattle, Washington, area is one of the most important industries in the state.

In Washington and Oregon cherry season starts in June and ends in August.

Water, Water Everywhere

Water is an important resource in Washington and Oregon. The Pacific Ocean and the Columbia River add greatly to the economies of both states. Freshwater runs through dams on the Columbia River. Water from this river is used for irrigation, power generation, fishing, and recreation.

Water transportation is also important to both states. The harbors on Puget Sound in Washington offer easy access to the ocean. Portland is one of Oregon's most important ports. It is located on the Columbia River. From here ships head to the Pacific Ocean and then to places all over the world.

Ships destined for the Pacific Ocean make their way through Portland Harbor.

Grand Coulee Dam

The Grand Coulee Dam is located on the Columbia River in the state of Washington. It generates more than one-fourth of the hydroelectric power in the United States and is one of the largest hydroelectric power plants in the world.

The Grand Coulee Dam is one of eleven dams on the Columbia River that contribute to the region's power supply.

A Land of Mountains and Trees

Water isn't the only resource in the Pacific Northwest, though. The Olympic Mountains and the Cascade Range are important mountain ranges here. Surrounding the mountains are forests, which provide Washington and Oregon with trees for the timber industries.

The Douglas fir is the dominant lumber tree in Washington and Oregon. Because of the freeways and railways in these states, lumber can easily be transported all across the country. Washington is also a leading paper producer in the United States.

But not all trees here are used for lumber and paper. Did you know Washington grows more apples than any other state?

Presidential City

There is one city in the United States that uses the full name of a president when combined with the state name: George, Washington. The city's main street is named Montmorency. This is the kind of cherry tree the President is said to have chopped down when he was a boy. Additional streets are named after other varieties of cherries to honor Washington State's large cherry industry.

California, Here We Come!

We have visited Washington and Oregon. So now it's time to head south and visit the state of California.

California produces enough crops to supply the United States with about half its fruits and vegetables. Central Valley, which runs for more than 400 miles down the center of the state, contains rich farmland.

California's coastline offers both sandy beaches and **rugged** cliffs. Many people visit the California coast. Tourism and recreation add to the economy of this region. Since the 1970s California has been a leading force in computer technology. Other important industries include electronics manufacturing, airplane manufacturing, and fishing.

California's Central Valley produces more than three hundred different crops. Apricots, rice, and pistachios are just a few!

South of San Francisco, California, is Silicon Valley, which is home to many electronics and computer companies.

High and Low

California is home to the Sierra Nevada, the Coast Ranges, and the Cascade Range. Many forests grow close to these mountain ranges. The substantial amount of rainfall in the northern Coast Ranges helps the timber industry thrive.

The Sierra Nevada is the largest mountain range in California. It has the highest mountain anywhere in the United States, except for Alaska. Mount Whitney rises to 14,494 feet. Just 85 miles away from Mount Whitney is Death Valley, the lowest and hottest place in North America.

Redwood Forest

Nearly half of the remaining old growth redwoods are found in California's Redwood National and State Park system. In these protected forests, visitors can enjoy hiking, biking, kayaking, and bird watching among other outdoor activities.

Many tourists come to California to visit the redwood parks, which are home to the giant redwood trees. Many redwood trees grow to be 300 feet tall!

Lights, Camera, Action!

A tour of California wouldn't be complete without a visit to Hollywood. An important part of California's economy is the movie industry. Many movies are produced and **filmed** in Hollywood, California. Even the geography of this region is used as the setting for movies. The movie industry provides jobs for many people.

The Hollywood sign is a famous landmark in Los Angeles, California. It was originally built to

Mount McKinley, the highest mountain in the United States, has an elevation of 20,320 feet. It is also called Denali, a Native American name meaning "the high one."

Off the Mainland

The last stops on our tour of the Western Region are Alaska and Hawaii. The state of Alaska is the largest in land area and one of the smallest in population. Alaska has many miles of forest and is home to an oil pipeline that runs for 800 miles. Fishing is also a prominent part of Alaska's economy. And because visitors love Alaska's rugged beauty, the state's economy is also helped by tourism.

Tourism is also important to the economy of Hawaii. Its warm climate and beautiful beaches draw many visitors. People also come here to experience Hawaii's unique landscape, which includes the volcanoes that formed all of the islands.

Kilauea in Hawaii is one of the most active volcanoes in the world.

History and Culture

Many Native American groups, such as the Chinook, were the first to live near the Pacific Coast. They fished for salmon in the Columbia River and gathered berries and nuts. The Native Americans constructed large homes and canoes out of the red cedar trees that grow in the forests here.

Other Native American groups, such as the Inuit, lived farther north in what is now Alaska. The cold, snowy environment did not allow for gathering or farming, so Native Americans lived mostly off foods they hunted, such as fish, caribou, seal, and whale. During the winter many wore clothing made from caribou furs to keep warm. Winter homes were made from stone, sod, or blocks of snow.

Dogsleds were the primary form of transportation for the Inuit. Today some Inuit continue to use them.

Heading West

When Lewis and Clark reached the Columbia River in 1805, they sent reports to the East of all the riches the region had to offer. By the 1830s, American **missionaries**, such as Marcus Whitman, arrived in present-day Washington and Oregon.

One of the most important events in this region happened in 1848. James Marshall found some gold nuggets at Sutter's Mill in California. Marshall's discovery set off the Gold Rush to California. Between 1848 and 1854, the Gold Rush brought about 300,000 people here!

In the 1880s and 1890s, two major railroads, the Northern Pacific Railroad and the Great Northern Railroad, made it faster to move people and goods to the West Coast.

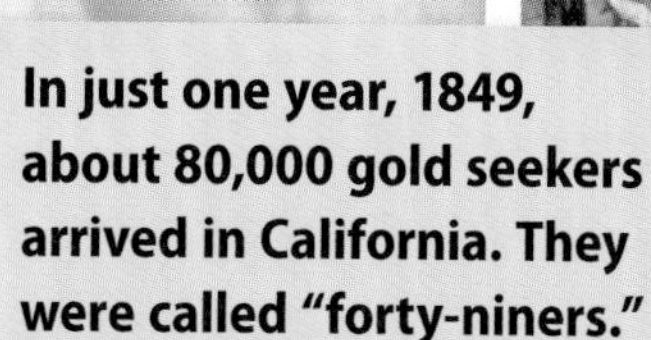

In just one year, 1849, about 80,000 gold seekers arrived in California. They were called "forty-niners."

The Last Two States

In 1778 Captain James Cook sailed to what is now known as the Hawaiian Islands. American missionaries came to Hawaii in 1820, and in the early 1900s the U.S. government built a naval base at Pearl Harbor. This brought many people to Hawaii. When Japan attacked Pearl Harbor in 1941, the United States entered World War II. Hawaii became the fiftieth state in 1959.

Earlier that year Alaska became the forty-ninth state after being purchased by William Seward in 1867. The addition of Alaska increased the size of the United States by almost 20 percent! However, some people disagreed with the purchase of this cold, distant land, and the purchase was called "Seward's Folly."

The USS *Arizona* Memorial at Pearl Harbor honors the people who died in the Pearl Harbor attack.

The hula is a Hawaiian religious dance that is hundreds of years old.

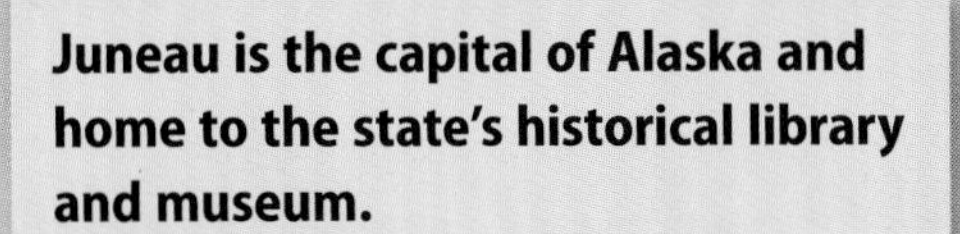

Juneau is the capital of Alaska and home to the state's historical library and museum.

A Coast of Cultures

The culture of the Pacific States is very diverse. People come from all over the world to live here. They come to enjoy the beautiful cities, such as Seattle, Washington, and Portland, Oregon. Portland earned the name "The City of Roses" because of its many rose gardens. People also enjoy art at famous museums, such as the Getty Museum in Los Angeles, California.

San Francisco, California, is also one of the great cultural centers of our country. Several songs have been written about this coastal city. Many famous writers have lived in San Francisco, including Mark Twain, Jack London, and Robert Louis Stevenson.

At the Experience Music Project in Seattle, Washington, visitors can see musical artifacts and learn about the ways that musicians make music.

Life in the Western Region is influenced by geography, economy, history, and culture. The natural resources of the Mountain States make them good for mining and farming. Lumber, fruit, paper, and even movies come from the Pacific States. The Pacific Ocean and the many rivers here help the economy of the Pacific States too.

Workers from all over the world come to the Western States to find jobs, and they bring their cultures with them to share with others. People come from many places to appreciate the beauty and cultural attractions of this region. The Western Region is a fascinating place to live and visit.

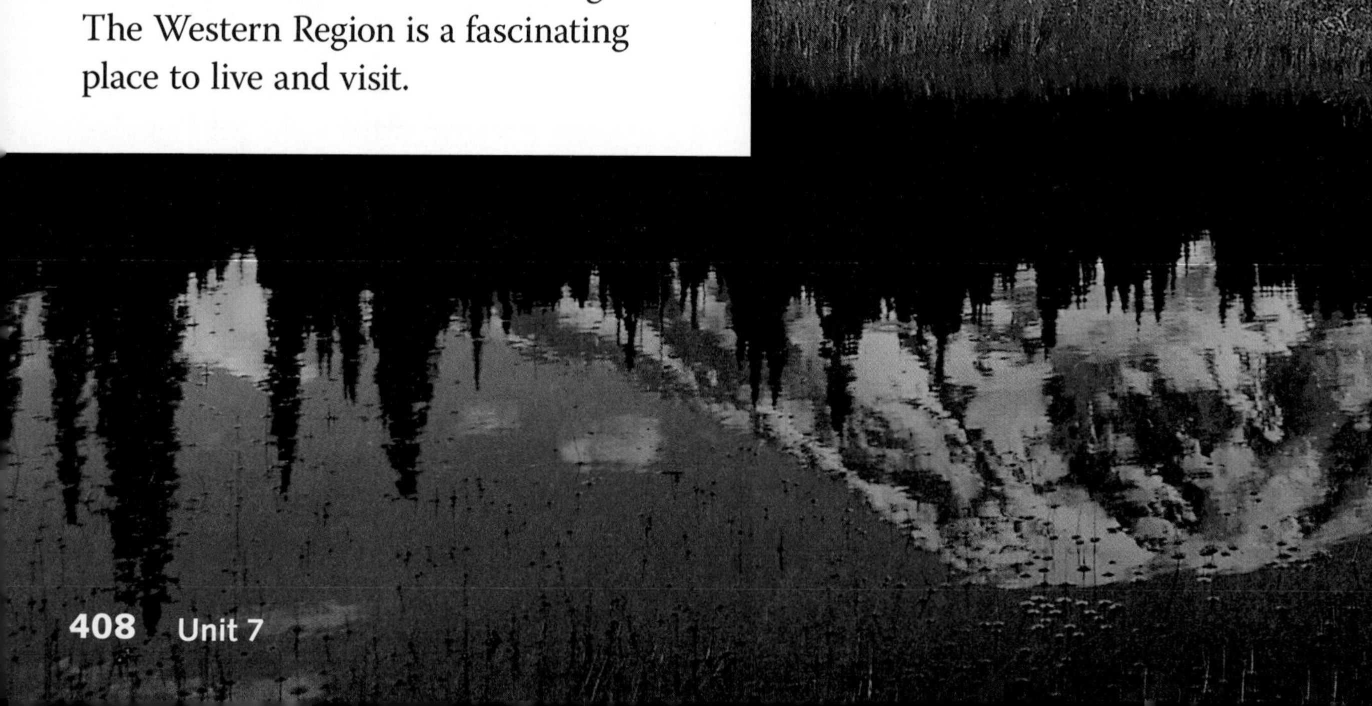

Juan Verdades

The Man Who Couldn't Tell a Lie

retold by **Joe Hayes** • illustrated by **Joseph Daniel Fiedler**

For all who recognize the truth in the old tales,
whether the story ever happened or not

—J.H.

To Kristy

—J.D.F.

ONE LATE SUMMER DAY a group of wealthy rancheros was gathered on the village plaza, joking and laughing and discussing events on their ranches.

One of the men, whose name was don Ignacio, had a fine apple tree on his land. The rancher called the apple tree *el manzano real*—the royal apple tree—and was extremely proud of it. It had been planted by his great-grandfather, and there was something about the soil it grew in and the way the afternoon sun struck it that made the apple tree flourish. It gave sweeter and more flavorful fruit than any other tree in the country round about.

Every rancher for miles around knew about *el manzano real,* and each year they all hoped don Ignacio would give them a small basket of its sweet fruit. And so each of the ranchers asked don Ignacio how the fruit of the apple tree was doing. To each one don Ignacio replied, "It's doing beautifully, amigo, beautifully. My foreman takes perfect care of the tree, and every evening he reports how the fruit is ripening."

When don Ignacio said this to his friend don Arturo, the other man replied, "Do you mean to say, don Ignacio, that you don't tend your magnificent tree yourself? How can you have such faith in your employee? Maybe he's not doing all he says he is. Maybe he's not telling you the truth."

Don Ignacio wagged a finger at his friend. "*Mi capataz* has never failed me in any way," he insisted. "He has never told me a lie."

"Are you sure, *compadre?*" said don Arturo. "Are you sure that he has never lied to you?"

"Absolutely certain, *compadre,* absolutely certain. The young man doesn't know how to tell a lie. His name is Juan Valdez, but everyone calls him Juan Verdades because he is so truthful."

"I don't believe it. There never was an employee who didn't lie to his boss. I'm sure I can make him tell you a lie."

"Never," replied the proud employer.

The two friends went on arguing good-naturedly, but little by little they began to raise their voices and attract the attention of the other men on the plaza.

Finally don Arturo declared loudly, "I'll bet you whatever you want that within two weeks at the most I'll make this Juan Verdades tell you a lie."

"All right," replied don Ignacio. "It's a deal. I'll bet my ranch against yours that you can't make my foreman lie to me."

The other ranchers laughed when they heard that. "Ho-ho, don Arturo," they said, "now we'll see just how sure you are that you're right."

"As sure as I am of my own name," said don Arturo. "I accept the bet, don Ignacio. But you must allow me the freedom to try anything I wish." The two friends shook hands, and the other men in the group agreed to serve as witnesses to the bet.

The gathering broke up, and don Arturo and don Ignacio rode confidently away toward their ranches. But as don Arturo rode along thinking of what he had just done, he no longer felt so sure of himself. When he arrived home and told his wife and daughter about the bet, his wife began to cry. "What will we do when we lose our ranch?" she sobbed. And don Arturo began to think he had made a terrible mistake.

But his daughter, whose name was Araceli and who was a very bright and lively young woman, just laughed and said, "Don't worry, *Mamá*. We're not going to lose our ranch."

Araceli suggested to her father that he make up some excuse for them all to spend the next two weeks at don Ignacio's house. "If we're staying on don Ignacio's ranch," she said, "we'll surely discover a way to come out the winners."

The next day don Arturo rode to don Ignacio's ranch and told his friend, "My men are mending the walls of my house and giving them a fresh coat of whitewash. It would be more convenient for my family to be away. Could my wife and daughter and I stay at your house for a while?"

"Of course, my friend," don Ignacio answered. "Feel perfectly free."

That afternoon don Arturo and his family moved into don Ignacio's house, and the next morning Araceli rose at dawn, as she always did at home, and went to the ranch kitchen to prepare coffee. The foreman, Juan Verdades, was already there, drinking a cup of coffee he had made for himself and eating a breakfast of leftover tortillas. She smiled at him, and he greeted her politely: "*Buenos días, señorita.*" And then he finished his simple breakfast and went off to begin his day's work.

That night don Arturo and his daughter made up a plan. Araceli rose before dawn the next day and went to the kitchen to prepare coffee and fresh tortillas for the foreman. She smiled sweetly as she offered them to Juan. He returned her smile and thanked her very kindly. Each morning she did the same thing, and Juan Verdades began to fall in love with Araceli, which was just what the girl and her father expected.

What Araceli hadn't expected was that she began to fall in love with Juan Verdades too and looked forward to getting up early every morning just to be alone with him. She even began to wish she might end up marrying the handsome young foreman. Araceli continued to work on the plan she and her father had made—but she now had a plan of her own as well.

Of course, Juan knew that he was just a worker and Araceli was the daughter of a wealthy ranchero, so he didn't even dream of asking her to marry him. Still, he couldn't help trying to please her in every way. So one morning when they were talking, Juan said to Araceli, "You're very kind to have fresh coffee and warm food ready for me every morning and to honor me with the pleasure of your company. Ask me for whatever you want from this ranch. I'll speak to don Ignacio and see that it's given to you."

This is exactly what the girl and her father thought would happen. And she replied just as they had planned. It was the last thing Juan expected to hear.

"There's only one thing on this ranch I want," she said. "I'd like to have all the apples from *el manzano real.*"

The young man was very surprised, and very distressed as well, because he knew he couldn't fulfill her wish.

"I could never give you that," Juan said. "You know how don Ignacio treasures the fruit of that tree. He might agree to give you a basket of apples, but no more. I would have to take the fruit without permission, and then what would I say to don Ignacio? I can give you anything else from the ranch, but not what you're asking for."

With that the conversation ended and they separated for the day. In the evening Juan reported to don Ignacio, and they exchanged the exact words they said every evening:

"Good evening, *mi capataz*," the rancher said.

"Good evening, *mi patrón*," replied the foreman.

"How goes it with my cattle and land?"

"Your cattle are healthy, your pastures are green."

"And the fruit of *el manzano real*?"

"The fruit is fat and ripening well."

The next morning Juan and Araceli met again. As they sipped their coffee together, Juan said, "I truly would like to repay you for the kindness you've shown me. There must be something on this ranch you would like. Tell me what it is. I'll see that it's given to you."

But again Araceli replied, "There's only one thing on this ranch I want: the apples from *el manzano real*."

Each day they repeated the conversation. Araceli asked for the same thing, and Juan said he couldn't give it to her. But each day Juan was falling more hopelessly in love with Araceli. Finally, just the day before the two weeks of the bet would have ended, the foreman gave in. He said he would go pick the apples right then and bring them to the girl.

Juan hitched up a wagon and drove to the apple tree. He picked every single apple and delivered the wagonload of fruit to Araceli. She thanked him very warmly, and his spirits rose for a moment. But as he mounted his horse to leave, they sank once again. Juan rode away alone, lost in his thoughts, and Araceli hurried off to tell her father the news and then to wait for a chance to talk to don Ignacio too.

Juan rode until he came to a place where there were several dead trees. He dismounted and walked up to one of them. Then he took off his hat and jacket and put them on the dead tree and pretended it was don Ignacio. He started talking to it to see if he could tell it a lie.

"Good evening, *mi capataz,*" he pretended he heard the tree say.

"Good evening, *mi patrón.*"

"How goes it with my cattle and land?"

"Your cattle are healthy, your pastures are green."

"And the fruit of *el manzano real?*"

"The . . . the crows have carried the fruit away . . . ."

But the words were hardly out of his mouth when he heard himself say, "No, that's not true, *mi patrón.* I picked the fruit . . . ." And then he stopped himself.

He took a deep breath and started over again with, "Good evening, *mi capataz.*"

And when he reached the end, he sputtered, "The . . . the wind shook the apples to the ground, and the cows came and ate them . . . . No, they didn't, *mi patrón.* I . . ."

He tried over and over, until he realized there was no way he could tell a lie. But he knew he could never come right out and say what he had done either. He had to think of another way to tell don Ignacio. He took his hat and coat from the stump and sadly set out for the ranch.

All day long Juan worried about what he would say to don Ignacio. And all day long don Ignacio wondered what he would hear from his foreman, because as soon as Araceli had shown the apples to her father he had run gleefully to tell don Ignacio what had happened.

"Now you'll see, *compadre,*" don Arturo gloated. "You're about to hear a lie from Juan Verdades."

Don Ignacio was heartsick to think that all his apples had been picked, but he had agreed that don Arturo could try whatever he wanted. He sighed and said, "Very well, *compadre,* we'll see what happens this evening."

Don Arturo rode off to gather the other ranchers who were witnesses to the bet, leaving don Ignacio to pace nervously up and down in his house. And then, after don Ignacio received a visit from Araceli and she made a request that he couldn't deny, he paced even more nervously.

All the while, Juan went about his work, thinking of what he would say to his don Ignacio. That evening the foreman went as usual to make his report to his employer, but he walked slowly and his head hung down. The other ranchers were behind the bushes listening, and Araceli and her mother were watching anxiously from a window of the house.

The conversation began as it always did:

"Good evening, *mi capataz.*"

"Good evening, *mi patrón.*"

"How goes it with my cattle and land?"

"Your cattle are healthy, your pastures are green."

"And the fruit of *el manzano real?*"

Juan took a deep breath and replied:

"Oh, *patrón,* something terrible happened today.
Some fool picked your apples and gave them away."

Don Ignacio pretended to be shocked and confused. "Some fool picked them?" he said. "Who would do such a thing?"

Juan turned his face aside. He couldn't look at don Ignacio. The rancher asked again, "Who would do such a thing? Do I know this person?"

Finally the foreman answered:

"The father of the fool is my father's father's son.
The fool has no sister and no brother.
His child would call my father 'grandfather.'
He's ashamed that he did what was done."

Don Ignacio paused for a moment to think about Juan's answer. And then, to Juan's surprise, don Ignacio grabbed his hand and started shaking it excitedly.

The other ranchers ran laughing from their hiding places. "Don Arturo," they all said, "you lose the bet. You must sign your ranch over to don Ignacio."

"No," said don Ignacio, still vigorously shaking Juan's hand. He glanced toward the window where Araceli was watching and went on: "Sign it over to don Juan Verdades. He has proved that he truly deserves that name, and he deserves to be the owner of his own ranch as well."

Everyone cheered and began to congratulate Juan. Don Arturo's face turned white, but he gritted his teeth and forced a smile. He shook Juan's hand and then turned to walk away from the group, his shoulders drooping and his head bowed down.

But Araceli came running from the house and put her arm through her father's. "*Papá*," she said, "what if Juan Verdades were to marry a relative of yours? Then the ranch would stay in the family, wouldn't it?"

Everyone heard her and turned to look at the girl and her father. And then Juan spoke up confidently. "*Señorita* Araceli, I am the owner of a ranch and many cattle. Will you marry me?"

Of course she said she would, and don Arturo heaved a great sigh. "Don Juan Verdades," he said, "I'll be proud to have such an honest man for a son-in-law." He beckoned his wife to come from the house, and they both hugged Juan and Araceli.

The other ranchers hurried off to fetch their families, and a big celebration began. It lasted all through the night, with music and dancing and many toasts to Juan and Araceli. And in the morning everyone went home with a big basket of delicious apples from *el manzano real*.

Note to Readers and Storytellers

The origin of the tale I call "Juan Verdades" is clearly European. The story turns up in many lands and languages. It is a variant of tale number 889 ("The Faithful Servant") in the Aarne-Thompson index of tale types. Early in the twentieth century, a version was collected in Spain by Aurelio M. Espinosa and published in *Cuentos populares españoles*. In the 1920s two versions were found in New Mexico by Juan B. Rael and included in his monumental work *Cuentos españoles de Colorado y Nuevo México*. The tale has been collected in Latin America as well.

In telling "Juan Verdades," I have given the tale a more literary treatment than I usually do. For example, I have assigned names to all of the principal characters so that the reader can keep them straight. In a traditional telling, only the main character would be given a name, and even he might simply be identified as *el joven* or *el muchacho*. I have also used dialogue to carry the narrative and clarify the characters' motivations to a greater extent than would be found in a true folktale.

Finally, I have changed the content of the story a bit. In traditional versions the daughter isn't a strong character. She just follows her father's orders. The prized possession of the employer is usually an animal, a bull or an ox, and the girl demands that it be killed and served to her. In my retelling I have softened her request. The final riddle spoken by Juan is my invention, but the conversation in verse between the servant and master is traditional. And the episode of the young man talking to a tree or a stump seems especially typical of Hispanic versions of the tale. It was the element that first captured my imagination and made me want to retell the story.

UNIT 8

Achieving Dreams

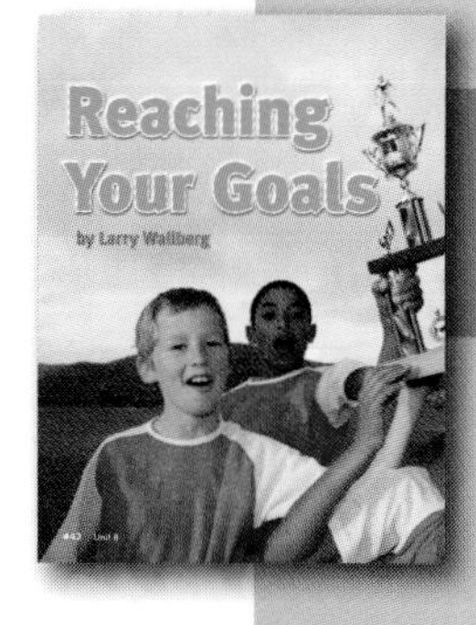

How do people set and meet goals?

Focus Questions

What things do people strive for?

What kinds of challenges do people face when working toward their goals?

How do people stick with their goals, even when they face challenges?

What does it feel like to achieve something you've worked hard for?

Reaching Your Goals

by Larry Wallberg

Contents

What Are Your Goals?

Have you thought about what you want to be when you grow up? Most likely, you aren't sure yet. Someday, however, you may choose a career like teaching or medicine. That career, or profession, will become your **goal**.

A goal is something you work toward. Like having a road map, setting goals helps you arrive at a place that is important or interesting to you. A short-term goal, such as finishing your homework, may take only a day to complete. A long-term goal, such as working toward a career, can take several years. It may require a college degree or time spent as a trainee.

On November 4, 2008, Barack Obama was elected President of the United States. He had to work hard for many years to reach that goal.

Learning how to swim might be one of your short-term goals.

Here are some goals that students your age might have.

- learn a new sport
- write a poem
- make new friends
- get good grades in school
- do volunteer work

What are your goals? Which ones can be broken down into a series of short-term goals?

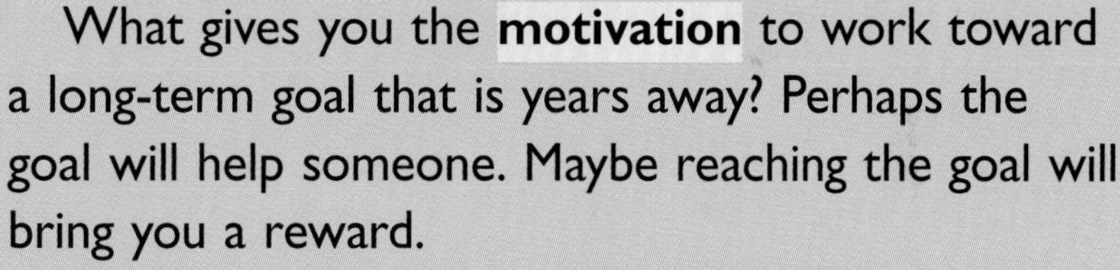

What gives you the **motivation** to work toward a long-term goal that is years away? Perhaps the goal will help someone. Maybe reaching the goal will bring you a reward.

Sometimes it helps to create several short-term goals that lead to the long-term goal. If you want to become a nurse, for example, you might set three short-term goals: Excel in your science class. Volunteer in a hospital during the summer. Take a first-aid class.

There will be challenges along the way. You may need to revise your goals. You may need more time to reach a goal. Find people who will give you their advice and encourage you not to give up!

Chapter 1

How Goals Change

You have already set—and met—many challenging goals. When you were younger, you worked hard to learn many new things. You learned to play new games and sports. Maybe you tried to learn a song you heard your teacher or family sing.

Those goals may seem simple now, but they weren't then. Learning to catch a ball, for example, took a lot of work. To achieve that goal, you had to learn to judge where the ball was going, how to get there in time, and how to hold your hands so you wouldn't drop the ball when it finally arrived.

If your teacher or family taught you a song, it might have had words that you didn't understand, so you had to learn how to pronounce them. That may seem easy now, but try to remember how hard it was when you were young! You had to learn the words, the tune, and the rhythm. That was not such a simple goal when you think about it, was it?

These girls practice hard to learn to play their instruments.

Some people want to learn their family's customs, such as traditional dances.

Your Goals Today

As you get older, your goals change. You can think further into the future and set long-term goals. You may have more than one goal at a time.

You may want to go to camp next summer (your long-term goal), which will take saving some of your allowance each week (your short-term goal). You may want to learn to skateboard. This goal will wait until spring when the weather is warm enough to practice outdoors. You may also want to learn first aid by taking a Red Cross class because you want to know what to do in an emergency.

Some goals last a lifetime. If you start a collection of coins, hats, or comic books now, you may add to the collection throughout your life.

Some people who want to become a nurse or a doctor start working toward that goal by volunteering in a hospital.

Maybe your goal is to get a big part in a class play. You will have to **strive**, or work really hard, to get that starring role and perform well.

Some young people set goals to learn how to play an instrument or take beautiful photographs. Others set goals to invent a video game or write a funny story. Whatever the goal, when they reach it, they feel a sense of triumph, or great success. What do you strive for?

You might set a goal to learn how to play a difficult piece of music.

Chapter 2

Saying "Yes" to Confronting Challenges

Most of the goals you've read about would take hard work to reach. But sometimes even hard work is not enough!

Some goals are difficult to reach because challenges stand in the way. A challenge can make any goal seem almost impossible at first. But most problems can be overcome if you are determined not to give up.

Here's how some young people said "yes" to confronting challenges.

Kyle

Kyle is a typical ten-year-old. He never imagined that he would have the important short-term goal of saving his younger brother's life.

Kyle was watching TV at his grandmother's house when his sister came running up to him. She was too scared to speak, but she pointed outside the window at the covered swimming pool.

When Kyle looked out he saw something move under the cover, and he jumped into action. He raced to the pool and pulled his baby brother from the water.

At a Cub Scout meeting, Kyle had learned how to breathe air into another person's lungs. He never imagined how scary it would be to use that skill, but he knew he had to overcome his fear to help his brother. Kyle met the challenge. He stayed calm, followed the steps he was taught, and saved his brother's life.

Kyle and his younger brother

Danielle

Some people must overcome physical challenges in order to reach their goals. Danielle faces a physical challenge in her everyday life. She has been blind since the age of two.

In school Danielle learned about tae kwon do. She made it her goal to learn this form of self-defense. She had to do this through touch, not sight. Several years of hard work paid off, because in November 2007, Danielle earned the rank of black belt.

Danielle was not surprised that she achieved her goal. She says, "I don't let the blindness stop me from doing anything. If there's something in my way, I'll find a way around it."

Like tae kwon do, karate requires discipline and concentration.

Joe

Joe also faced a physical challenge when he made it his goal to compete in the Virginia Swing Dance Championships one year. What was his challenge? Joe is deaf—he is unable to hear sounds.

Joe learned to "hear" the music by paying careful attention to his partner. He learns the rhythm of the dance by watching and feeling how quickly or slowly she moves. He says, "My eyes will see the music the way people hear the music."

Joe overcame his challenge and met his goal in a big way. He and his partner took first place in two different dances!

In swing dancing, partners hold hands and swing, flip, and throw each other. These students are swing dancing in a competition like Joe did.

Hannah

Some goals are too big for one person to face alone. When Hannah was five years old, she set a challenging goal like that.

One day Hannah saw a homeless man, a person who has no place to live, looking in a garbage can for food. Later that year she saw a homeless woman who kept everything she owned in a shopping cart. Hannah felt sad. She couldn't understand why anyone had to live that way.

Hannah set a goal to make homeless people's lives better. She knew it was a big challenge. After all, there were many people who needed help, and she was only a child.

Hannah has spoken at more than 200 events to encourage people to help the homeless.

Hannah realized that she would need plenty of help to meet her goal. She decided to start a foundation, or charitable group. She called it the Ladybug Foundation because Hannah believes that the ladybug is a symbol, or sign, of good luck.

The Ladybug Foundation raises money to give to charities that help homeless people. She visits schools, businesses, and places of worship, asking people to help her meet her goal.

Hannah discovered that many people wanted to help her reach her goal. So far, she and the Ladybug Foundation have raised over one million dollars.

Homeless Population in the United States

Although Hannah lives in Canada, there is an equally huge homeless problem in the United States. Unfortunately, many homeless people are families with children.

Meeting Your Own Challenges

You have just read about what happens when people say "yes" to confronting challenges. Kyle overcame his fear in an emergency. Danielle and Joe figured out how to work with their disabilities. Hannah asked many people to join her in order to reach her goal of helping homeless people.

What challenges might you face as you work toward your goals? What will it take to overcome them? As you meet your own challenges, remember these people. If they can do it, so can you.

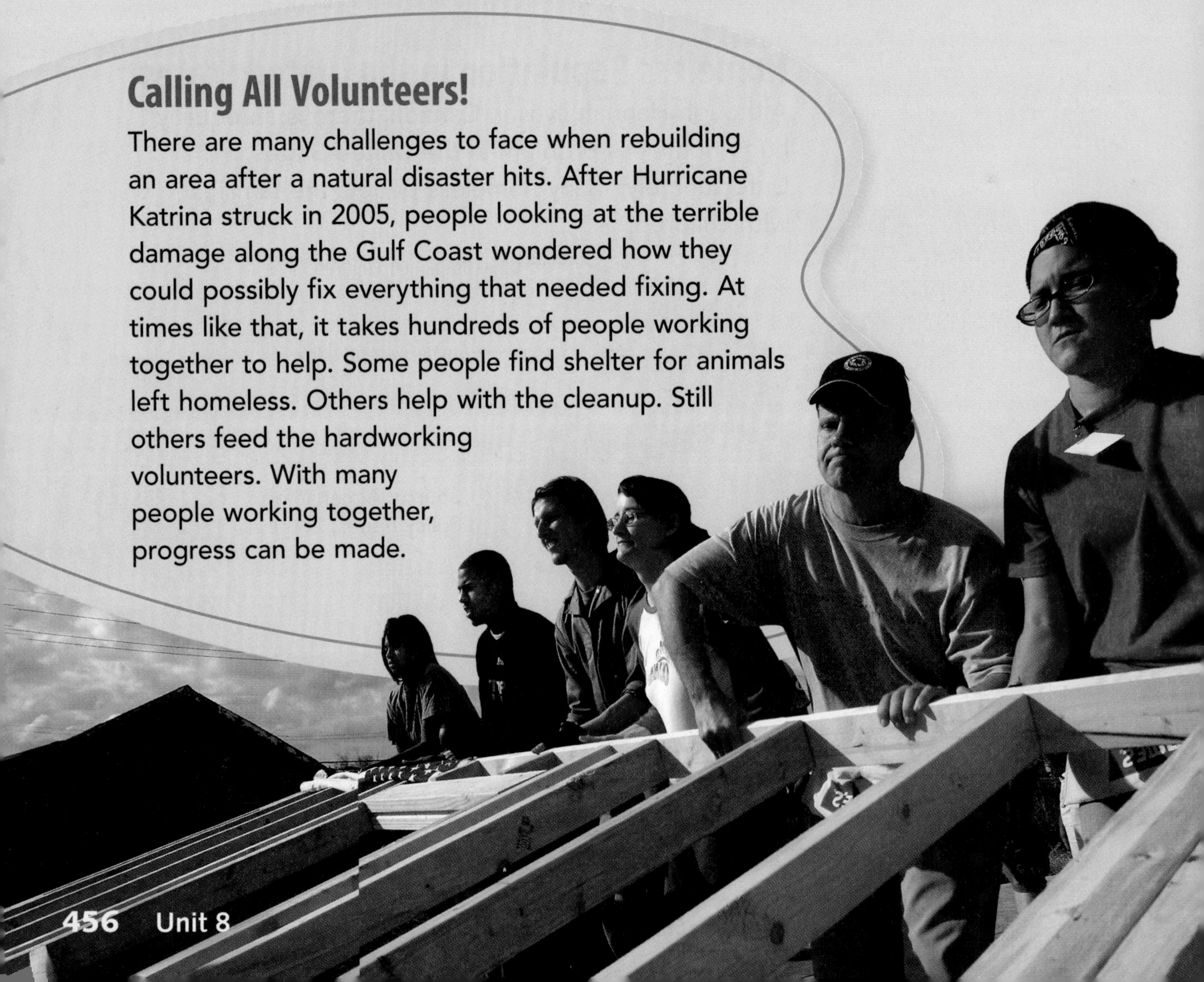

Calling All Volunteers!

There are many challenges to face when rebuilding an area after a natural disaster hits. After Hurricane Katrina struck in 2005, people looking at the terrible damage along the Gulf Coast wondered how they could possibly fix everything that needed fixing. At times like that, it takes hundreds of people working together to help. Some people find shelter for animals left homeless. Others help with the cleanup. Still others feed the hardworking volunteers. With many people working together, progress can be made.

Chapter 3

Learning from Past Challenges

Many people in the past achieved their goals in spite of great challenges, even ones that involved **risk** and danger. Frederick Douglass faced great risks just to learn to read! Elizabeth Blackwell strived to become a doctor during a time when many people disapproved of women doctors. As a boy, Native American Carl Gorman vowed to speak his Navajo language, even when he was punished for doing so.

These three people were not deterred by the challenges they faced. They all made amazing contributions to the world.

Frederick Douglass

Carl Gorman

Elizabeth Blackwell

Frederick Douglass

As a boy in the early 1800s, Frederick Douglass was an enslaved African American. He believed that he had to read and write if he wanted to be free someday, so he made it his goal to get an education. But he faced a big challenge. It was against the law to teach enslaved people how to read.

Young Frederick worked in a place where men built ships. The workers labeled each piece they made with a letter that stood for where the piece would go. By watching the men, Frederick learned to identify and write a few letters.

Frederick Douglass

Time Line of Frederick Douglass's Life

1818
Frederick Douglass is born near Easton, Maryland.

1829
Douglass secretly practices reading and writing while working in a shipyard.

1838
Disguised as a sailor, Douglass escapes from slavery.

1845
His autobiography, *Narrative of the Life of Frederick Douglass, An American Slave*, is published.

Whenever he met another boy who could write, Frederick would boast that he could write just as well. Frederick would write the few letters he knew and dare the other boy to do better. As the other boy wrote different letters, Frederick would pay careful attention.

Over time, Frederick learned to write well. When he grew up, he **fled**, or escaped, from slavery. He used his powerful writing and speaking skills to fight for human rights. He became famous as an abolitionist, a person who fought to end slavery.

Frederick first met President Lincoln in 1863. Lincoln valued Frederick's opinions and friendship. The Civil War ended in 1865. That year, the Thirteenth Amendment abolished slavery in the United States.

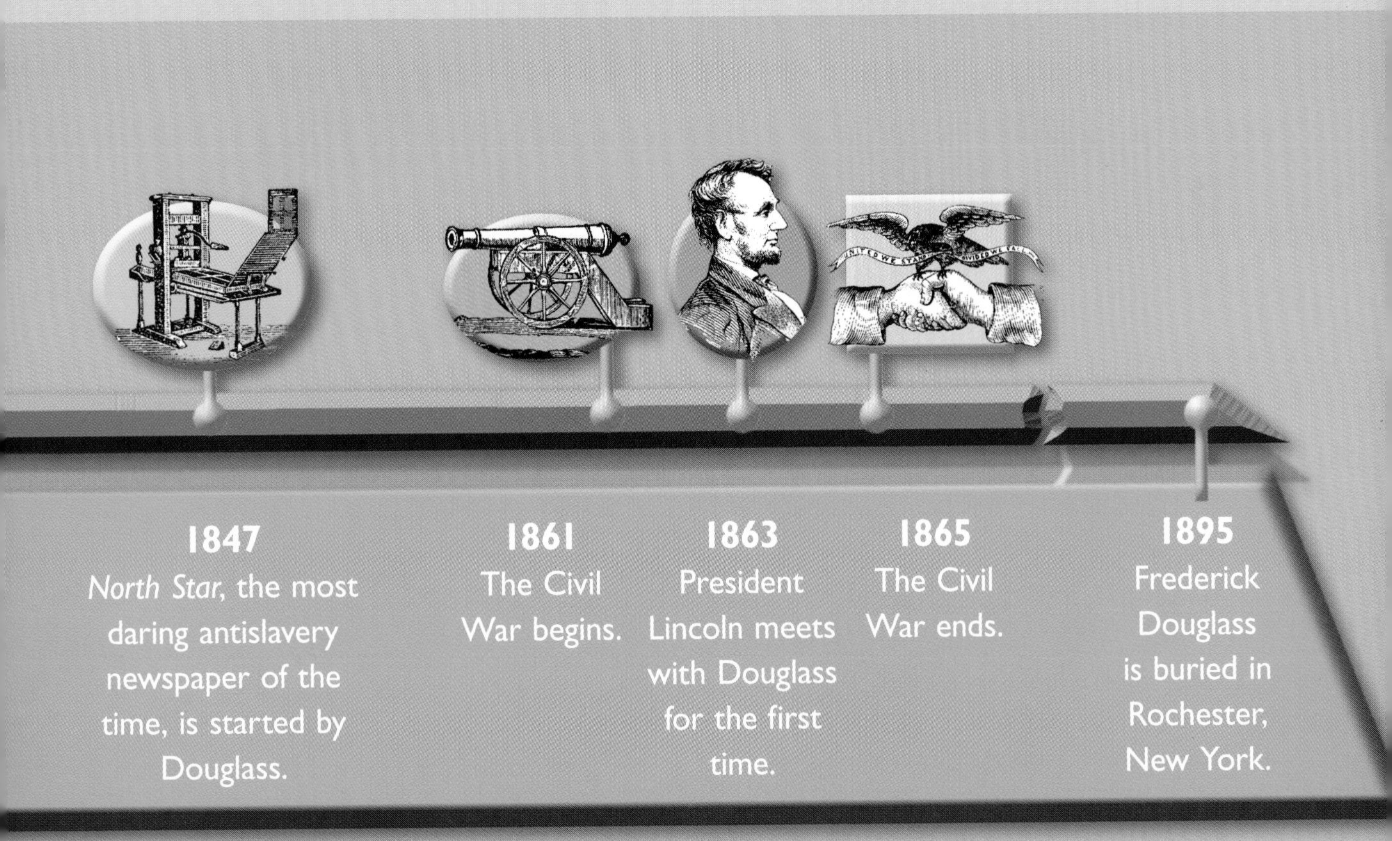

Elizabeth Blackwell

Elizabeth Blackwell wanted to become a doctor. She should have been able to achieve that goal by just working hard, because she was smart and excited about studying. But when Elizabeth tried to get accepted into medical school, she faced a huge challenge. The year was 1847, and many Americans did not believe that women should be doctors.

Elizabeth applied to dozens of schools, but they all turned her down. Finally she wrote to Geneva College in New York.

The school's teachers let the male students vote whether or not to let a woman attend. Many of the students thought that Elizabeth's application was a joke, written by friends at another school, so they all laughed and voted yes.

Elizabeth Blackwell

The U.S. Postal Service honored Elizabeth Blackwell with a postage stamp.

Nobody laughed when Elizabeth arrived to start school. "A hush fell over the class," one student wrote. Everyone was shocked. During Elizabeth's time at Geneva, the men in her classes jeered and bothered her. People in the town avoided her and made fun of her.

But Elizabeth stuck with her goal. She became the first woman to graduate from medical school in the United States. When she graduated she was first in her class, the best student.

In meeting her personal challenge, Elizabeth Blackwell opened up the field of medicine to women.

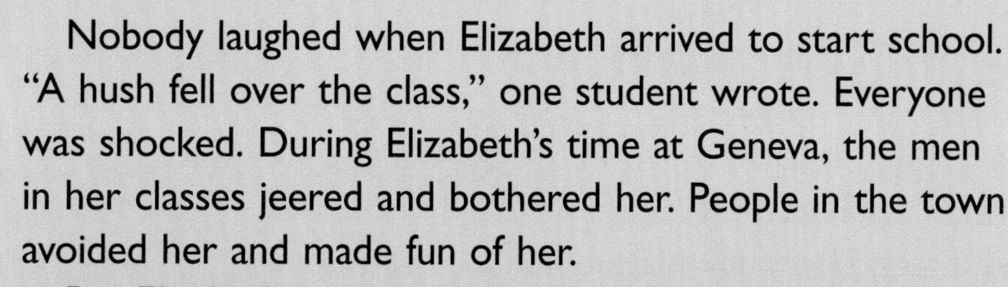

Today many woman are physicians. We have Elizabeth Blackwell to thank for paving the way.

Carl Gorman

As a young Navajo boy in the early 1900s, Carl Gorman learned the Navajo language known as Diné. Later, like many Navajo children at that time, he was sent to live at a boarding school. There he experienced harsh rules and prejudice directed toward students who spoke their Native American languages.

At school Carl was once chained to an iron pipe because he wouldn't stop speaking Navajo. Finally he ran away. Carl was determined to honor his culture and language.

Many years passed. In 1941 the United States began fighting Japan in World War II. The American military tried to keep its radio messages secret by using codes, but the Japanese military always broke the codes.

The Marines came up with a brilliant idea. Navajo was a complicated language, with no written alphabet. Few people besides about 50,000 Navajos could speak it. Could the Marines find a group of code talkers, or people who could create a code, based on Navajo? Surely the Japanese could never break that code!

Carl Gorman was one of the men the Marines picked. Carl had struggled to retain his Navajo language, and now it paid off. The secret information passed along in Navajo code talk by Carl and the others helped to defeat the Japanese.

Carl Gorman

Navajo code talkers, including Carl Gorman, sent important messages during World War II. Their skill and courage saved many American lives.

Chapter 4

The Rewards of Reaching Goals

Did you ever study hard for a test and receive an A, hit a home run to win a game, or finally master a skateboard trick you'd been practicing? How did you feel?

Some **rewards** are internal. They include the sense of pride and accomplishment you feel when you know you did a great job. Sometimes you may receive an actual physical reward for reaching a goal. It may be a trophy, a ribbon, or your photo in the newspaper.

Whether someone presents you with a reward in front of millions of people or you simply have a good feeling inside, there is nothing better than the sense of personal satisfaction that accompanies reaching a goal.

Becoming a good athlete gives you a sense of pride and accomplishment.

Most people do the work they do because it's important to them and they believe in it. Still, it is nice to be recognized and honored for a job well done, such as earning a good grade on a test

To win a Nobel Prize is a great honor. The Nobel Prize is given in such areas as literature, physics, and peace. In 2007 former Vice President Al Gore accepted the Nobel Peace Prize. He was part of a group that won for their work on the topic of global climate change.

Nobel Prize Medal

Al Gore

A Sense of Accomplishment

A Nobel Prize tells the whole world what you've accomplished. However, winning a Nobel Prize was not the goal of the winners. Their goals focused on their work, which turned out to be important enough to win this international award. The prize is like icing on a cake. It makes achieving the goal even more special.

Even if you win a blue ribbon for your efforts, the sense of accomplishment is the best reward of all. You know that all the hard work, the hours of practice, and the times you overcame challenges, even when you felt like giving up, all paid off. You did it!

As you set goals for yourself, remember that reaching even small goals is worthwhile. Each small step you take will lead you closer to the realization of your dream! In fact, many people who have accomplished great things began their slow, steady climb to success as young people. Many movie stars began by acting in class plays. Some scientists can trace the roots of their careers to school science-fair projects that captured their imaginations.

Everybody in this photo has the goal of winning the race. But regardless of who wins, they will all have a sense of accomplishment for trying their best.

3
2

Sharing a Sense of Accomplishment

When you are part of a group that is working toward the same goal, you share a sense of accomplishment with others. Anyone who has played a team sport or has been part of a performing arts group knows what that's like.

Imagine that you live in a neighborhood that needs a new playground. You and others who live nearby work together to build it. Once the playground is completed, it leads to a new goal. People in the neighborhood vow to work hard to keep the playground clean and safe.

Sometimes people come together from different places with a common goal in mind. Hurricane Katrina destroyed many homes, schools, and other buildings in the Gulf Coast region in August 2005. During spring break of 2006, about 30,000 college students headed for the Gulf Coast. They all wanted to help rebuild houses and other places damaged by the storm. The students worked together to fix walls, replace windows, repair roofs, and paint rooms. The students felt a great sense of accomplishment for the work they completed.

What goals have you reached, either by yourself or with a group? Did you have a sense of pride in what you accomplished? How did that feel?

J. W. Johnson Elementary School in New Orleans was destroyed by Hurricane Katrina. Many volunteers helped to rebuild its playground.

Sum It Up

Every day, people set goals of different kinds. Sometimes those goals are just for them, and sometimes those goals are shared with others.

It takes hard work to achieve a goal. Often you'll have to say "yes" to facing challenges to overcome them, as Kyle, Danielle, and Joe did. A challenge may be too big for just you to overcome, so you may have to learn to ask for help from others, like Hannah did.

Many people in the past were determined to meet their goals. Even though they faced tough challenges, Frederick Douglass, Elizabeth Blackwell, and Carl Gorman didn't give up. They became well known for reaching their goals.

When you meet a goal, you will get a wonderful reward: a sense of accomplishment.

AMERICA'S CHAMPION SWIMMER

Gertrude Ederle

WRITTEN BY

David A. Adler

ILLUSTRATED BY

Terry Widener

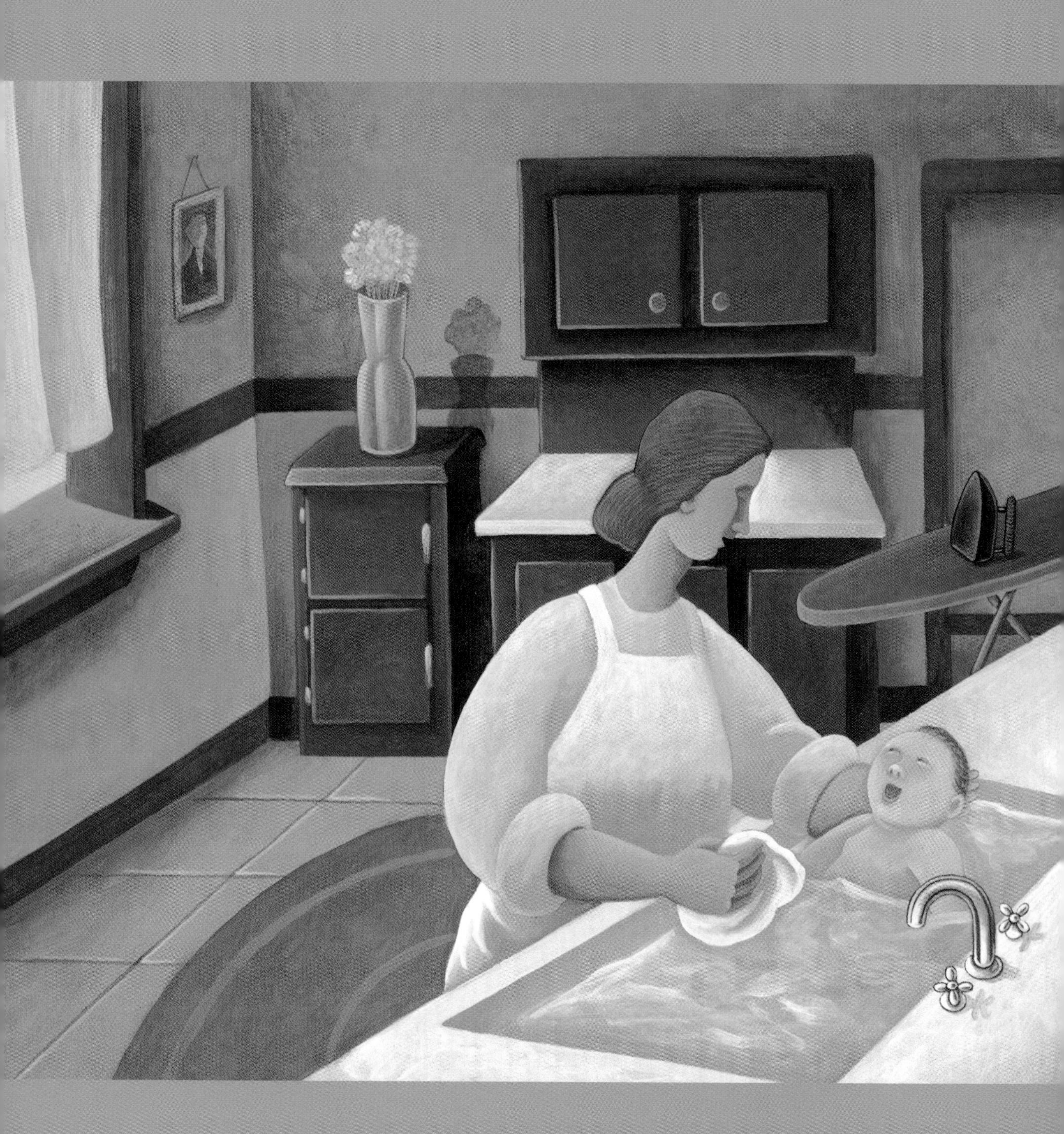

In 1906 women were kept out of many clubs and restaurants. In most states they were not allowed to vote. Many people felt a woman's place was in the home.

But Gertrude Ederle's place was in the water.

Gertrude Ederle was born on October 23, 1906. She was the third of six children and was raised in New York City, where she lived in an apartment next to her father's butcher shop. Her family called her Gertie. Most everyone else called her Trudy.

Trudy spent her early years playing on the sidewalks of New York. It wasn't until she was seven that she had her first adventure in the water. While visiting her grandmother in Germany, Trudy fell into a pond and nearly drowned.

After that near disaster, Trudy's father was determined to teach her to swim. For her first lesson, he tied one end of a rope to Trudy's waist and held on to the other end. He put Trudy into a river and told her to paddle like a dog.

Trudy mastered the dog paddle. She joined her older sister Margaret and the other children in the water and copied their strokes. Soon Trudy swam better than any of them.

From that summer on, it was hard to keep Trudy out of the water. She *loved* to swim. At the age of thirteen she became a member of the New York Women's Swimming Association and took lessons there.

At fifteen Trudy won her first big race.

The next year, she attempted to be the first woman to swim the more than seventeen miles from lower Manhattan to Sandy Hook, New Jersey. When Trudy slowed down, her sister Margaret yelled, “Get going, lazybones!” And Trudy did. She finished in just over seven hours. And she beat the men’s record.

People were beginning to notice Gertrude Ederle. Newspapers described her as courageous, determined, modest, and poised. They called her the most perfect swimmer. Trudy's mother said she was "just a plain home girl."

In 1924 this "plain home girl" was good enough to make the U.S. Olympic team. Trudy won three medals at the games in Paris. Her team won more points than all the other countries' swimming teams combined.

By 1925 Trudy had set twenty-nine U.S. and world records. She was determined to take on the ultimate challenge: the English Channel. Many had tried to swim the more-than-twenty-mile-wide body of cold, rough water that separates England from France. But only five men—and no women—had ever made it all the way across.

Many people were sure Trudy couldn't do it. A newspaper editorial declared that Trudy wouldn't make it and that women must admit they would "remain forever the weaker sex."

It didn't matter to Trudy what people said or wrote. She was going to swim the Channel.

Early in the morning on August 18, 1925, Trudy stepped into the water at Cape Gris-Nez, France, the starting point for the swim. For almost nine hours she fought the strong current. Then, when Trudy had less than seven miles to go, her trainer thought she had swallowed too much water and pulled her, crying, from the sea.

Trudy did not give up her dream. She found a new trainer, and a year later, on Friday, August 6, 1926, she was ready to try again.

Trudy wore a red bathing cap and a two-piece bathing suit and goggles that she and her sister Margaret had designed. To protect her from the icy cold water, Margaret coated Trudy with lanolin and heavy grease. The greasing took a long time—too long for Trudy. “For heaven’s sake,” she complained. “Let’s get started.”

Finally, at a little past seven in the morning, she stepped into the water. “Gee, but it’s cold,” Trudy said.

Trudy's father, her sister Margaret, her trainer, and a few other swimmers were on board a tugboat named *Alsace*. The boat would accompany Trudy to make sure she didn't get lost in the fog and was safe from jellyfish, sharks, and the Channel's powerful currents. There was a second boat, too, with reporters and photographers on board.

As the *Alsace* bobbed up and down in the choppy water, Margaret wrote in chalk on the side of the boat, "This way, Ole Kid." She drew an arrow that pointed to England.

← THIS WAY, OLE KID

THIS

To entertain Trudy, Margaret and some of the others sang American songs, including "The Star-Spangled Banner" and "East Side, West Side." Trudy said the songs kept her "brain and spirit good."

At first the sea was calm.

Trudy swam so fast that her trainer was afraid she would tire herself out. He ordered her to slow down.

Trudy refused.

At about ten-thirty in the morning, Trudy had her first meal. She floated on her back and ate chicken and drank beef broth. A while later, she ate chocolate and chewed on sugar cubes. Then she swam on.

At about one-thirty in the afternoon, it started to rain. A strong wind stirred the water. For a while, Trudy would swim forward a few feet only to be pulled back twice as far.

By six o'clock the tide was stronger. The waves were twenty feet high. The rough water made the people aboard the *Alsace* and the news boat seasick.

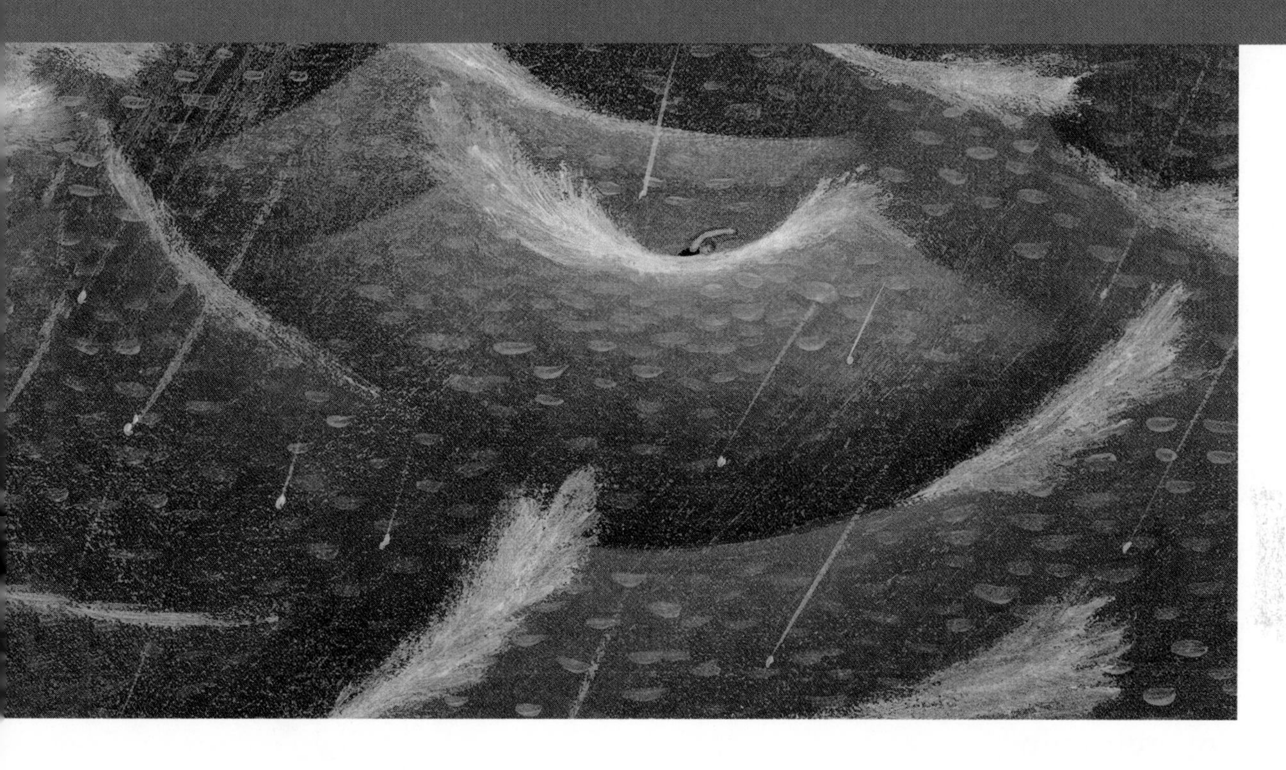

Trudy's trainer was sure she couldn't finish the swim. He told her to give up.

"No, no," Trudy yelled over the sound of the waves. She kept swimming.

In the next few hours, the rain and wind became stronger and the sea rougher. At times the rough water pulled the boats away, out of Trudy's sight. She was scared. It was eerie being out there all alone.

Now Trudy began to have trouble kicking in the water. When the *Alsace* came close again, Trudy said her left leg had become stiff. Her trainer was frightened for her. He yelled, "You must come out."

"What for?" Trudy shouted, and kept swimming.

Trudy continued to fight the tide and the **constant** stinging spray of water in her face. She knew she would either swim the Channel or drown.

As Trudy neared Kingsdown, on the coast of England, she saw thousands of people gathered to greet her. They lit flares to guide her to shore.

At about nine-forty at night, after more than fourteen hours in the water, Trudy's feet touched land. Hundreds of people, fully dressed, **waded** into the water to greet her. When she reached the shore, her father hugged Trudy and wrapped her in a warm robe.

"I knew if it could be done, it had to be done, and I did it," Trudy said after she got ashore. "All the women of the world will celebrate."

Trudy swam the Channel in just fourteen hours and thirty-one minutes. She beat the men's record by almost two hours. In newspapers across the world, Trudy's swim was called history making. Reporters declared that the myth that women are the weaker sex was "shattered and shattered forever."

Trudy sailed home aboard the SS *Berengaria*. After six days at sea, the ship entered New York Harbor.

Two airplanes circled and tipped their wings to greet Trudy. People on boats of all kinds rang their bells and tooted their horns to salute her. Foghorns sounded.

Trudy climbed into an open car for a parade up lower Broadway. An estimated two million people, many of them women, stood and cheered. They threw scraps of newspaper, ticker tape, pages torn from telephone books, and rolls of toilet paper.

When her car arrived at the New York city hall, Mayor Jimmy Walker praised Trudy for her courage, grace, and athletic prowess.

"American women," he said, "have ever added to the glory of our nation."

President Calvin Coolidge sent a message that was read at the ceremony. He called Trudy "America's Best Girl." And she was. Gertrude Ederle had become a beacon of strength to girls and women everywhere.

Notes from the author:

While it's twenty-one miles across the Channel, the rough water makes the actual swim much longer. It was estimated Trudy had to swim thirty-five miles to get across.

Trudy's 1925 swim was cut short because of terrible conditions and because her trainer, Jabez Wolffe, touched her in the water. That touch disqualified the swim. Wolffe had tried to swim the Channel more than twenty times but had never succeeded.

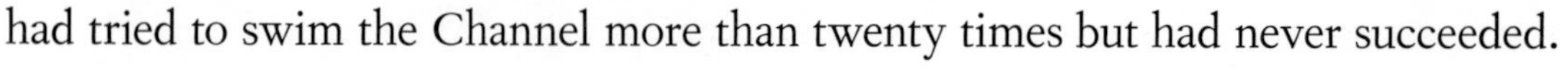

For the 1926 swim Trudy's trainer was Thomas W. Burgess, who in 1911, after many failed attempts, was the second man to swim the Channel.

Someone who witnessed Trudy's swim and more than a dozen other attempts commented that in good weather Trudy would have finished at least four hours sooner.

A London Daily News editorial declared women "the weaker sex" the very day of Trudy's successful 1926 swim. The next day, the newspaper didn't back down from that statement but explained that "Miss Ederle is evidently a superwoman."

According to New York City Police Inspector Kuehne, many women felt empowered by Trudy's swim. At Trudy's welcome back to New York, he tried to help one very old woman. He was afraid she would get hurt in the crowd. "I guess I can take care of myself," she told him. Inspector Kuehne said later, "That seemed to be the attitude of most of the women."

On August 28, 1926, three weeks after Trudy's swim, another woman, Mrs. Millie Corson, left the coast of France. Two other swimmers, both men, made the attempt with her. Only Millie Corson made it across. Millie Corson was the first mother to swim the Channel. She got across in fifteen hours and thirty-two minutes, not fast enough to beat Trudy's record but faster than any of the previous male swimmers. Two days later, on August 30, 1926, Ernst Vierkoetter, a German, swam the Channel. He did it in just twelve hours and forty-three minutes, setting a new record.

Gertrude Ederle never married. She lost much of her hearing after her swim, perhaps because of the cold Channel water but more likely the result of childhood measles. She fell sometime in the 1940s and was in a cast for more than four years. Doctors were sure Trudy would be confined to a wheelchair, but she was determined to walk again—and she did. Trudy worked as a dress designer and taught deaf children to swim. She was also a member of the President's Council on Youth Fitness.

The sources for much of the information for this book were periodicals of the time, including the *New York Times*, the *New York World*, and the *Literary Digest*, as well as more recent collective biographies.

Comprehension Strategy Handbook

How will this handbook help me?

Each page of this handbook will help you choose and use comprehension strategies while you read. Comprehension strategies are tools you can use to help you understand what you read:

Ask and Answer Questions
Determine Important Information
Make Connections
Make Inferences
Make Predictions
Monitor Comprehension
Summarize
Visualize

How do I use the handbook?

The box at the top of each page will remind you what each strategy is and help you decide if you want to use it.

The steps will remind you exactly what you need to do.

The tip will show you a way to keep track of information as you read.

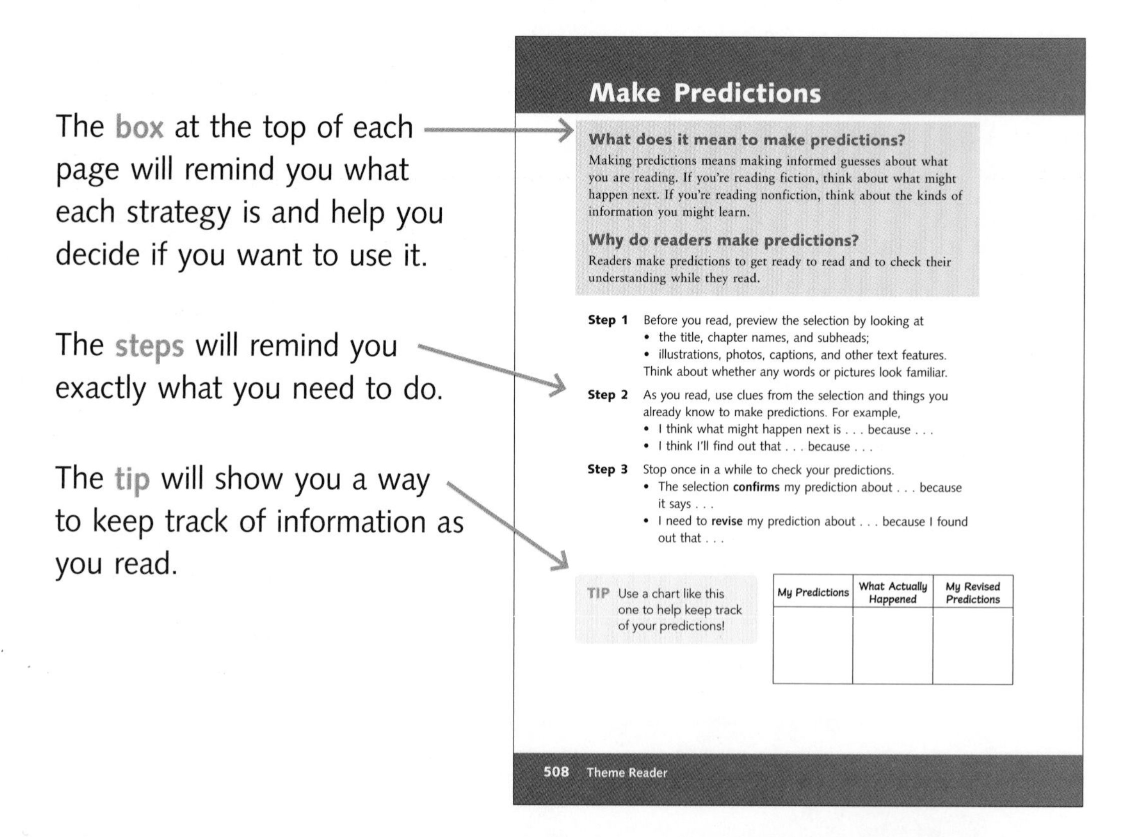

Make Predictions

What does it mean to make predictions?
Making predictions means making informed guesses about what you are reading. If you're reading fiction, think about what might happen next. If you're reading nonfiction, think about the kinds of information you might learn.

Why do readers make predictions?
Readers make predictions to get ready to read and to check their understanding while they read.

Step 1 Before you read, preview the selection by looking at
- the title, chapter names, and subheads;
- illustrations, photos, captions, and other text features.

Think about whether any words or pictures look familiar.

Step 2 As you read, use clues from the selection and things you already know to make predictions. For example,
- I think what might happen next is . . . because . . .
- I think I'll find out that . . . because . . .

Step 3 Stop once in a while to check your predictions.
- The selection **confirms** my prediction about . . . because it says . . .
- I need to **revise** my prediction about . . . because I found out that . . .

TIP Use a chart like this one to help keep track of your predictions!

My Predictions	What Actually Happened	My Revised Predictions

508 Theme Reader

Can I use multiple strategies?

Yes! Experienced readers use more than one strategy at a time. Read this paragraph to see how each strategy helps you notice and understand different things.

Rani pushed the door open slowly. **Creeaaak!** She peered down the stairs into the pitch-black darkness of the basement. *Should I really be doing this?* She took a deep breath and swallowed hard.

"He-hello?" she called timidly. Her voice was barely a whisper.

There was no answer. Then she heard it again! *What was that noise?* It sounded almost like a giggle.

Rani crept quietly down the stairs, grasping the railing and feeling for each step in front of her, counting as she went. One, two, three, four . . . finally her foot hit the last step. She reached for the light switch, but something grabbed her arm! She squeezed her eyes shut and began to scream when all of a sudden—

"Surprise! Happy birthday to you . . . " her friends began to sing.

Visualize I can really picture this scene in my mind. It gives me the chills!

Make Predictions I've read stories like this before! I think that giggle means her friend is hiding down there.

Make Connections Wow, is she brave! I would never walk into a dark room like that!

Check Predictions Aha! I knew it was going to be her friends!

Ask and Answer Questions

What does it mean to ask and answer questions?

Readers ask themselves questions before, during, and after reading. Sometimes there are questions someone else asks at the end of a selection. Readers find answers in the selection, from their own experiences, or both!

Why do readers ask and answer questions?

Asking and answering questions helps readers check their understanding. It helps them think more deeply about the selection so that they better understand it.

Step 1 **Before You Read** As you preview the selection, ask questions to activate prior knowledge and set purposes for reading. For example,

- What is this selection going to be about?
- What do I already know about this topic?
- Is this picture going to be important?

Step 2 **As You Read** Continue asking questions about things you don't understand or things you'd like to find out more about. Keep reading to look for answers to your questions.

Step 3 **After You Read** Are there any questions you have not yet answered? Is there anything new you wonder about now that you have finished reading?

TIP Keep track of your questions in a chart like this one. When you find the answer, write it down! If you don't find the answer, write down other places you could look for it.

Questions	Did you find the answer?		
	Yes	No	Need more information
	✔		

Determine Important Information

What does it mean to determine important information?

Fiction and nonfiction selections include many details that make the writing interesting. But the most interesting ideas may not always be the most important. Determining important information means figuring out the big ideas in the selection.

Why do readers determine important information?

Separating the big ideas from the details helps readers understand the important information the author wants them to know.

Step 1 Look for key words. Key words may be

- in the title, chapter names, and subheads;
- boldface or highlighted;
- repeated in many parts of the selection.

Step 2 Look at the text features. They could be clues about the important ideas in that chapter.

Step 3 Carefully read the first and last sentences in each paragraph. Authors often put important information here.

Step 4 Stop after each section and ask questions.

- What is the most important idea of this section?
- Can I pick out a sentence that tells the most important idea?
- Which information is interesting but not that important?

TIP Use a chart to help you determine important information as you read. Write the big ideas in the left column. Write the supporting details in the right column.

Big Ideas	Supporting Details

Make Connections

What does it mean to make connections?

Readers make connections when something they read reminds them of other things they know. Readers make connections to their own experiences, to other things they have read, and to what they know about the world around them.

Why do readers make connections?

Readers understand a selection better when they can find ways to connect it to things they already know.

Step 1 Before you read, preview the selection and look for words, pictures, or ideas that are familiar to you. Ask yourself:

- What do I already know about this topic?
- What else have I read about this topic?

Step 2 When you read a part of the selection that reminds you of something, stop and jot it down.

- **Text-to-Self** Does it remind you of your own experiences?
- **Text-to-Text** Does it remind you of something else you have read?
- **Text-to-World** Does it remind you of something you know about the world?

Step 3 Think about how the connection you made helps you better understand the selection.

TIP Use sticky notes to record connections you make! Label them like this:
S = self
T = other texts you've read
W = the world

S: *This character reminds me of my friend Brian. They both get into trouble, but they mean well.*

T: *I read an article online about this! It also talked about how birds fly.*

W: *I don't think the character understands that it's hard for everyone to make friends sometimes.*

Make Inferences

What does it mean to make inferences?

Readers make inferences by using what they know to fill in information that is not stated in the selection.

Why do readers make inferences?

Authors don't always include every detail, so readers need to make inferences. Readers understand a selection better when they add what they already know to the information on the page.

Step 1 As you read, pause to ask yourself:
- What information is the author giving me?
- What other information do I need to understand this?

Step 2 Think about what you already know.
- Think about your own experiences.
- Recall other books you have read about the topic.
- Think about the world around you.

Step 3 Use what you know to better understand the information in the selection.

TIP You can also make inferences to figure out unfamiliar words and understand text features. Use a chart like this one to help you.

What I read in the text:	+	What I know about this:	=	Inference:

Make Predictions

What does it mean to make predictions?

Making predictions means making informed guesses about what you are reading. If you're reading fiction, think about what might happen next. If you're reading nonfiction, think about the kinds of information you might learn.

Why do readers make predictions?

Readers make predictions to get ready to read and to check their understanding while they read.

Step 1 Before you read, preview the selection by looking at

- the title, chapter names, and subheads;
- illustrations, photos, captions, and other text features.

Think about whether any words or pictures look familiar.

Step 2 As you read, use clues from the selection and things you already know to make predictions. For example,

- I think what might happen next is . . . because . . .
- I think I'll find out that . . . because . . .

Step 3 Stop once in a while to check your predictions.

- The selection **confirms** my prediction about . . . because it says . . .
- I need to **revise** my prediction about . . . because I found out that . . .

TIP Use a chart like this one to help keep track of your predictions!

My Predictions	What Actually Happened	My Revised Predictions

Monitor Comprehension

What does it mean to monitor comprehension?

Experienced readers pay attention not only to *what* they read but also to *how* they read. They recognize when they don't understand something. When their comprehension is breaking down, they use fix-up strategies.

Why do readers monitor comprehension?

At some point, all readers have trouble understanding something they read. Monitoring comprehension helps readers notice when they don't understand something and figure out how to fix it.

Step 1 Pause and ask yourself: Do I understand? Try to summarize what you just read. If you can summarize it, keep reading.

Step 2 If you are not sure you understand, use a fix-up strategy.

- **Reread** the section.
- **Keep reading** to see if the author explains further.
- **Slow down** so you don't miss important information.
- **Speed up**—reading one word at a time makes it difficult to put ideas together.
- **Use the images** to see if they *show* what the text *says*.
- **Seek help** from a dictionary; ask someone to help you.

Step 3 Ask yourself again: Do I understand? If not, try another fix-up strategy.

TIP Follow the arrows to help you decide what to do when you get stuck!

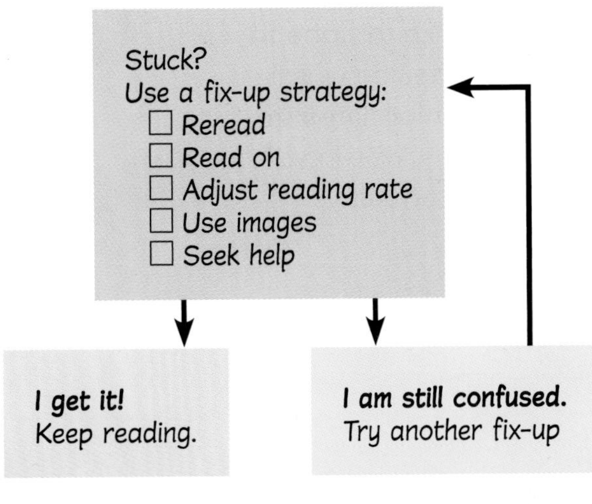

Summarize

What does it mean to summarize?

Summarizing means using your own words to explain the most important ideas of a selection you have read. A summary of a nonfiction text tells the most important information. A summary of a story tells who the main characters were and what happened to them.

Why do readers summarize?

Readers summarize to check their understanding and to help them remember what they have read. Readers might stop as they read to summarize part of the text. They might also summarize the entire text once they have finished reading.

Step 1 When you finish a paragraph, chapter, or selection, stop and think about the most important ideas. Make a list.

Step 2 Look over the list and cross out details that are interesting but not that important.

Step 3 Think of a topic sentence that tells the main idea. Ask yourself: What is this paragraph or selection mostly about?

Step 4 Use your list to write sentences that explain the big ideas.

TIP Use a chart like this one to decide which information to include in your summary.

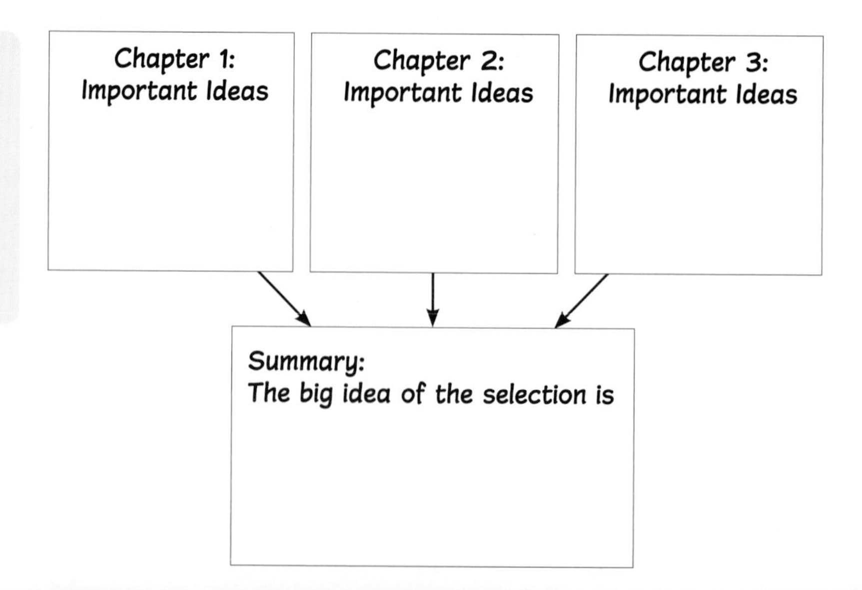

Visualize

What does it mean to visualize?

When readers visualize, they use the words on the page to create pictures in their minds. Readers picture the people, places, and things the author describes.

Why do readers visualize?

Visualizing helps readers see, feel, and hear what the author describes. When readers visualize, they can imagine being a part of the story.

Step 1 Look for clues in the selection that signal it might be a good time to visualize:

- Descriptive words
- Actions
- Comparisons

Step 2 Think about your own experiences. Use the selection and your own ideas to create a picture in your mind.

Step 3 As you read on, use new information from the selection to add to or revise your mental picture.

TIP You can draw pictures to help you visualize!

Words from the Selection	The Picture in My Mind

Strategies at a Glance

Use this chart to help you decide which strategies to use.

Ask and Answer Questions Do you find yourself wondering about something you read? Asking and answering questions helps build understanding.
Determine Important Information Which ideas are important, and which ones are supporting details? Figuring out what is important will help you better understand the selection.
Make Connections Does something you read remind you of your own experiences? Does it remind you of something else you have read or something in the world?
Make Inferences Did the author leave out some information? Sometimes readers need to "fill in the blanks" by using what they already know. Making inferences helps you make sense of what you read.
Make Predictions Are you wondering what is going to happen next? Make a prediction and then check it as you read.

Monitor Comprehension
Not sure you understand something? Stop and check your understanding. Then try using a fix-up strategy, such as rereading, using images, or reading on.

Summarize
Can you sum up what you just read using your own words? Try summarizing to help you remember what you have read.

Visualize
Is the author using descriptive words or figurative language? Use the words to make a picture in your mind.

Glossary

Pronunciation Key

a	bat	oi	toy
ā	ape	ou	shout
air	air	ŏŏ	book
ä	park	ōō	moon
e	let	s	sun
ē	easy	sh	pressure
i	if	th	the, thing
ī	lie	u	nut
îr	dear	ûr	circle
k	cause	ə	ago
o	lot	ər	mother
ō	go	′	primary stress
ô	all	′	secondary stress

affect (ə fekt′) *v.* to influence or change;

Two months without rain will affect the amount of water in the river. **339**

alternative (ôl tûr′ nə tiv) *adj.* being or giving a choice between two or more things;

His alternative idea was that we could swim today instead of play basketball. **80**

ancestor (an′ ses′ tər) *n.* a family member from a distant generation;

Your great-grandmother is your ancestor. **11**

arid (a′ rid) *adj.* land that gets very little rain;

The arid desert has many interesting features. **389**

basin (bā′ sin) *n.* all the land that is drained by a river and the streams that run into that river;

Illinois, Missouri, and Arkansas are in the basin of the Mississippi River. **258**

boundary (boun′ drē) *n.* a limit;

I broke a boundary when I became the first female quarterback on the school team. **61**

cautiously (kô′ shəs lē) *adv.* acting with caution or care;

The girl looked both ways, but she still crossed the street cautiously. **122**

compete (kəm pēt′) *v.* to be in a state of rivalry, or to try to win or gain something;

The teams compete to win the game. **333**

competition (kom′ pi ti′ shən) *n.* a contest;

I think I can win the 50 meter dash competition. **48**

consequence (kon′ si kwəns′) *n.* the result of an action;

A consequence of skipping lunch is to be hungry. **152**

constant (kon′ stənt) *adj.* continuing and not changing;

We heard the constant roar of the ocean waves. **492**

custom (kus′ təm) *n.* a practice common to many people;

Dancing is an important custom in many cultures. **27**

dazzling (daz′ ling) *adj.* showy or brilliant;

She hoped her dazzling outfit would impress her friends. **176**

delta (del′ tə) *n.* an area of land at the mouth of a river, formed by mud, sand, and pebble deposits;

There are many farms on both sides of the river delta. **274**

disappear (di′ sə pîr′) *v.* to pass from view, to stop existing;

The hot sun made the rain puddles dry up and disappear. **339**

diverse (di vûrs′) *adj.* different from one another, not all the same;

My diverse neighborhood has families from all over the world. **282**

economy (i ko′ nə mē) *n.* how people in an area make a living;

The economy of a rural community is different from the economy of an urban community. **134**

ecosystem (ē′ kō sis′ təm) *n.* the living and nonliving things that interact within a community;

The plants and animals are all part of the ecosystem. **320**

endangered (en dān′ jərd) *adj.* in danger of becoming extinct, or disappearing from Earth;

The Hawaiian goose is an endangered bird. **88**

exchange (eks chānj′) *v.* to give and receive things of the same kind;

It makes me happy to exchange gifts at holiday time. **425**

extremes (ek strēmz′) *n.* the farthest points, complete opposites;

The coldest winter temperature and the hottest summer temperature are extremes. **382**

fertile (fûr′ təl) *adj.* able to easily produce crops and plants;

Many plants grow on the fertile land. **152**

film (film) *v.* to use a motion-picture camera to take pictures;

The camera operator will film the actors. **402**

flee (flē) *v.* to run away;

Many animals will flee from danger rather than attack. **459**

flourish (flûr′ ish) *v.* to grow or develop strongly;

Orange trees flourish in Florida. **268**

formation (fôr mā′ shən) *n.* something that is made, arranged, or formed, as in a pattern;

The marching band made an interesting formation on the field. **241**

fragrant (frā′ grənt) *adj.* having a pleasing smell;

The baking bread made the kitchen fragrant. **372**

fulfill (fŏŏl fil′) *v.* to carry out or finish;

We can fulfill Mom's wish to clean our rooms. **422**

generation (je′ nə rā′ shən) *n.* a group of people born around the same time;

My friends and I are from the same generation. **11**

glide (glīd) *v.* to move along smoothly;

Jason loves to glide along the ice on the pond. **301**

goal (gōl) *n.* a purpose or something a person wants to achieve;

Lina's goal was to make the track team. **444**

gravity (gra′ vi tē) *n.* the force that pulls things toward Earth;

If you throw a ball up in the air, gravity pulls it back to Earth. **198**

habitat (ha′ bi tat′) *n.* the place where a plant or animal naturally lives and grows;

My fish tank looks like an underwater habitat. **88**

heritage (her′ i tij) *n.* something that is handed down from one generation to another;

Certain foods are part of my family's heritage. **10**

hesitate (he′zə tāt′) *v.* to hold back because of feeling unsure;

If you hesitate you will lose your place in line. **376**

interdependence (in′ tər də pen′ dəns) *n.* when two or more people or things depend upon each other;

The interdependence of the family members helps make doing chores easier. **322**

irrigated (ir′ i gā ′ tid) *adj.* being watered through streams, pipes, or other means;

The irrigated lawn was greener than the lawn that didn't have a sprinkler. **387**

issue (i′ shōō) *n.* something that is being talked about or considered;

My brother and I spoke about the issue of sharing our games. **140**

keen (kēn) *adj.* excellent or sharp in seeing, thinking, or hearing;

The cat's keen eyes saw the mouse in the dark. **106**

landform (land′ fôrm) *n.* a natural feature of the land;

Sandstone arches are a landform found in Utah. **260**

lunar (lōō′ nər) *adj.* having to do with the moon;

The astronaut walked across the lunar surface. **217**

magnificent (mag ni′ fə sənt) *adj.* very grand and beautiful;

The magnificent building was made of pink stone. **247**

marvel (mär′ vəl) *v.* to feel a sense of wonder or astonishment;

I marvel at the skill of pole vaulters. **237**

missionary (mi′ shə ner ′ ē) *n.* someone sent by a group to spread their beliefs, usually religious;

Our aunt was a Methodist missionary in China. **405**

motivation (mō′ tə vā′ shən) *n.* an influence or the reason that makes a person do something;

My motivation for joining the debate team was watching our local candidates debate important issues. **445**

mutter (mu′ tər) *v.* to speak in a voice that is low and not clear;

I will mutter something when I don't want my sister to hear me. **292**

nonrenewable (non′ ri nyōō′ ə bəl) *adj.* not able to make new again;

Coal is a nonrenewable resource. **74**

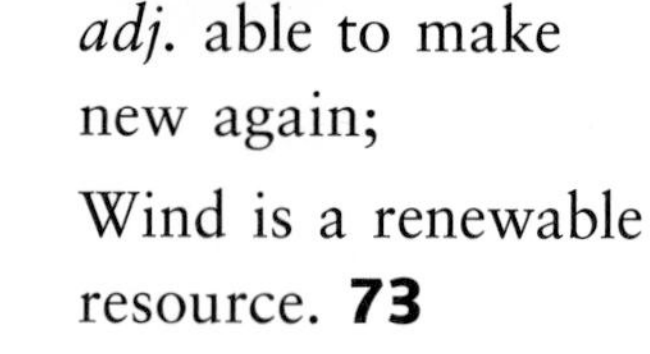

plod (plod) *v.* to walk heavily or slowly;

The boys plod through the deep puddles. **366**

recipe (re′ sə pē) *n.* the instructions and ingredients for making something to drink or eat;

I have a great recipe for chicken and rice. **23**

reel (rēl) *v.* to pull by winding something in;

It took all my strength to reel in the big fish. **175**

reflect (ri flekt′) *v.* to give back, bounce off;

The lakes reflect the snow-capped mountain. **198**

region (rē′ jən) *n.* a large area or territory;

The view of the mountain region is beautiful. **134**

religious (ri li′ jəs) *adj.* showing faith in, or relating to a religion;

My religious grandparents enjoy teaching me about our religion. **33**

renewable (ri nyōō′ ə bəl) *adj.* able to make new again;

Wind is a renewable resource. **73**

rescue (res′ kyōō) *v.* to save or free;

I was relieved to rescue the cat from the storm. **108**

revolve (ri volv′) *v.* to move in a circle around a center point;

Earth revolves around the sun. **198**

reward (ri wôrd′) *n.* something given or received in return for doing something;

Mrs. Falco took me to see my favorite movie as a reward for helping her. **464**

risk (risk) *n.* the possibility of great loss, harm, or danger;

A tornado chaser runs the risk of becoming hurt. **457**

rotate (rō′ tāt) *v.* to turn on an axis;

The Ferris wheel can rotate five times in one minute. **200**

rugged (ru′ gid) *adj.* being rough, irregular;

The rugged cliff was difficult to climb. **400**

shimmer (shi′ mər) *v.* to shine with a faint light;

The water in the pool will shimmer in the sunlight. **41**

species (spē′ shēz) *n.* a group of plants or animals that have similar characteristics;

There are many species of birds. **87**

stretch (strech) *v.* to reach out or extend;

My little brother has to stretch to reach the kitchen counter. **286**

strive (strīv) *v.* to try very hard or make a great effort;

We should strive to do our best, even in our most difficult subjects. **449**

support (sə pôrt′) *v.* to provide for;

The money that tourists spend helps to support many businesses in our state. **144**

survive (sər vīv′) *v.* to remain alive;

The dog cannot survive without food and water. **326**

swoop (swōōp) *n.* the act of rushing down suddenly;

The bird caught the fish with a swoop. **170**

telescope (te′ lə skōp′) *n.* an instrument that makes faraway objects seem larger and closer;

When I look through my telescope, the moon seems as if it is right outside my window. **196**

transport (trans pôrt′) *v.* to carry or bring from one place to another;

Ships transport goods around the world. **263**

treasure (tre′ zhər) *v.* to cherish or consider to have great value;

Grandma and Grandpa treasure the handmade cards we send them. **422**

wade (wād) *v.* to walk in or through water;

Small children often wade in shallow water. **494**

Index

Acknowledgments

Photo Credits

6 (br) ©Ronnie Kaufman/Corbis, (bl) ©Rolf Bruderer/Corbis; **6-7** (t) ©Digital Vision; **7** (br) ©Tim Boyle/Getty Images, (bl) ©Corbis Super RF/Alamy; **8-9** ©Tony Mextaxas/Getty Images; **10-11** (b) ©D. Hurst/Alamy; **11** (t) ©Allison Dinner/Getty Images; **12-13** (b) ©Harman Singh Narula; **13** (t) ©Arif Ali/AFP/Getty Images; **14-15** (b) ©AFP/Getty Images; **15** (t) ©Jim Pickerell/Stock Connection Blue/Alamy; **16** ©Lucian Coman/Shutterstock; **17** (t) ©Faith Ringold, (b) ©Panoramic Images/Getty Images; **18-19** (t) ©Dennis MacDonald/PhotoEdit; **19** (bl) ©Jeff Greenberg/PhotoEdit, (br) ©Chris Johnson/iStockphoto/Getty Images; **20** (b) ©Michael Greenlar; **20-21** ©Photodisc/Getty Images; **22** (b) ©Corbis Super RF/Alamy, (t) ©Used With Permission from Penguin Group; **23** (b) ©Lawrence Migdale/Getty Images, (t) ©Eric Futran/Getty Images; **24** ©Jeff Greenberg/PhotoEdit; **25** ©Koichi Kamoshida/Getty Images; **26** (b) ©Cristina Fumi/Alamy, (t) ©Joseph Project-Malawi/Alamy; **26-27** ©Brittany App's Photography/IAI Presentations, Inc.; **28-29** (b) ©Jeff Greenberg/Photoedit; **29** (tc) ©Photodisc/Getty Images, (t) ©Brand X Pictures/Punchstock, (b) ©Ingram Publishing/Alamy, (bc) ©Ingram Publishing/Fotosearch; **30** ©Time & Life Pictures/Getty Images; **31** ©Kim Karpeles/Alamy; **32-33** (t) ©Peter Sandground/Unique Events/Getty Images, (b) ©Associated Press; **34** (b) ©Tim Boyle/Getty Images; **34-35** ©altrendo images/Getty Images; **35** (t) ©Donna Day/Getty Images; **36** ©Will Hart/Photoedit; **68** (br) ©PhotoLink/Getty Images, (bl) ©Don Smith/Getty Images; **68-69** (t) ©Ron and Patty Thomas/Photographer's Choice/Getty Images; **69** (bl) ©Jason Edwards/National Geographic/Getty Images, (br) ©Creatas/PunchStock; **70-71** ©Punchstock/Brand X Pictures, (t) ©Creatas/PunchStock; **72** (b) ©Imagebroker/Alamy; **72-73** ©Don Smith/Lifesize/Getty Images; **74-75** ©Ding Jianzhou/Imaginechina/Associated Press; **75** (br) ©David Young-Wolff/PhotoEdit, (bl) ©David Trevor/Alamy Images; **76** (b) ©E.B. Boyd; **76-77** ©Steve Prezant/Corbis; **77** (inset) ©Corbis Premium RF/Alamy; **78-79** ©Photofusion Picture Library/Alamy; **79** (b) ©AGE Fotostock/SuperStock; 80 (b) ©Associated Press; **80-81** ©David R. Frazier Photolibrary, Inc./alamy; **82-83** (bkgrd) ©mediacolor's/Alamy; **84** (t) ©AGStockUSA, Inc./Alamy, (b) ©Jim Parkin/Alamy; **84-85** ©ICP/Alamy; 85 (t) ©Peggy Greb/USDA; **86** (t) ©RIA Novosti/Photo Researchers, Inc.; **86-87** ©Associated Press; **87** (b) ©Tim Laman/National Geographic Stock; **88-89** ©Morales/AGE Fotostock, (t) ©Flip Nicklin/Minden Pictures; **90** ©Jason Edwards/National Geographic/Getty Images; **91** ©Nature Picture Library/Alamy Images, (cr) ©Associated Press; **92-93** ©Jeff Greenberg/AGE Fotostock; **93** (t) ©Betsy Fresen, (b) ©Jeff Greenberg/PhotoEdit; **94** (b) ©Findlay/Alamy; **94-95** ©Dave Bevan/Alamy, (t) ©Allstair Berg/Digital Images/Getty Images; **95** (b) ©Getty Images; **96** (bl) ©Tom Schierlitz/The Image Bank/Getty Images; **96-97** ©Andersen Ross/Iconica/Getty Images; **98** ©Ron and Patty Thomas/Photographer's Choice/Getty Images; **130** (bl) ©Sean Gallup/Getty Images, (br) ©Creatas Images; **130-131** (t) ©Image Ideas/PictureQuest; **131** (bl) ©C. Borland/PhotoLink/Getty Images, (br) ©Purestock/Getty Images; **132** (bl) ©Image Ideas/PictureQuest, (cl) ©Punchstock/Photodisc; **132-133** (bkgrd) ©Masterfile; **133** (tc) ©BananaStock/Punchstock, (tr) ©Melba Photo Agency/Punchstock, (br) ©David Frazier/Corbis, (c) ©Photodisc/Getty Images, (bcr) ©Brand X Pictures/Punchstock, (tcr) ©Oleg Moiseyenko/Alamy; **134** (tr) ©Punchstock/Comstock Images; **136** (bl) ©StillmanRogers/Alamy, (br) ©Roy Morsch/AgeFotostock/Photolibrary, (tr) ©Bananastock/Punchstock; **136-137** (bkgrd) ©Erin Paul Donovan/Alamy; **137** (c) ©The Stcck Asylum, LLC/Alamy, (c) ©Mike Chew/Corbis; **138** ©W.A. Hamilton/Alamy; **139** (c) ©North Wind/North Wind Picture Archives, (b) ©Michael A. Schwarz/The Image Works; **140** (tr) ©The Granger Collection, New York; **140-141** (bkgrd) ©Michael Springer/Getty Images; **141** ©North Wind/North Wind Picture Archives; **142** (b) ©Michael Dwyer/Associated Press, (c) ©Royalty-Free/Corbis, (t) ©Rhode Island School of Design; **143** (b) ©Michael S. Yamashita/National Geographic/Getty Images, (tr) ©Royalty-Free/Corbis, (tl) ©Corbis-Royalty-Free; **144-145** (bkgrd) ©Ball Miwako/Alamy; **145** (t) C. Borland/PhotoLink/Getty Images, (b) ©P. Michael Photoz/AKA/AGE Fotostock; **146** (c) ©Philip Scalia/Alamy; **146-147** (bkgrd) ©Racheal Grazias/Shutterstock; **148** (b) ©Visions of America, LLC/Alamy, (t) ©Photodisc/Getty Images; **148-149** (bkgrd) ©Mira/Alamy; **149** (tr) ©Sandra Baker/Alamy, (c) ©Lee Foster/Alamy, (b) ©Brand X Pictures/Punchstock; **150** (b) ©AGE Fotostock/SuperStock, (tl) ©David Lyons/Alamy; **150-151** (bkgrd) ©Digital Vision/Punchstock; **151** (c) ©Ferenc Cegledi/Shutterstock; **152** (t) ©Photodisc/Getty Images; **152-153** (t) ©inga spence/Alamy; **153** (t) ©Jeff Greenberg/Alamy, (c) ©PhotoAlto/Punchstock; **154** (b) ©Russell Kord/Alamy, (t) ©Photodisc/Getty Images; **155** ©Marilyn Angel Wynn/Nativestock.com/Getty Images; **156** (t) ©Photodisc/Getty Images; **156-157** (bkgrd) ©David Forbert/SuperStock; **157** (b) ©Library of Congress, (t) ©Popperfoto/Getty Images; **158** (t) ©Robert Harding Picture Library Ltd./Alamy, (b) ©David Caton/Alamy; **158-159** (bkgrd) ©Purestock/Getty Images; **160** ©Photodisc/Getty Images; **192** (bl) ©Geoff du Feu/Alamy, (br) ©Leda_d/Shutterstock; **192-193** (t) ©NASA; **193** (bl) ©Comstock Images/Alamy, (br) ©NASA/Johnson Space Center; **194-195** ©Digital Stock/Corbis; **196-197** (bkgrd) ©Alamy Images; **197** (b) ©Photodisc/Getty Images; **198** ©NASA/Corbis; **199** ©Peter Arnold, Inc./Alamy, (c) ©Brand X Pictures/PunchStock; **200-201** (bkgrd) ©StockTrek/

Getty Images, (t) ©Royalty-Free/Corbis; **201** (t) ©Studio Photogram/Alamy Images; **202-203** (bkgrd) ©NASA; **203** (b) ©Royalty-Free/Corbis; **204-205** (bkgrd) ©Gerard Lodriguss/Photo Researchers, Inc.; **205** (b) ©Geoff du Feu/Alamy; **206** (c) ©Hrana Janto; **206-207** (bkgrd) ©Leda_d/Shutterstock; **207** (b) ©Stefano Bianchetti/Corbis; **208** (b) ©Brad Sheard/SuperStock; **208-209** (bkgrd) ©James Gritz/Getty Images; **210** (b) ©Gianni Tortoli/Photo Researchers; **210-211** (bkgrd) ©Royalty-Free/Corbis; **211** (t) ©Digital Vision/Alamy; **212-213** (bkgrd) ©Comstock Images/Alamy; **214** (t) ©ImageState/Alamy; **214-215** (bkgrd) Angelo Cavalli/Getty Images; **215** (b) ©Daniel Berehulak/Getty Images, (t) ©McGraw-Hill Companies; **216-217** (bkgrd) ©Brand X Pictures/PunchStock; **217** (t) ©NASA, (b) ©NASA; **218-219** (bkgrd) ©NASA; **219** (b) ©NASA, (t) ©NASA; **221** (b) ©NASA; **222** ©Royalty-Free/Corbis; **254** (bl) ©Scenics of America/PhotoLink/Getty Images, (br) ©Jim Parkin/Shutterstock; **254-255** (t) ©Phil Degginger/Alamy; **255** (bl) ©Robert Laberge/Stringer/Getty Images Sport/Getty Images, (br) ©Ariel Skelley/Getty Images; **256-257** ©Curt Maas/AGE Fotostock; **260-261** ©Digital Vision/Getty Images; **261** ©Scenics of America/PhotoLink/Getty Images; **262** ©Mike Boyatt/AGE Fotostock; **263** (t) ©Dennis MacDonald/Age Fotostock, (b) ©Marvin Dembinsky Photo Associates/Alamy; **264** ©Getty Images/Digital Vision, ©Russell, Charles Marion/Private Collection/The Bridgeman Art Library International; **266** (inset) ©North Wind Picture Archives/alamy, (b) ©Visions of America/Joe Sohm/Getty Images; **266-267** ©State Historical Society of Iowa - Des Moines; **268-269** (bkgrd) ©Bettmann/Corbis; **269** ©SuperStock, Inc; **270** (l) ©Jeff Greenbert/Alamy; **270-271** (b) ©Robert Laberge/Stringer/Getty Images Sport/Getty Images; **271** (t) ©Eric Meola/Riser/Getty Images; **272** (t) ©Shutterstock; **272-273** ©Digital Vision/Punchstock; **273** (b) ©PhotoStock-Israel/Alamy, ©AGStockUSA, Inc./Alamy; **274-275** ©Danny Lehman/Corbis; **275** (inset) ©M. A. Battillana/Alamy; **276-277** ©Jim Parkin/Shutterstock; **277** (t) ©James P. Blair/National Geographic Stock; **278** (b) ©Allan Friedlander/SuperStock, (t) ©Shutterstock; **278-279** ©The Granger Collection, New York; **280** (b) ©The Granger Collection, New York; **280-281** ©Bettmann/Corbis; **282** (b) ©Kevin R. Morris/Corbis; **282-283** (t) ©David R. Frazier Photolibrary, Inc./Alamy; **316-317** (t) ©Specta/Shutterstock; **283** ©Ping Amranand/SuperStock; **284** ©Mike Boyatt/AGE Fotostock; **316** (bl) ©Klaus-Peter Wolf/imagebroker/Alamy, (br) ©Pawel Strykowski/Shutterstock; **317** (bl) ©Bruno Morandi/Getty Images, (br) ©Photodisc/Getty; **318-319** ©Photolibrary; **320** (c) ©Specta/Shutterstock, (t) ©Doug Sherman/Geofile; **220-221** (bkgrd) ©NASA; **321** (c) ©Ron and Patty Thomas/Photographer's Choice/Getty Images, (t) ©Digital Vision/Getty Images, (b) ©V.J. Matthew/Shutterstock; **322** (b) ©Pawel Strykowski/Shutterstock; **322-323** (t) ©Photos.com/Jupiter Images; **324** (t) ©Digital Archive Japan/Alamy; **324-325** ©Punchstock; **326** (inset) ©Corel; **326-327** (t) ©Digital Archive Japan/Alamy; **327** (b) ©Paul Edmonson/Getty Images; **328** (b) ©Christian Musat/Shutterstock, (c) ©Danno3/Shutterstock, (t) ©Jeff Foott/Getty Images; **329** (b) ©Photodisc/Getty Images; **330** (t) ©Rick & Nora Bowers/Alamy, (b) ©Stephen P. Lynch; **331** (t) ©John Cancalosi/Alamy, (c) ©Craig K. Lorenz/Photo Researchers, Inc., (b) ©Nature's Images, Inc./Photo Researchers, Inc.; **332-333** (t) ©Bruce Coleman Inc./Alamy, (c) ©Photodisc/Getty Images, (b) ©Michael Melford/The Image Bank/Getty Images; **334** ©Visuals Unlimited/Getty Images; **335** (l) ©Neale Cousland/Shutterstock, (r) ©Warren Stone/Bruce Coleman Inc.; **336-337** ©Alan and Sandy Carey/Getty Images; **337** ©Photodisc/Getty Images; **338** (t) ©Martin Horsky/Shutterstock, (b) ©Comstock/PunchStock; **339** (b) ©Gallo Images-Anthony Bannister/Getty Images; **340-341** (b) ©Ethan Miller/Getty Images, (t) ©Bruno Morandi/Getty Images; **341** (br) Photodisc/Getty Images; **342** (b) ©Gary Meszaros/Getty Images; **342-343** (t) ©Roger Bamber/Alamy; **344** (t) ©John E. Fletcher/Getty Images; **344-345** (b) ©Wayne Lawler/AGE Fotostock; **345** (t) ©Noam Armonn/Shutterstock; 346 ©Photolibrary; **378** (bl) ©Stephen Simpson/Getty Images, (br) ©Digital Stock/Corbis; **378-379** (t) ©U.S. Fish and Wildlife Service, Alaska; **379** (br) ©Bruce C. Murray/Shutterstock, (bl) ©Tom Till/Getty Images; **380-381** (bkgrd) ©Tim Fitzharris/Minden Pictures/National Geographic Stock; **381** (c) ©Brand X Pictures/PunchStock; **382-383** (top banner, left) ©Digital Stock/Corbis, (top banner, center) ©Stockbyte/Getty Images; **384-385** (bkgrd) ©Brand X Pictures/PunchStock; **385** (b) ©U.S. Department of Energy/Photo Researchers, Inc.; **386** (br) ©William Albert Allard/Getty Images, (bl) ©Comstock Images/Alamy; **386-387** (bkgrd) ©Chuck Pefley/Alamy; **387** (b) ©David R. Frazier Photolibrary, Inc./Alamy; **388** (br) ©Ron Niebrugge/Alamy, (bl) ©Digital Stock/Corbis; **388-389** (bkgrd) ©Ian Shive/Getty Images; **389** (b) Stephen Simpson/Getty Images; **390** (c) ©Whit Richardson/Getty Images, (b) ©Brand X Pictures; **390-391** (bkgrd) ©Ralph Lee Hopkins/Getty Images; **391** (b) Digital Vision; **392** (top banner) ©Michael T. Sedam/Corbis, (top banner) ©Photodisc/Getty Images, (b) ©Siede Preis/Getty Images; **392-393** (bkgrd) ©Tom Till/Getty Images; **393** (b) ©Panoramic Images/Getty Images, (top banner) ©Radius Images/Jupiterimages; **394** (top banner) ©Image Source, (b) ©Fribus Ekaterina/Shutterstock; **394-395** (t) ©Associated Press, ©Danita Delimont/Alamy; **395** (r) ©Digital Stock/Corbis, (br inset) ©Ken Usami/Getty Images; **396-397** (bkgrd) ©Digital Stock/Corbis, (top banner) ©Royalty-Free/Corbis, (top banner) ©MedioImages/Punchstock; **397** (c) ©AGStockUSA, Inc./Alamy; **398** (t) ©Associated Press, (b) ©Royalty Free Corbis; **398-399** (bkgrd) ©Andre Jenny/Alamy; **399** (b) ©Emma Lee/Life File/Getty Images, (br) ©Imagestate Media (John Foxx)/Imagestate; **400** (b) ©Christoprudov Dmitriy Gennadievich/Shutterstock; **400-401** (bkgrd) ©Peter Arnold, Inc.; **401** (br) ©Dynamic Graphics Group/Creatas/Alamy, (bl) ©Jose Carillo/Photoedit; **402** (b) ©Bobbi Lane/Getty Images; **402-403** (bkgrd) ©Prisma/SuperStock; **403** (b) ©G. Brad Lewis/Getty Images; **404** (b) ©PhotoAlto/PunchStock; **404-405** (bkgrd) ©Bryan & Cherry Alexander Photography/Alamy, (top banner) ©Dynamic Graphics Group/Creatas, (top banner) ©SuperStock/Alamy, (top banner) ©Digital Vision/Getty Images; **405** (b) ©Library of Congress; **406** (br) ©Greg Wright/Alamy, (bl) ©Bruce C. Murray/Shutterstock; **406-407** (bkgrd) ©Ron Niebrugge/Alamy; **407** (b) ©Bernard

Photo Credits, cont.

O'Kane/Alamy; **408** ©Digital Stock/Corbis; **440** (bl) ©Brand X Pictures/PunchStock, (br) ©NBAE/Getty Images, (bl) ©IT Stock Free; **440-441** (t) ©Bigshots/Getty Images; **441** (br) ©AFP/Getty Images, (bl) ©Doug Pensinger/Getty Images; **442-443** ©Digital Vision/Getty Images; **444-445** ©Stan Honda/AFP/Getty Images; **445** ©Tony Freeman / PhotoEdit; **446** ©IT Stock Free; **446-447** ©Karen Moskowitz/Getty Images; **448** (l) ©blue jean images/Getty Images, (b) ©Jules Frazier/Getty Images, (c) ©JupiterImages/Brand X/Alamy; **448-449** ©Bob Daemmrich/PhotoEdit; 450 (bl) ©The McGraw-Hill Companies, Inc./Andrew Resek, photographer, (br) ©Timothy A. Clary/AFP/Getty Images, (t) ©2007-2008 The Ladybug Foundation Inc. All rights reserved.; **451** Photo Courtesy Daytona Beach News-Journal; **452** (b) ©The McGraw-Hill Companies, Inc./Andrew Resek, photographer; **452-453** ©Timothy A. Clary/AFP/Getty Images; **454** ©2007-2008 The Ladybug Foundation Inc. All rights reserved.; **455** ©Jim West/Alamy; **456** ©NBAE/Getty Images; **457** (l) ©American School/Bridgeman Art Library/Getty Images, (r) ©Museum of the City of New York/Hulton Archive/Getty Images, (c) ©Zonnie Gorman; **458** ©Time & Life Pictures/Getty Images; **458-459** (b) ©McGraw-Hill Companies, Inc./Silver Editions; **460** (bl) ©Hulton Archive/Getty Images, (br) ©Tony Freeman / PhotoEdit; **460-461** ©David Hanover/Getty Images; **462** (t) ©Zonnie Gorman; **462-463** ©Associated Press; **464** ©Michael Newman / PhotoEdit, ©Jim Cummins/Taxi/Getty Images; **465** (t) ©Topham/The Image Works, (bkgrd) ©AFP/Getty Images; **466-467** ©Bigshots/Getty Images; **468-469** ©Doug Pensinger/Getty Images; **470** (bkgrd) ©Nicole Hill/Getty Images, (r) ©JupiterImages/Brand X.

Art Credits

The McGraw-Hill Companies, Inc. would like to thank the following illustrators for their contributions: Ortelius Design and Robert Schuster/©The McGraw-Hill Companies, Inc.

Text Credits

A Symphony of Whales by Steve Schuch, illustrated by Peter Sylvada. Text copyright © 1999 by Steve Schuch. Illustrations copyright © 1999 by Peter Sylvada. Reprinted by permission of Houghton Mifflin Harcourt Publishing Company. All rights reserved.

America's Champion Swimmer: Gertrude Ederle by David A. Adler, illustrated by Terry Widener. Text copyright © 2000 by David A. Adler. Illustrations copyright © 2000 by Terry Widener. Reprinted by permission of Houghton Mifflin Harcourt Publishing Company. All rights reserved.
2001 Notable Children's Book

"Birdfoot's Grampa" from *Entering Onondaga* by Joseph Bruchac. Used by permission of Barbara Kouts Literary Agency.

Galileo's Journal 1609-1610. Text copyright © 2006 by Jeanne K. Pettenati. Illustrations copyright © 2006 by Paolo Rui. Used with permission by Charlesbridge Publishing, Inc. All rights reserved.

First published in the United States under the title *Henry and the Kite Dragon* by Bruce Edward Hall, illustrated by William Low. Text Copyright © 2004 by Bruce Edward Hall. Artwork Copyright © 2004 by William Low. Published by arrangement with Philomel Books, a division of Penguin Young Readers Group, a member of Penguin Group (USA) Inc. All rights reserved.

From *Juan Verdades: The Man Who Couldn't Tell A Lie* by Joe Hayes, illustrated by Joseph Daniel Fiedler. Scholastic Inc./Orchard Books. Text copyright © 2001 by Joe Hayes, illustrations copyright © 2001 by Joseph Daniel Fiedler. Reprinted by permission.

Marven of the Great North Woods by Kathryn Lasky, illustrated by Kevin Hawkes. Text copyright © 1997 by Kathryn Lasky Night. Illustrations copyright © 1997 by Kevin Hawkes. Reprinted by permission of Houghton Mifflin Harcourt Publishing Company. All rights reserved.
1998 Notable Children's Book

My Name is Celia by Monica Brown, illustrated by Rafael López. Text Copyright © 2004 by Monica Brown. Illustrations copyright © 2004 by Rafael López. Translation © by Northland Publishing. Used by permission of Cooper Square Publishing, Lanham, MD.
2006 Belpré Award Honor

The Great Kapok Tree: A Tree of the Amazon Rain Forest by Lynne Cherry. Copyright © 1990 by Lynne Cherry. Reprinted by permission of Houghton Mifflin Harcourt Publishing Company. All rights reserved.